# UNDAUNTED VALOR

AN ASSAULT HELICOPTER UNIT IN VIETNAM

UNDAUNTED VALOR
BOOK 1

MATT JACKSON

MATT JACKSON BOOKS

# INTRODUCTION

This is a fictional work, based on actual events that occurred between February 5, 1968, and August 1, 1970. Some names are fictitious, as I wish to protect individuals' identities in some cases. Names that appear on the Vietnam Memorial in the National Mall have been used, as it is my intent to honor those individuals that gave all. Conversations depicted are fictitious but represent what was said or would have been said under the circumstances. I have attempted to use slang that was typical of pilots, such as "niner" for the number nine. Racial slurs towards the Vietnamese have been included for accuracy and are not appropriate by today's standards, but soldiers in combat, even today, still apply slurs towards their enemy. Not every event that impacted the company during this period is covered, but only those that I felt highlighted the various missions we undertook. Some events I would just rather not recall, but it was wisely pointed out to me that those events are just as important as other events. Events portrayed are close to the actual sequence in which they occurred.

I have focused on one company of the 227th Assault Helicopter Battalion, 11th Aviation Group, 1st Air Cavalry Division. In addition, I have focused mostly on the pilots of that one company, Alpha Company, as that is the unit I flew with and knew the best. It should be noted, however, that the 227th Assault Helicopter Battalion consisted of three assault helicopter companies, an attack helicopter company and a headquarters company. Each played a vital role in the battalion's success, making it one of the most highly decorated units of the US Army. Without the effort of everyone in each unit, the 227th AHB would have been just another aviation unit, to be disbanded after the war. It is still serving today at Fort Hood, Texas, upholding the traditions established in Vietnam. Missions indicated were flown by each of the assault helicopter companies in both the 227th AHB and our sister battalion, the 229th AHB.

I have thought about writing this for the past forty-eight years. As I wrote, I felt it was important to relate to those great soldiers that made this such a great company. We all have a journey in life, with many crossroads, curves and offshoots. The synergistic effect created by individual journeys coming together at this point in time, at this location, created an organization that truly stood above the rest. The quality of an organization ebbs and flows with the quality of the leadership and the dedication, personalities and expertise of the individuals present at a particular time. During this time period, I witnessed the synergism of the unit only increase further with each passing month.

This story is important so that people know who the helicopter crews were and what they were asked to do and did. In 1964–65, the Army ramped up the Warrant Officer Candidate Program to meet the expanding need for helicopter pilots in Vietnam. Between 1965 and 1971, 44,000 warrant officer cadets were awarded flight wings. Most were high school graduates and some had some college. The average age of pilots, crew chiefs and door gunners was twenty years old. Badly needed, they were trained quickly and given enormous responsibility to maintain a very complex piece of equipment. Our aircraft were not as sophisticated as the machines today, but the UH-1D and the UH-1H models were exceptional, forgiving workhorses without which this war could not have been waged. Of the 5,000 UH-1 helicopters that went to Vietnam starting in 1962, over 3,300 were destroyed in combat. This undeclared war also could not have been waged without the young men that supported, maintained, and crewed these aircraft.

Today's Army Aviation crews are some of the best in the world. They can be on target in thirty seconds plus or minus with the latest in GPS navigation equipment and can operate at night with night vision goggles. Vietnam crews had no night vision goggles, and navigation was by a map, compass and clock, but we flew formations at night, operated at night and were also on target in thirty seconds plus or minus.

It is also important that this story be told because there are unique lessons to be learned when flying in a hot, humid jungle environment. Too often, the US military is accused of preparing today for the last war and not the next war. Only through historical writings, be they official Army publications or historical novels, can current pilots learn lessons for future operations. Not since the Vietnam Conflict has the US Army had to operate in a jungle environment on any large scale. Ignore history and we will repeat history. Ignore the lessons we learned in this environment and they will only be taught again, tragically.

# 1

## IT BEGIN

THE TRIP STARTED ON FEBRUARY 5, 1968, AT THE Military Entrance and Processing Station (MEPS) in Portland, Oregon. It was a long day of filling out paperwork, stripping naked with sixty other guys and being examined by what appeared to be a doctor. After having blood drawn, I was informed I had syphilis.

Fortunately, being raised a Navy brat, with a father that had come up through the ranks, I had been around the military long enough to recognize that some of those serving were not the sharpest knives in the drawer, and this guy struck me as among the dullest. And since I was older than most present for this medical news—and not officially in the military yet—questioning the informant was not a problem.

"Hey, medic, you want to check that again?"

Annoyed, he double-checked his clipboard, the sign of authority around here, it appeared.

"All right, what's your number again?"

"Number fifty-one."

"Oh, this isn't you. Number fifteen, come in here."

Had the medic passed his reading test? Late that afternoon, the MEPS staff deemed me worthy to join the ranks. Raising our right hands, we all took the Oath of Allegiance. Those of us that were flight school wannabes were escorted to a waiting cab that was to take us to the airport. There were antiwar protesters blocking the front door, so we went out the back, through an abandoned storefront. Instead of bands playing as we went off to combat as our grandfathers had experienced, we were sneaking out the back door.

The flight to Fort Worth, Texas, was an all-night affair as it was the last flight out of Portland that night. The flight was half-full. A flash-in-the-pan rock band was on board, corralling the attention of the stewardess for the whole flight. Two future soldiers were of no interest to her, and we didn't even look like soldiers yet.

Changing planes in Fort Worth, we boarded a prop airplane from Trans-Texas Airways along with thirteen other guys heading to Fort Polk, Louisiana. I had some flight training and held a private pilot's license, so I noticed little things, like the fuel cap dangling from a chain on the wing. Small detail. I notified the stewardess, who informed someone in the cockpit. The pilot wasn't happy, stopping the plane on the taxiway, getting out and placing the cap in position. I should have paid more attention to Fort Worth, as I would be returning here after basic training.

Arriving in Fort Polk, Louisiana, the plane taxied to a shed that appeared to be left over from World War II. Everyone deplaned and went inside to be greeted by military police, MPs. The MPs directed us to empty our shaving kits, as that was all we were allowed to bring besides the clothes on our backs. That was good because that was all I owned anyway. We were asked if we were carrying any contraband, such as legal or illegal drugs, knives, guns, or straight razors. We were then directed to turn our pockets inside out. Some contraband was found on a couple of individuals, and their Army experience started very badly. Once cleared, we were loaded on a bus and taken to the reception station, where we were greeted by a noncommissioned officer, a staff sergeant.

The staff sergeant was polite, almost fatherly. No screaming, no yelling. He took us on a tour of the reception station. The reception station was all wooden buildings that appeared to have been left over from World War II. In fact, Fort Polk was left over from World War II and had only been reopened in 1966 during the buildup for the Vietnam Conflict. Between World War II and 1966, the post had been in "caretaker" status, being used only for National Guard and Army Reserve training on weekends and in summer. No active Army forces had been stationed there, so most of the post was in disrepair.

The barracks were two-story wooden buildings with open sleeping bays for twenty men on each level. They had been upgraded with a gas furnace instead of a coal furnace. Each level had a bathroom with four showerheads, ten toilets, and ten sinks. The toilets had no dividers between the seats, so guys could have conversations while seated. How convenient!

The staff sergeant directed us to the mess hall as none of us had eaten since we'd started for Fort Polk. After breakfast, he returned us to one of the barracks buildings, assigned each of us a bunk, for which we drew bedding, and told us to wait, and wait, and wait. Throughout the day, new people arrived and went through a similar procedure.

The next five days were filled with in-processing procedures. Haircuts were the very first thing. For the cost of one dollar, everyone received their first GI haircut. It took the barber about twenty seconds to deliver this haircut, which was like shearing sheep. All individual identity was lost after this as everyone was a skinhead when they got out of the chair. Then off to draw uniforms. First, we were instructed to strip naked.

"If the Army wants you to have something, the Army will issue it to you," bellowed the staff sergeant. As we walked down a long row of clothing, butt naked, civilians began to dress us. The first item they handed me was a duffel bag.

"What's your waist size?" a civilian clerk asked.

"Ah, thirty-two, sir," I stuttered.

"Here's size thirty. You're going to drop a few pounds in the next weeks," he replied while handing me four pair of boxer shorts. "Put one pair on and three in the duffel bag," he directed. "Next! What's your waist size?" he asked the next guy. By the time you reached the end of the line, you were fully clothed and had a duffel bag of clothing.

The afternoon was another exercise in rapidly moving two hundred bodies through another process: immunizations. We formed a single line. On each side stood two medics, with one holding what appeared to be an air gun. "Shirts off!" came the command. "Forward march." The first medic on each side wiped my shoulder with an alcohol pad, then the second placed the air gun on my shoulder and fired. No needles required, and it hurt like hell. Well, two shots wasn't so bad. Oh no, it was every afternoon for four days! The whole process took about thirty minutes, and then it was off to a classroom for more testing. I guess they didn't trust the tests we'd taken before we joined, so we took the same tests all over again.

Finally, the day came when we were assembled on the street with our duffle bags and prepared to move to the appropriate training company. The renowned Army two-and-a-half-ton trucks arrived and were positioned for us to load. As our names were called, we were told to load the trucks. Since my last name began with a C, I was one of the first to climb up on the back of the truck and moved to the front. As more men climbed in, the front filled up. At last, the final sardine was packed in, and the back flap of the truck's canvas cover was closed so we couldn't see where we were being taken. It was so dark in there I couldn't see the guy standing next to me either.

The ride was short. The driver deliberately screeched to a halt at every stop sign and hit every pothole, just so we could enjoy the experience of our first ride in the back of the truck. Eventually, the truck stopped and the back flap opened.

"Get out of my truck, you maggots! Move, move, move! Here, let me help you, maggot!" yelled a voice surrounded by a blinding outside light.

"Ahhh!" came a reply, followed by the sound of a body hitting the ground, then another, and another in rapid succession. A groping arm reached into the truck, grabbing for me.

"What are you waiting for, Princess? I said get out of my truck!" In seconds, I was out of the truck and running for dear life with a drill sergeant right on my ass.

"Now get in formation on the cables!" bellowed another drill sergeant. How many drill sergeants did they have in this company? They were everywhere; almost one drill sergeant per trainee, it seemed. We were all trainees now. Running down the length of the street were four steel cables staked to the ground. We were directed to line up, toes only touching the cables and duffel bags in front of us. Some of the trainees managed to screw up these simple orders.

"You people don't want to listen and follow instructions? Fine! Every last one of you mothers drop and give me fifty!" Being from a military family, I knew this meant we all had to get into a front leaning position and push out fifty pushups. However, some trainees didn't understand and moved too slow for the drill sergeant.

"Recover!

What are you doing, maggots? Who told you to wipe your hands off? Why are you not at the position of attention? Now, together, on my command, you will take the front leaning rest position, and together we will do our fifty pushups. And don't let me see one of you out of step. Now, drop!"

Down we went. "On my command. One, two, three—

recover! Why can't you keep up? Yeah, you, Little Sister!" There was no telling who the offender was because the drill sergeant was looking at everyone. Everyone was looking straight ahead as they should be when in the position of attention. Well, not everyone.

Suddenly a drill sergeant appeared in front of a trainee who had been looking at the drill sergeant leading this exercise. "Why are you looking at Sergeant Spruce? Do you want to make out with Drill Sergeant Spruce? Is he that pretty you want to stare at him? You don't need to see him to hear him! Do you listen with your eyes? Are you some kind of freak?"

The exercise and tirade went on for a good hour. I doubt anyone completed fifty pushups, but we were all smoked and our arms were shaking by the end of the ordeal. We were told to pick up the contents of our duffel bags, which had been dumped on the ground for contraband inspection. A drill sergeant ordered us to our assigned barracks. As he called out names, he assigned each trainee a bunk, a wall locker and a footlocker. We were told to stand next to our footlockers at parade rest. After everyone was assigned a place, three other drill sergeants strolled into the barracks. One was a staff sergeant, the other two being just sergeants—Staff Sergeant Van B. Ford, assisted by Sergeant Bradshaw from Texas and Sergeant Thomas from Ohio.

Staff Sergeant Van B. Ford was a short black man with a calm voice. He simply told his soldiers what he expected and never raised his voice. His sentences usually followed a "Normally this, however that" pattern. "Normally these barracks are spotless. However, with you people here, it's a pig sty."

"When I call yo' name, sound off," he said as he looked at a clipboard. "I need a platoon guide and four squad leaders. Are any of you trainees prior service?" he asked. One trainee raised his hand. "What's yo' name, trainee?"

"Crawford, Drill Sergeant," he responded.

"Crawford, Crawford." He consulted his clipboard. "Oh yeah, you was Navy. What you joining the Army for anyway?"

"To go to flight school, Drill Sergeant," Crawford said.

"Flight school! You got to get through basic training before you can fly. You the platoon guide now. Anyone had ROTC training?" Staff Sergeant Ford looked around the room, and two other trainees raised their hands. Addressing the closest, he declared,

"You going to be first squad leader. What's yo' name?"

"Hanna, Drill Sergeant."

"Where you from, Hanna?"

"Puerto Rico, Drill Sergeant."

"Puerto Rico my ass, Hanna. With that blond hair, blue eyes and lily-white skin, you can't be from Puerto Rico. Sergeant Lopez is from Puerto Rico, but not you. What's yo' daddy do?"

"Dad is an engineer for a company there, and we moved there when I was born. Been there ever since."

Looking at the other trainee, Drill Sergeant Ford tagged him as the second squad leader.

"You, what's yo' name?" he asked, pointing at a tall, thin black soldier.

"Me?" he answered, pointing at himself. "Johnson, sir."

"Don't you sir me, trainee. I work for my pay. Where you from, Johnson?"

"Lickskillet, Kentucky, Drill Sergeant." The rest of us were attempting to suppress our laughter.

"Lickskillet! What kind of place is that?"

"That's a small place, Drill Sergeant," Johnson answered with a thick Southern drawl. Some trainees could not suppress their laughter on that note.

"Well, in the interest of equality, you're the second squad leader. Any military brats?" Staff Sergeant Ford asked.

I raised my hand.

"Yo' daddy Army?" He walked up to me.

"No, Drill Sergeant. Navy, submarines," I responded.

"Well, you is now the third squad leader. Hope he taught you something. What's your name?"he asks.

"Cory, Dan, drill Sergeant," I respond.

"Well, which is it? Dan Cory or Cory Dan?"he asks with some frustration.

"Dan Cory, Drill Sergeant."

He wrote my name on his clipboard. "Why didn't you join the Navy?"

"I want to go to flight school," I answered.

"Another flight school wannabe! Anyone else here a wannabe flight school peeloot?" He looked around the room. Over half the guys in the room raised their hands, to include the three selected squad leaders.

"You too, Johnson?" This surprised all of us. Johnson just didn't seem that swift.

"Yes, Drill Sergeant," Johnson answered.

Staff Sergeant Ford looked down and shook his head as he started laughing. Looking up finally, he said, "Let me tell y'all something. You learn real good here in basic, because over half of y'all are going to fail in that there flight school and find yourselves in the infantry, humping a rucksack in Vietnam. So, y'all learn good here. Understood!"

"Yes, Drill Sergeant," the group responded.

After selecting his fourth squad leader, Staff Sergeant Ford stated, "Now when I tell y'all to fall out, y'all do so quickly and line up on yo' four squad leaders with yo' toes on the cables. Normally, we would go to chow now. However, I do believe y'all need some exercise, so we will be going to the Hill on the way to the mess hall. Crawford!"

"Yes, Drill Sergeant," he responded.

"Crawford, when y'all get back from the mess hall, I expect you to show these ladies how to set up their wall lockers, footlockers and bunks. They did teach you that in the Navy, didn't they?"

"Yes, Drill Sergeant."

"Now, fall out on the cables!" And we bolted out of the barracks and fell in a platoon formation.

The Hill was a hundred-yard dirt-and-gravel field with a steep slope of fifty feet at one end. We were lined up by squad in four ranks of ten. On command, we had to crawl to the top of the slope. When I reached the top, my hands, knees and elbows were raw. For the next three days, we revisited the Hill each evening before chow. On the third day, I was really feeling sorry for myself. Suddenly, I had a come to Jesus moment. *Hey, dumbass, you volunteered to be here. You weren't drafted, you quit college and "volunteered" for this shit, so stop your crying and suck it up!*

And I did. Suddenly that crawl wasn't so bad. In fact, I found myself enjoying it. I picked up my pace and reached the top in record time, whereupon I became a damn cheerleader, screaming words of encouragement to my fellow soldiers. If I'd had pompoms, I would have used them, I was so fired up. Next thing I knew, everyone who had made it to the top was yelling words of encouragement to the guys still coming up. That was the last time we crawled the Hill.

The mess hall entry entailed an interesting exercise as they moved two hundred trainees through there for breakfast and dinner. Lunch was usually served wherever we were training. We lined up by platoons outside the mess hall on the cables. Never missing an opportunity to conduct physical training, the drill sergeants would have us doing pushups, flutter kicks or sit-ups until it was our turn to enter. However, before entering, one had to negotiate the overhead bars and then do six pull-ups. Those who did not accomplish these tasks received extra training from the drill sergeant supervising the chow line.

As we entered the mess hall, we grabbed eating utensils and a cafeteria tray that was also our dinner plate and moved along the cafeteria line. The mess hall dining area was about fifty feet long and thirty feet wide with a center aisle. Tables with bench seats for ten trainees on each side of the table radiated from the center to the walls. We didn't talk; we just moved, and other trainees that were on kitchen police put food on our trays. No one cared if the food was appetizing or eaten; that was up to the recipient.

We quickly found a seat and started to eat. A drill sergeant hovered around the room, and if we took longer than two minutes to consume our food, we were told to get out. "Eat fast and haul ass!" was a common command. We didn't even consider having a cup of coffee or a cigarette after eating. Generally, we started eating before we sat down and kept shoveling food in as we moved out the back door.

After dinner that first night, it was back to the barracks to prepare our footlockers and living area.

Crawford took charge and coached everyone through how to set up our footlockers so that uniformity was established. The wooden footlockers had a top shelf and a lower area. In the lower area, he demonstrated that every pair of boxer shorts and T-shirt should be rolled instead of folded and each should be nine inches in length. He explained that this way, rolled items did not wrinkle as folded items did, and rolled items fit better in duffle bags, with less wasted space. Long johns went into the bottom as well and were also rolled. The top shelf, which was removable to expose the bottom, was first lined with a towel, neatly folded to fit snugly in the top. On the left side, in precise positions, went our razor, shaving cream, toothbrush, toothpaste, and soap dish with an unused bar of soap. On the other side went socks, also rolled, and an extra towel. Everyone laid their footlockers out the same. Then he explained that we would not touch anything on the top shelf, ever, if we wanted to stay on the good side of Staff Sergeant Ford.

"Look, we have to play the game, and the game is discipline. The quicker we learn that, the better off we'll be. Setting up uniform displays, footlockers and wall lockers will get the drill sergeants off our backs much quicker. The first chance we have to go to the PX, you buy a new toothbrush, razor, shaving cream and toothpaste, and you put it in a shaving kit in the top of your wall locker. That's the one safe place we are authorized that the drill sergeants won't look into or have a shit fit about unless we give them a reason. Also, get a second towel—no, make that two more towels, with a hanger to hang one in your wall lockers with one in your butt pack. You're going to need it in the field. Now let me show you how to lay out the wall lockers." I was thinking that if Mother had seen my room this squared away, she would have been very happy.

He moved over to his wall locker, and we all followed as he had our undivided attention. "On the top shelf, place your additional shaving kit in the back, right side. Hang each of your fatigues with the left sleeve out so they're all facing the same way. The hanger hook should be facing the rear of the locker. Your low-quarter shoes go on the lower left side with your extra pair of boots on the right side, toes back an inch from the front. Change your boots every day, so each night you will be shining boots. Change your socks each day, and every day at noon. Might want to buy extra socks when you get a chance. Any questions?"

"Where do we put our laundry bags?" asked another trainee.

"Laundry bags are tied to the top rung at the foot of the bed, centered. Let me show you." And he proceeded to demonstrate how to tie it. For a guy that was prior service Navy, Crawford sure knew a lot about how to set up an Army barracks.

"What about our TA-50 field gear?" came the next question.

"Everyone get your field gear and meet back here in the bay, and I'll show you how to set it up. They were probably going to do that tomorrow, but let's get it done tonight." Once everyone was assembled with their equipment, Crawford walked us through how to put our field gear together. First, the web belts were adjusted to fit each other; then came the positioning of the suspenders, followed by the positioning of two ammo pouches. Next was our butt packs, centered on our backs. Canteen on left hip was next, followed by first aid pouch on the left shoulder.

"When you're in the barracks, hang your field gear on the top left side of the bunk if you sleep on top and top right side if you sleep on the bottom, aisle side. Okay, now let's get to putting everything in its place."

Everyone moved to their respective areas and commenced putting things away, as well as making beds. Thank goodness we'd learned at the reception station how to make beds. Lights out was at 2200 hours, and most of us were quickly asleep as our bodies were sleep-deprived.

At 0500 hours every morning for the first week, the barracks exploded, with Staff Sergeant Van B. Ford turning on lights and kicking over garbage cans. Ten minutes later, everyone was outside doing pushups and flutter kicks, running, and low-crawling. Breaks included fireman carry races with one trainee being carried on the back of another trainee over a fifty-yard racecourse. An hour later, we were off to the mess hall for breakfast and back to the barracks to get our stuff for training. Somewhere in there, we were expected to brush our teeth, wash and make our beds. As time went on, we soon learned to shower the night before, make our beds as tight as possible so it was easy to make them up in the morning, and get up around 0430 hours to be ready when Staff Sergeant Ford came through the door.

After the first week, he came in at 0500 hours and found every one of us standing next to our footlockers, dressed, beds made and ready for training. "Normally, I have to wake dumbass trainees up for all eight weeks of training. However, y'all are a little smarter than the average trainees." A new bond was formed with Staff Sergeant Ford. His job became much easier, resulting in our lives becoming more pleasant. We were still trainees, but we weren't getting our butts chewed anymore. Not only were we smarter than the average trainees, but our bodies were becoming harder.

The physical training continued to be hard, but the ass chewing and intimidation subsided. We soon realized that the physical training we were doing was actually the same as the physical fitness test we would have to take at the end of our basic training. The test included low-crawling fifty feet out and back; the two-man fireman carry race; the overhead bars; run, dodge and jump; and a two-mile run. All events were for time. No one failed. At the end of our eight weeks, we were certainly different, both physically and mentally. The night before graduation, Staff Sergeant Ford was noted by the company commander as the Drill Sergeant of the Cycle for having the best platoon, which made the entire platoon really feel good about what we had done. The fact that over half the platoon would be heading to flight school also added to the good feelings. In fact, the only trainee that was supposed to be going but wasn't was Crawford[1]. He was being held over. The next morning, Johnson, Hanna and I loaded a Greyhound bus along with thirty-seven others for our next assignment at Fort Wolters, Texas.

# 2

## WELCOME TO PREFLIGHT

THE TRIP FROM FORT POLK, LOUISIANA, TO FORT Wolters, Texas, took about seven hours on the Greyhound bus. This was the first time the forty flight-school-bound wannabes had been off a military installation in three months. We enjoyed sitting back in comfortable seats, also for the first time in three months. Almost everyone slept on the road trip. As we drew closer to Fort Wolters, the level of anticipation rose.

Fort Wolters had been an active basic training base in World War II and remained so through the Korean War but then had been placed in caretaker status, like so many other installations after Korea. Besides World War II wooden buildings, there were three-story concrete block barracks as well. These had two-man rooms and a community bathroom on each floor. Fort Wolters had only been reopened since 1966, when the demand for pilots had exceeded the capabilities of the traditional Army Aviation Center at Fort Rucker, Alabama.

We were met at the main gate to Fort Wolters by another warrant officer cadet, or WOC, as all cadets were called.

After giving directions to the driver, he addressed us. "Hi, I'm Brian Brady, and I'm a cadet just like you guys. When we get to the barracks, gather up your stuff and fall into two ranks on the street next to the bus. I will then conduct a roll call and assign you a barracks." He then turned his attention back to the bus driver.

The designated barracks were World War II wooden buildings like we'd had in basic training. Other buses were already there, offloading cadets. We removed our duffel bags from the bus and lined up as Brian had asked. We looked more like a mob than a military formation. As he called our names, we answered and moved to the designated building. There sat another cadet.

"Hi, Dan Cory," I said as I extended my hand.

Taking my hand, he said, "Hi, Bob Atwell. Dan, you're assigned to the fourth bunk on the right side. Footlocker is in front of your bunk and the wall locker is behind along the wall. Your blankets and sheets are on the bed, so you might start making it up. Once everyone gets in, I'll be giving a quick briefing here on the first floor."

"Okay," I said, moving down to my assigned bunk and making the bed. Once everyone was in the building, Bob called those assigned upstairs and asked them to come downstairs for a briefing.

"Welcome to Preflight. You'll get to meet our TAC officer tomorrow morning, and it will not be pleasant. Just try and laugh it off. Enough said about that. You need to remove all rank from your uniforms tonight and replace it with WOC brass. The post exchange will be open for a couple more hours, so when you leave here, get over there and get at least three sets of brass. The PX is down two blocks. Can't miss it. After that, head over to the mess hall, which is one block behind this building. At eighteen hundred tonight, there will be a briefing back here on how to set up your wall locker and footlocker, as well as what you can expect in the morning. Okay, now you're free until eighteen hundred."

Heading back to my bunk to retrieve my cap, I noticed Bob standing next to his bed. His area looked pretty squared away.

"You going to the PX?" he asked.

"Yeah. Just looking at how you have your stuff set up. Looks pretty much like we did in basic," I said.

"Really does, but note the attention to details. All the shirts are facing left, but note the spacing between each hanger —two inches. And my low-quarter shoes are exactly one inch from the end of the shelf and one inch from the left side, with my extra boots' toes one inch from the front of the shelf and one inch from the right side."

"Bob, I think I'm beginning to see the picture here," I said.

"You have no idea. A little tip for you—buy a small ruler at the PX and keep it hidden from the TAC officers. Also get a black magic marker to cover any black threads on your uniforms. Basic training taught us discipline. Preflight is going to teach us attention to detail. When you come back, give me a holler and I'll go to chow with you," Bob offered.

As I was leaving the building, Johnson was coming down the stairs.

"Dan, you goin' to the PX?"

"Yeah, you?"

"I'll walk over witch'u if you don't walk too fast." Johnson's Southern accent was coming through loud and clear.

"What's the matter?" I noticed his limping walk. "What'd you do?"

"Dee low-quarter shoes. I ain't never worn dees before, and dey're killing my feet."

"What, you've never worn low-quarters before!"

"Nah. Growing up, we was too poor for anything but sneakers, and in basic we wore boots, but not dese. Dey hurt."

Johnson was right—we never had worn our issued low-quarters in basic training, only boots. Low quarter shoes were made in the federal prison system, and not of the most supple leather.

"When you get back from chow, go up to the shower wearing your shoes. Soak those shoes good in hot water and keep them on until you go to bed tonight. That will break them in quick. You may get your ass ripped tomorrow for wet shoes, but I suspect we're going to get our asses ripped for everything tomorrow, so the TACs may not even notice the shoes are damp."

When we returned from the PX, Johnson and I walked over to the mess hall with Bob. In basic training, "Eat fast and haul ass" had been the motto. Here was different. We entered the mess hall without having to do pushups or overhead bars. No one was screaming as we moved along the cafeteria line with a tray and real dishes. Tables were arranged to seat four people. We knew when we entered how much time we had for the meal. It was always long enough to eat, drink a second cup of coffee and have a smoke if you were so inclined. I was a bit gun-shy, expecting the TAC officers to burst in and start screaming at any minute. When they didn't, I started to relax.

I became more relaxed when Bob said, "Hey, no need to shovel food in. Remember the table manners your parents taught you. The TACs will be around after tomorrow, and if you're eating like an animal, they'll put your tray on the floor and have you get down and eat with no utensils. Eat like your mom was sitting here, which means no foul language." I suddenly remembered my table manners and started acting appropriately.

Cadet Brady chaired the 1800 briefing. "Welcome to Preflight. I'm a holdover from a previous class, so me and the other cadets were directed to meet you and get you settled in. After tomorrow morning, we're just like you and in this with you. First formation will be at zero five thirty, and it will be frightening. Our TAC officers are warrant officers who finished their tours flying in Vietnam. Now they're babysitting us instead of being instructor pilots, and they're not happy about it. You can expect to get your ass smoked in the morning. Nothing you do will make them happy, so be prepared for it. This is my second time going through this, and I'll try to laugh my way through tomorrow morning, 'cause it's the only thing to do," he explained.

Bob picked up the briefing. "Preflight is four weeks long. You will be in classrooms all day, every day, learning how to behave as an officer. There will be classes on etiquette and manners. You will receive classes on the Uniform Code of Military Justice, UCMJ, and just how fast you can be kicked out of this program." The rest of the briefing went into detail on how to prepare our footlockers and wall lockers for inspections. Inspections were conducted every day, whenever the TAC officer felt like doing it, whether we were in the barracks or in class.

It was agreed that everyone would start waking up at 0430 hours. That would give us an hour to clean up and have our areas prepared for inspection after we spent the previous night setting everything up as instructed. At 0530 hours, all forty cadets were stacked one behind the other and ready to burst onto the company street. When the whistle blew, cadets poured out of the barracks as if they were on fire. And we did it again, and again, and again, interspersed with pushups as we just could not vacate the barracks fast enough.

While we were outside getting smoked doing pushups, some of the TAC officers were in the barracks tossing everything out of our wall lockers and footlockers. If they noticed Johnson's shoes, they said nothing about them being wet. Of course, the barracks weren't clean enough for the TAC officers, so mops, brooms, pails and garbage cans were flying around squad bays as well. Obviously, no one made their bed that morning, because mattresses were upside down and bedding pulled apart.

After two weeks, the barracks were in a clean enough condition to satisfy the TAC officers. The level of cleanliness was achieved when a cadet wore a pair of white gloves while conducting a pre-inspection before the TAC's inspection. Satisfied that attention to detail was being paid to the large items like the barracks, the TAC officers turned their attention to small things, such as the cleanliness of the inside of our brass belt buckles or the inside of our razors or our toothbrushes. "This is filthy, Cadet. It is only good for cleaning the latrine. Now get in there and clean those toilets. Take your damn toothbrush."

More than one of us was accused of growing penicillin in our belt buckles. A loose thread on a shirt would obtain an ass chewing for the offender. Faded black thread required a black magic marker touch-up in order to pass inspection. Attention to detail was the name of the game. We would learn on the flight line why it was so important.

We received more shots, as well as our flight gear. Our flight gear consisted of two one-piece flight suits, a pair of leather gloves and a flight helmet with carrying bag. The flight suits would not be going to Vietnam with us. A lot of bravado was displayed in the barracks as cadets modeled before the camera in their flight gear for pictures to be sent home. For many, that would be the extent of their aviation experience. Counseling by our TAC officer also began with each of us being called into his office. When it was my turn, I knocked on the door.

"Get in here, Cadet!" shouted the TAC officer, Chief Warrant Officer 2 Barbie. Chief Warrant Officer Barbie was a tall, skinny man with an unhandsome pockmarked face. However, he did have a knockout wife that frequently came to the barracks to pick him up in a new Corvette Stingray. We couldn't help but notice her.

Approaching his desk, I came to attention and rendered the proper salute. "Sir, Cadet Cory reporting as ordered." He returned my salute and told me to stand at ease, which really meant stand at parade rest. He was looking at my chart and had not looked at me.

"Cadet Cory, you're older than most cadets we see here. You have almost three years of college."

"Yes, sir," My father had taught me that statements of fact got a "yes, sir" or "no, sir" response and nothing more.

"Didn't you like college? Or were you just too stupid to finish? Are you a quitter, Cadet Cory?" he asked, leaning forward across his desk, staring at me with his beady black eyes.

"No, sir!"

"Are you going to waste the Army's money, and my time, quitting before you even start?"

"No, sir!" This line of questioning was becoming annoying.

"I suppose you're going to take that nice pay raise and buy yourself one of those new Corvettes, aren't you?" he needled me.

We did get a pay raise coming to flight school as we were promoted from E-1 or E-2 privates to E-5 sergeants. Our pay went from ninety-eight dollars to two hundred and twenty-five dollars a month. Almost all the extra pay went to two things—haircuts and laundry bills. We were expected to have high and tight haircuts, which meant a haircut each weekend. We were also expected to break starch every day. Our fatigues were so heavily starched that it took some effort to get your foot down the pant leg and your arm down the sleeve. A few cadets attempted to wear the same uniform two days in a row. The penalty for such an action wasn't worth the price.

"No, sir, I don't even like Corvettes and couldn't afford one anyway," I responded, deviating from Dad's advice by giving more information than necessary.

"You don't like Corvettes! I suppose you're a Mustang lover, aren't you?" he fired off.

Now this was really starting to bother me. What kind of "counseling" was this anyway? "No, sir, I really am not crazy about cars, to be truthful. A car is only transportation to me, and I have never owned one." This response seemed to calm him down.

He paused and looked down at my file. "This says your next of kin lives in Morocco. What's with that?"

"Yes, sir. My father is a naval officer stationed there."

"Why didn't you join the Navy?" he asked.

"I thought about it. I had been a merchant sailor and thought about going back to sea, but when I quit college, I knew I wanted to do this," I answered.

"Why?" he asked with a questioning expression as he leaned back in his chair.

"Sir, I believe that our fight in Vietnam is the right thing for this nation to be doing. If we do not stop the spread of communism, then it will surround our shores. I believe the people of Vietnam deserve and want the same liberties that our forefathers fought for with the help of the French in the American Revolution."

Shaking his lowered head, he said, "Okay, keep yourself out of trouble and you'll probably make it. Send in Brewster. You're dismissed."

I came to attention, rendered that proper salute and did an about-face out of the office. What the hell was this about? I never spoke to the man again. Three months later, he would be shot by the military police while attempting to rob the PX one evening. Chief Warrant Officer 2 Barbie lost the gun fight. It was suspected that he was involved in a couple of robberies in Fort Worth, one involving a shooting death. The Criminal Investigation Division questioned us about his possibly attempting to recruit someone to assist him in his criminal behavior. We always wondered what happened to his "hot" wife. There was some speculation that her expensive tastes may have contributed to his actions.

We received weekend passes but were required to wear our uniforms. The adjacent town was Mineral Wells, Texas. *Oh my God*, I thought when I arrived downtown. It had one stop light. Every guy was dressed like a cowboy, as were the girls—at least, we thought they were girls. It became obvious quickly that our kind, soldiers, were not really appreciated in their town. My future roommate Bill was only nineteen, so the two of us found a small tavern that didn't ask for ID. We took a table by ourselves and quietly drank our beer. We decided to leave after one beer. Some of the cowboys were staring at us, and we thought it best to get out before some trouble started. The other option was to go into Fort Worth, but you had to have a car and neither of us did. There was a WOC club on base, but there were no women there. We could go to the NCO club as we were all E-5s, but the real NCOs really didn't want us hanging around. Did you ever get the feeling you aren't loved?

About this time, we lost the first member of our class.

"Someone get Hanna and have him report to me," bellowed CW2 Barbie. Dave came downstairs and headed for the TAC's office. A few minutes later, Dave came out and said nothing to anyone but went upstairs. A half hour later, he left the building in his khaki uniform with a shaving kit and a small bag. He was going home on emergency leave. He would be starting Preflight over again in a later class.

Seldom did physical training fall on the training calendar. The result was that we were all packing on the pounds we'd lost in basic training. While in preflight training, we were fitted for our officer's uniforms. Warrant officer cadets were required to purchase one set of the Class A green uniform, which consisted of a coat and pants with a black stripe up the pant legs and around the jacket cuffs. Also, one set of the dress blues uniform, a dark blue coat and light blue pants with gold stripes instead of black, worn for formal occasions. The tailor would measure us and then add half an inch or an inch to each waist and chest measurement. He told us he anticipated we would be packing on a few pounds. He was right. Officers weren't issued uniforms but had to buy them and were given a one-time payment of two hundred and fifty dollars for that purpose, regardless of how long they remained on active duty. Enlisted soldiers were issued their uniforms and got a monthly uniform allowance to maintain them. The one question we had was, if flight school was another seven months and the chance of dropping out was about fifty-fifty, why were we buying our uniforms now? Never got an answer to that one, but I suspected someone was making money under the table.

# 3

## PRIMARY FLIGHT TRAINING

ONCE WE COMPLETED PREFLIGHT, WE ENTERED primary flight training. At any one time in 1968, there were ten flight companies in session. All those companies were located on that portion of the base known as the Hill, where all the Korean War barracks were located, as well as three new additional barracks. These were concrete block buildings. Each class started with about three hundred and fifty cadets. Half of the day would be spent in the classroom, learning a variety of subjects, to include Federal Aviation Administration flight regulations, navigation, and aircraft operating systems. The other half of the day would be spent on the flight line and flying. There were three types of helicopters at Fort Wolters at that time: the Hughes TH-55; the Bell OH-13, which was the aircraft shown in the TV series *M*A*S*H*; and the Hiller OH-23. Whichever aircraft you started with was the aircraft you would be flying your entire time at primary flight school. I drew the TH-55 and came to love that aircraft as it had plenty of power on warm Texas days.

On our first day of flying, my platoon was directed to a classroom, as was each of the other platoons in the company.

Seldom would we come together as a company again. Our instructors, some military and some civilian, were already in the classroom. We were told to take a seat anywhere at a table where an instructor was already seated. Each table had two seats for students. Standing, the instructor introduced himself.

"Gentlemen, I'm Mr. West," he said, extending his hand to each of us. "I will be your instructor for the next four months. The first thing we're doin' is makin' a solemn pledge to each other. 'I won't get you killed if you don't get me killed.' Do we have a deal?" he asked in his Texas drawl. He was wearing cowboy boots, so he must be a civilian.

Looking at each other, Bob Atwell and I said, "Deal!" Truth be told, we hadn't even thought about it. Bob was from Cleveland and had been in basic training with me. Likable but cocky, he was a ladies' man, quick-witted and good looking, with dark wavy hair and blue eyes, a regular chick magnet.

"Good." Mr. West indicated for us to sit down. "Let me get some information and we'll get out to the flight line. Who wants to fly first?" he asked. This was different. We were being asked instead of told. I told Bob to take it.

"Now that that's settled, Cadet Cory, you will ride the bus to the stage field and we'll meet you there. Each of you will fly for an hour and a half and then switch. If you fly out, then you ride the bus back. Each day you switch on who flies first. Any questions?" We both indicated that we had no questions, and he completed the paperwork.

"Okay, let's go preflight. When that's done, Cory, you come back here and an instructor will gather everyone up for the bus ride. Leave your helmet here. Let's go." And out to the flight line we walked.

As we walked out to our assigned aircraft for the day, Mr. West went into a dissertation on the nomenclature of the TH-55 helicopter. "The TH-55 is an off-the-shelf civilian aircraft known as the Hughes 300. It's a gas-fueled, piston-engine-driven aircraft with a transmission and clutch. Once you start the engine and reach operating rpm, you begin to engage the clutch, which tightens eight fan belts that turn the transmission and thus the rotor head and tail rotor. In your classroom work, you will learn all about the workings of the aircraft. Learn it well."

When we arrived at the aircraft, Mr. West reached in and pulled out a small laminated book, handing it to me.

"Cory, you read off the checklist for the preflight. As he reads it off, Atwell, we'll check the aircraft. You must pay attention to the details. A broken safety wire, a misaligned slippage mark, a missing nut or bolt or a loose Jesus nut can get you killed. Pay attention to the details."

The Jesus nut was a large nut that sat on the very top of the rotor and held the rotor head to the rotor mast that came out of the transmission. It was called the Jesus nut because if it came off, you'd be meeting Jesus very shortly.

As I read off each item, Mr. West pointed it out to us and showed us how to inspect that item. As he finished up, he said, "Tomorrow I'll read the checklist and you will do the inspection, Cory."

"Yes, sir."

He sent me back to the classroom to join the others for the bus ride. Fort Wolters had two major heliports, each with about seven hundred and fifty aircraft on them. Each morning at 0800 hours, all fifteen hundred aircraft took off. They returned at 1200 hours, then launched again at 1300 hours and returned at 1700 hours. Those aircraft would scatter across the countryside around Mineral Wells, Texas, to stage fields leased from local ranchers and farmers where training would be conducted. In addition to the stage fields, there were designated training locations where cadets could practice pinnacle approaches and slope landings. The students flying these aircraft had less than one hundred hours flying time, and the safety record was truly amazing considering the number of aircraft each day in the air and the low level of experience most of the pilots possessed.

As the bus pulled into the stage field where we were to meet our flight instructor, there were four asphalt lanes about the length of a football field with each lane about ten feet wide. Painted on each of these lanes, twenty yards apart, were four white squares designated as touchdown points for landing. Except, no one was landing there. All the helicopters were in the large field adjacent to the asphalt lanes, and those aircraft appeared to be in controlled crashes! Some were spinning wildly, others going up and down like yo-yos, and still others were doing both. Eventually each aircraft came back to the one building on the field to exchange students and refuel.

As Mr. West shut our aircraft down to refuel, Bob climbed out and walked over to me.

"How was it?" I asked.

"Oh my God! The flight out was nice, and he let me fly the thing. When we got here, he made the approach and took the aircraft over to the field at a hover. He set it down, explained each of the controls to me again and told me to hover. It was like riding a bucking bronco and Brahman bull all at once. And he was laughing! Scared the crap out of me."

"No shit!" I said.

"Finally he took the controls and set the thing on the ground, and then, one at a time, he would let me take a control while he handled the others. That wasn't bad, but when he gave me all four again, I was riding the bull, and someone had just opened the gate."

"Hey, Cory, get your ass over here and let's go," called Mr. West as he finished refueling the aircraft. As I climbed in and was getting my seat belt adjusted, he asked, "You have any flight experience, Cory?"

"Yes, sir. I have a private pilot's license, fixed-wing," I responded.

"That's good. You will have some air sense, but this is nothing like flying a plane. This is the cyclic." He indicated the control stick between my legs. "Go ahead and take it with your right hand. When you have it, state, 'I have the aircraft.' The response is, 'You have the aircraft.' This is the transfer of positive control of the aircraft. Whatever direction you move the cyclic in, that's the direction the aircraft is moving horizontally. That lever in your left hand is the collective and controls vertical movement. Take it with your left hand." I did.

"To go up, you pull it up, and to go down, you push it down. Your left hand has a death grip on the throttle. Relax. Every time you move the collective, you must increase or decrease the throttle and keep the engine rpm in the green arc here on the tachometer. Just a slight twist will be enough." He pointed at the tachometer.

"Now your feet are resting on the pedals. The pedals turn the nose of the aircraft to the left or the right. If you turn the nose to the left, you must increase your throttle, and because you increase your throttle, you may have to decrease your collective a bit to maintain your same hover height of three feet. Anytime you move the collective or the pedals, you will also have to move the throttle in order to maintain your hover height, which means you will have to move the collective as well. Pretty simple, really. Like a plane, all control movements are small and smooth. Any questions?"

Only about a thousand questions at this point. "No, sir," I lied, and I was sure he knew it, but he just smiled. He hovered the aircraft to the field, set it down and told me I had the controls. I repeated, "I have the controls," indicating positive control of the aircraft. Well, sort of.

"You have the aircraft. Okay, pick up to a hover," he

instructed me, and the next hour was a repeat of what Bob had experienced. Disneyland had nothing on this ride!

Gradually, over the next two weeks, things improved in our ability to hover and fly the aircraft. At about ten hours' flying time, cadets started soloing. At eleven hours, Mr. West told me to hover to the building. Climbing out of the aircraft, he said, "Cory, take it around the pattern three times, landing on strip four, panel four. Any questions?"

"No, sir." This time I wasn't lying, and I took the aircraft around the pattern three times. But I also talked out loud the whole time, repeating instructions to myself.

Besides hovering, takeoffs and landings, we were also instructed in how to execute autorotations. When the engine quits, then the helicopter goes into an autorotation, falling with the aerodynamics of a simonized brick. The pilot must a) identify he has a problem: "*Oh, my engine just quit!*"; b) respond correctly to the problem: immediately put the collective down and maintain rotor rpm in the green arc on the tachometer while maintaining sixty knot airspeed; c) pick a landing zone suitable to put the aircraft into: "*Where the hell is a field or highway that's clear of power lines or fences?*"; and d) land the aircraft. Okay, flare at fifty feet to decrease descent and slow forward motion, pop the collective at twenty-five feet, level the skids, pull more collective at three feet. From an altitude of one thousand feet, the pilot has about one minute to do that.

We were still expected to maintain our same standards for clean barracks. However, now we had only two students per room, so it was much easier to maintain our respective areas. The bathrooms were still communal, however. Our TAC officer, CWO2 Sloneger, set the standards the day we arrived, and we never had a problem, until he decided to go on leave and the senior TAC, CWO3 Robertson, filled in. On day one, he wasn't satisfied with the condition of the bathroom. This went on for about four days, until we'd had enough of using toothbrushes to clean the floors. That evening, we moved his entire office into the bathroom. Come morning, we held our breath as we assembled in the company street. He came into the building and went to his office. Expecting an explosion, we heard nothing. When he returned, he acted as if nothing was out of the ordinary. He took roll call and released us to go to breakfast. Damn, nothing! However, when we returned, one of our members went in to use the bathroom.

"What do you mean taking a shit in my office! How dare you take a crap in my office? Are you trying to be disrespectful to me?" screamed the senior TAC. Some poor schmuck had walked right into an ass chewing. We suddenly realized we were going to have to hold it until we got to the flight line. That evening, we reclaimed our bathroom. We moved everything back into his office, and he never complained about the condition of the bathroom again.

About two months into our flight training, we returned from the flight line and were told to get in company formation right away. Once all two hundred and seventy-five of us were assembled, as we'd had about seventy-five drop out at this point, the company commander came forward and addressed the class. One of our fellow classmates had crashed that day and was killed. That was something none of us had considered at this point in our training. His death would not be the last, either. Another student and his flight instructor were killed in a midair collision with another aircraft flown by someone from another class. How there weren't a lot more midair collisions always amazed me.

Primary flight training came to a close four months after it had started. We'd started with a class of three hundred and fifty and graduated a class of one hundred and seventy-five. Those who didn't complete the course in most cases found themselves in the infantry on their way to Vietnam. The big decision on graduation was where to go for our next phase of training. Fort Rucker, Alabama, had always been the home of Army Aviation, but with Vietnam in full swing, it had reached its capacity for taking student pilots. A new Advanced Rotary Wing Flight training facility had opened at Hunter Army Airfield in Savannah, Georgia. The Army actually asked for volunteers to go there. *Let's see*, I thought, *go to Fort Rucker, which sits in the middle of a dry county and the adjacent town is Enterprise, Alabama, or go to Hunter Army Airfield, with an adjacent major city, Savannah, and in a wet county.* That was a no-brainer decision for me.

Right after graduation that day, a group of us met at the post chapel. Bob had asked the girl back home to marry him and she'd accepted. Lin was as cute as could be and we had a grand party after the wedding, which was attended by Lin's sister and both sets of parents. Being married was frowned upon by the Army prior to primary flight but okay for advanced flight school. Lin and Bob were heading to Savannah along with me, Bill and Johnson.

# 4

## ADVANCED FLIGHT TRAINING

BILL MICHEL, MY ROOMMATE, AND I ARRIVED IN Savannah the night before we were due to report to Hunter Army Airfield, as had Bob and Lin as they sought out an apartment in town. Married men were allowed to live off post and not in the barracks. The city was covered in fog the next morning, which wasn't a problem for the cab driver who drove us to the base well prior to our noon reporting time. Unfortunately, most of the eighty members of our class were on the same commercial airliner that couldn't land that morning. Those cadets were delayed because of the fog and arrived after the 1200 formation. All those that arrived late were stopped at the entrance to the WOC company by a TAC officer, Chief Warrant Officer 2 Clinton. Since I'd arrived early, he made me the class cadet commander and had me stand next to him to meet the late arrivals.

"Cadet Cory, get these people in a formation," he growled at me. Mr. Clinton didn't really talk. He growled.

"Yes, sir." Picking four cadets that I knew out of the group, I made them the squad leaders and told them to line up.

"Everyone will fall in on these four squad leaders on my

command. Duffel bags in front of you. Fall in!" They did as instructed and stood in the position of attention. They all knew they were late and this could be trouble for them. Then Mr. Clinton stepped forward.

"You people had a twelve-hundred-hour report time, and you are late by sixty minutes. Evidently you don't want to be here. I suspect you have been screwing off in Savannah this morning," he stated as he walked along in front of the formation.

One cadet made the big mistake of offering an excuse. This was not the time to do that.

"Sir, we were all on the same flight and the fog..." He stopped as Mr. Clinton immediately got in his face.

"How dare you address me when you are at the position of attention and I am talking? Who the hell do you think you are? By tonight, Cadet, you will be in the infantry and out of this program. Now get out of this formation and go to the orderly room with your crap. You're done! Anyone else want to say anything?" Everyone just remained at attention and said nothing as our classmate picked up his bag with a look of shock on his face.

"Cadet Cory is your class commander. Cory, march this bunch of misfits to the orderly room. There you will all sign your Article 15s for missing formation—or, if you are as stupid as I think you all are, you can request a court-martial. I don't care." And he turned and walked back to the orderly room.

Everyone was in a state of shock that they were getting Article 15s, which could result in loss of pay and a blemish on their records. Worse, though we didn't realize it at the moment, this incident would be held against the entire class for some time.

The class cadet commander was responsible for all the class did or didn't do. If the barracks weren't cleaned to the standards set by the cadre, I heard about it. If someone failed a test, I heard about it. If the class was late getting someplace, I heard about it. Leadership positions were supposed to rotate after a week. For some reason, they did, but my position did not. After a week of being in this leadership position, I came to realize that I couldn't be a friend to anyone in the class. I would have to be the hard-ass if I was to get the cadre off my back as well as the class's. Our cadre consisted of one TAC officer, CWO2 Clinton, and one TAC NCO. The TAC NCO was a large, overweight man with numerous tattoos before tattoos became popular. I don't recall him ever saying anything. CWO2 Clinton, on the other hand, was quite vocal. Over time, it became obvious to all of us that he had a drinking problem.

The first major phase of our training was instrument training. This was conducted in the Bell TH-13 aircraft with full instrument packages. As in primary flight training, half of the day was spent in the classroom and the other half flying. Once the instructor and cadet were in the aircraft, the cadet would place a hood over his helmet so he couldn't see outside the aircraft and could only observe the instruments. Initially, the cadet was expected to maintain the aircraft in a level flight attitude, but we quickly transitioned to navigation and instrument approaches. Most of the cadets got through this phase of training, but not unscathed. Only one or two cadets weren't able to master the aircraft in a safe attitude and were recycled to the next class for additional training. A couple of cadets went on to gain full instrument tickets, which usually destined them for Boeing CH-47 Chinook transition after graduation. This training took approximately two more months. In addition to our instrument classroom instruction, we were taught how to adjust artillery fire and given extensive meteorology instruction.

We were approaching the end of our instrument training

when we returned to the barracks from the flight line the night prior to the meteorology exam. Mr. Clinton wasn't happy with the condition of the barracks and had gone on a rampage, aided by a bottle of Jack Daniels. Beds were turned over; wall locker contents were lying on the floor; the fire hose was spraying water, and the contents of everyone's footlockers were everywhere except in the footlockers. He was on a tirade. One cadet was singled out. Mr. Clinton was berating him. Evidently the cadet was responsible for his "five-o'clock shadow." Mr. Clinton told the cadet to get into the pushup position. Once there, he placed a razor on the floor in front of him and told him to shave! The cadet looked scared, and I was mad. I had had enough of Mr. Clinton's crap! With all the respect for his rank that I could muster, I stepped forward and got in Clinton's face.

"Sir, you have been drinking and you are drunk. If you do not leave this minute, I am going straight to the company commander and have him resolve this situation. Now leave!" I shouted. There was dead silence. Mr. Clinton just stood there and glared at me with his bloodshot eyes. Everyone was watching. Finally, he laughed, turned and staggered out of the barracks. Everyone, including me, sighed with relief. We spent most of the night getting the barracks back in order, and no one had an opportunity to study for the weather exam. It showed the next day.

The exam was in the morning. When we returned to the barracks after flying in the afternoon, we were immediately informed by the company first sergeant that we were all restricted to the barracks until further notice and I was to report to the company commander's office. When I arrived, the senior officer from the Weather Committee was present as well. I was told to sit down.

"Cadet Cory, do you know why I have restricted the company and called you here?" the company commander asked. Like I was some clairvoyant and could read his mind. This was the first time I had ever spoken to the man. Again, Dad's words of wisdom came to mind.

"No, sir," I replied, knowing this wasn't the time to be a smart-ass.

"It appears, Cadet Cory, that most of your class failed the weather exam. We need to know why," he stated. *Oh, shit! Most of the class, which includes me too.* Again, as class leader, it was my fault.

"Didn't you people study for the exam last night?" asked the Weather Committee instructor, who didn't look happy. Why did I suspect that shit rolled downhill here and it was all coming at me? However, I was seeing a U-turn for this shit storm.

"No, sir, we did not study last night. We had a party instead," I replied. Their eyes bulged, and I thought both men were going to drop dead from heart attacks.

"You did what?" gagged out the company commander. "You had a party the night before one of the most important exams of this course? Do you realize that by having a party and failing that exam, you all could fail flight school and be sent to the infantry immediately?"

"Yes, sir," I replied as I let them stew on this revelation.

Now the weather instructor had a grin on his face as he turned to the company commander. "Well, I guess the problem wasn't with the instruction but the discipline of these cadets."

I was beginning to see what was going on here. Somewhere above their level, the shit had hit the fan, and someone high up was looking for where to lay the blame. The Army needed helicopter pilots and at this point had spent considerable money training eighty cadets. The Army couldn't afford to wash out eighty cadets at one time. The company commander wasn't looking too good about now.

"Cadet Cory, why in the hell would you have a party the night before a major exam?" he asked in a dejected and resigned voice.

"Sir, we had no choice," I answered sheepishly. I was beginning to enjoy this. I had been around the military long enough to know when people were in a state of panic over something that had gone horribly wrong. *Oh, Dad, you taught me well.*

"What the hell do you mean you had no choice?" The company commander was starting to lose it.

"Sir, when we returned from the flight line last night, Mr. Clinton had torn the barracks apart, to include turning on the fire hose, and told us to get that mess cleaned up before morning. We had a barracks-cleaning party to get it squared away, and that took until midnight. Lights out was at twenty-two hundred hours, but we worked on stuff in the dark until we had it taken care of. Only the married men had a chance to study last night as they were free to leave once we got back from class." I had just let the cat out of the bag. They both sat in silence, staring at me with their mouths open. That lasted maybe fifteen seconds.

"You're dismissed, Cadet Cory," the company commander said, his face showing anger.

"Yes, sir." I came to attention, saluted smartly and did an about-face out the door. When I got back to the barracks, everyone wanted to know what was going on. When I told them that most of us had failed the weather exam, a quiet state of shock fell over the place. Then the questions started, focusing on whether we would all be washed out and sent to the infantry. About an hour later, I was called back to the company commander's office and told that the class would be restricted to the barracks but to go to dinner.

The next day appeared normal, until it came time to go to the flight line that afternoon. A clerk from the orderly room met me as we returned from class for lunch. "Cadet Cory."

"Yeah, what's up?"

"You are to report to the company commander, now, in Class B uniform," he said and left.

Normally we wore our flight suits to go to the flight line. Why was I getting dressed up in my khaki uniform? This wasn't good. As I arrived at the company commander's office, he was coming out and told me to follow him. We walked in silence to the battalion commander's office, which was in another building. The company commander entered the battalion commander's office first and shortly thereafter came out and directed me to go in. His only words were spoken in almost a fatherly manner.

"Just tell him what you told me last night. It's going to be all right."

The battalion commander directed me to sit down and asked me to explain what had happened. He listened and took some notes. He didn't ask questions, and at the end, he stood, picked up his hat and directed me to follow him. We left that building and walked to another building. The sign read School Commandant. This shit was rolling uphill now. The company commander and battalion commander entered the commandant's office first while I waited in the foyer. Then the battalion commander came out and I was directed into the office of the school commandant. Since joining the Army, I hadn't spoken to a full colonel, but here I was having an audience with one. Being a Navy brat, however, I had spoken to a lot of Navy captains, which is the same rank as an Army colonel. Dad had told me they all put their pants on the same way; don't ever lie and always talk straight and respectful. Also in attendance was the chairman of the Weather Committee, who had arrived before us.

Entering, I stopped three feet in front of the commandant's deck, came to attention and saluted. "Sir, Cadet Cory reporting as ordered, sir."

Returning my salute, he indicated a chair. "Sit down, Cadet Cory. Your company commander has told me what happened in the barracks the night before the weather exam, but I want to hear it from you." I repeated what I had stated before, almost word for word.

"Why do you think Mr. Clinton did that, Cadet Cory?" the school commandant asked. Time to play my hand.

"Sir, in my opinion, as on previous occasions, Mr. Clinton was intoxicated, as demonstrated by him putting Cadet Barker in the front leaning rest position and directing him to shave with a razor," I replied. This was the first time I'd mentioned those two details. You could have heard a pin drop. The colonel looked around the room at the others, who were looking at each other, and then all eyes came at me.

"Do you realize what you just said? You have made a serious allegation against an officer of the United States Army," asked the battalion commander, his voice slightly elevated.

"Yes, sir," I stated calmly.

"Cadet Cory, you will return to your classes. You will not repeat any of this to anyone. Do you understand?" The colonel glared. "You are dismissed."

I stood at attention, rendered the proper salute and departed. I began to wonder if I'd just sunk my own ship. When I walked into the classroom at the flight line, the instructor stopped in mid-sentence and everyone stared at me. Everyone wanted to know what had happened, but no one dared ask. The next day, three more cadets were told to get into their Class B khaki uniforms and report to the company commander, and all were instructed not to repeat what happened. And again the following day, three more were pulled from class.

Slowly, other items were coming out that the battalion commander and school commandant had not been aware of. Our class was in its eighth week of training and we were finishing up our instrument training. Since our arrival, our class hadn't been allowed off post on pass, except for the married men who lived off post. Every other class received blanket weekend passes, but not us. It appeared that the stigma of so many cadets arriving late on day one had tainted us. Other instances of our TAC officer being intoxicated began coming out as well, as the barracks incident hadn't been the first occasion. On Thursday we were informed that our class would retake the weather exam on the following Saturday. We were restricted to the barracks until such time but would all receive a weekend pass after the exam. Now if that wasn't an incentive to study, nothing was. We studied individually and as a group, asking questions and making a game of it. Come Saturday morning, we were ready, and everyone passed the exam with flying colors. Getting ready to go to town was on everyone's mind as we marched back to the barracks. Not so fast!

When we arrived back at the barracks, spirits were high. As we came through the door, there stood the battalion commander, and we immediately came to attention. He was standing in the middle of the hall along with another officer, a major.

"Cadet Cory, bring everyone in here and put them at ease," he directed me.

Once we were all assembled, the battalion commander introduced himself. "I am Lieutenant Colonel Barlow, your battalion commander. I have not met most of you and normally do not meet cadets until graduation. However, because of this incident, I have met some of you and thought I should meet all of you. What you have experienced is not typical of the treatment of cadets. Changes have been made, the first being you have a new company commander. Major

Kitter will be your company commander for the remainder of your training. Mr. Clinton and Sergeant First Class Moron will no longer be your TACs either. Major Kitter." And he turned the meeting over to the major.

*Oh shit*, I thought. They'd relieved our company commander over this. That was a ruined Army career. No love lost for the TACs. Our new company commander was a combat pilot, as was every officer at the flight school, but this guy had a reputation as a gunship pilot. Judging by the awards he was wearing, he had seen some action. Silver Stars and Distinguished Flying Crosses didn't get passed out easily.

"Thank you, sir. I know you're all anxious to get into town, so I'll be brief. You know what is expected of you for barracks standards and discipline. Maintain those standards and you can expect fair treatment from me. You will not have any TACs, but I will fulfill that role. Are there any questions?" No one did, or at least they were all smart enough not to ask at this point. Then the hammer fell, on me.

"Cadet Cory, you will remain as class leader. Any issues you have or I have, we will talk directly. Do you understand?" He was looking right at me, and so were all my classmates.

"Yes, sir." No discussion needed.

"Now, cadets, get changed and enjoy your pass for the weekend. Cadet Cory..."

I had been around long enough to know what that meant. "Class, attention!" I bellowed out and they did smartly. After he and the battalion commander left, I put everyone at ease. Naturally, there were a lot of questions. Some cadets still didn't understand that the company commander had been relieved and was probably being put out of the Army, as were the TAC officer and NCO. I closed the meeting with instructions on what time everyone had to be back on Sunday night and dismissed everyone. As I was changing clothes, another cadet from a lower class told me to report to the company commander's office in civilian clothes.

When I arrived, Major Kitter was by himself in his office and told me to come in and close the door.

"Sit down. Do you want some coffee? I just made a pot," he asked as he poured.

"Yes, sir, thank you." I was in shock that he was being so casual.

"Got any plans for this weekend, Cadet Cory?" he asked as he looked over the rim of his coffee cup. *This is not good*, I thought.

"Not really, sir. Just going to see some of the sights in Savannah," I responded slowly.

"Front Street is where most people go for the bars. You're over twenty-one, aren't you?" he asked with a grin.

"I am, sir, but I don't normally barhop. I find hotel cocktail lounges are a lot quieter and off the beaten path." *Where's this conversation going?* I wondered as I sipped my coffee.

"I understand you want to go home to Morocco on Christmas leave. Who is in Morocco?" he asked. *How the hell did he know that?*

"Sir, my father is a naval officer and stationed there. They're buying me a plane ticket."

"You do understand that you have to submit a DA Form 1049 requesting permission to leave the country along with your leave request, don't you?"

"No, sir, I did not." I was sinking here.

"Do you have a passport?"

"I have applied for one, sir. It hasn't come yet, but this being October, it should be here soon."

"Okay. Monday morning, you get to the orderly room and have them prepare the 1049 requesting permission to leave the country for Christmas leave. Understand that you best be back here for morning formation on January fourth or you will be dropped from the program," he cautioned me.

"Sir, I told my mom to have the plane bringing me back from Rabat to Savannah arriving on January first. I'm not taking any chances like what happened before with the fog."

"Okay, then, I'll sign it and recommend approval as soon as it comes across my desk." We made some small talk about different people in the class, those that were doing really good and those that were struggling.

"Well, I won't keep you. Just wanted to know if you had any questions. This was a messy situation, but we will get it resolved. I want you to understand that if there is a problem, you bring it to me, immediately. Here's my home phone number if you need to speak with me after duty hours for any reason." He handed a piece of paper to me.

"Oh, and one other thing. Your class moves on to Huey transition Monday morning and you are the senior class now, which means we have to have a cadet battalion commander overseeing the entire cadet corps. You're it, along with being your class leader. Pick your staff and give me their names Monday morning. Any questions?" I was sure he was smiling, or laughing, behind his coffee mug.

"No, sir, no questions," I stammered out.

"Good. Go enjoy your weekend. See you Monday morning." He set his coffee mug down and stood. That was my signal to get out, which I promptly did. A thousand questions ran through my head, not the least of which was *Why me?* I had been in a leadership position longer than anyone and now was going to be stuck in it for another eight weeks. How many times was I going to get my ass chewed out now, as I was responsible for the entire corps of cadets? Thoughts of what I had to do now plagued my mind over the weekend as I mapped out what I thought needed to be done. I spent

Sunday in my room, getting my notes in order to meet with the junior class leaders.

Monday morning began as usual, with one hundred percent of the company present for duty. We were to begin our transition into the UH-1 aircraft, the workhorse of the Vietnam War. Most of us would be flying this type of aircraft shortly in combat, so our training took on new meaning. We were riveted to our classroom and our flight instruction. Classroom work was understanding the different systems for the aircraft, to include flight control system, electrical system, engine and transmission. Flight training was one instructor with two students in the aircraft, and we were introduced to not only flying the aircraft but formation flying as well. Flying at two thousand feet with only a two-rotor-blade separation from the aircraft in front of you in different formations, including at night, was a bit hair-raising for me. I wasn't comfortable with it. This was nothing compared to night autorotations, however.

In primary flight, we hadn't done night flying or night autorotations. Night autorotations consisted of flying on the darkest night of the month and at one thousand feet, then closing the throttle so you immediately fell at a rate of one thousand feet per minute. At about one hundred feet, you turned on the landing light and executed a safe landing. We would joke that once you turned the landing light on, if you didn't like what you saw, just turn the light off and it would go away. How we didn't crash aircraft during this phase of training was beyond my comprehension. Very soon, I would learn different ways to do autorotations and proper formation flying, and at night.

Formation flying began in earnest when we moved to Fort Stewart, Georgia, for the last month of our training. We moved to a field camp that was representative of the living conditions in Vietnam. The hooches had fifty beds along the walls with a single corridor down the middle. We would receive our flight briefings in a hooch that served as the operations center. Two students would go with one instructor and conduct the mission. The instructor would sit in the jump seat behind and between the two students. If we screwed up, there was no way he could salvage a crash. We did not screw up.

Some days we practiced flying heavily loaded aircraft, which had water cans that added considerable weight to the aircraft. Some days we would conduct sling load operations with water bags tethered under the aircraft. Some days we would conduct formation flying with the formations changing while in flight. Once we had formation flying down pat, in daylight, we then got to practice it at night. Scared the crap out of me! Our passengers were Ranger students that initially had no idea we were students. They looked terrified for the rest of the flight once they found out. I really thought I would be better off flying gunships or medical evacuation missions.

The final exercise in our training was SERE training: Survival, Escape, Resistance and Evasion. We moved to a new field location, minus additional clothing, toilet articles or goodies. The first two days were spent attending lectures and demonstrations. The lectures were on land navigation by the stars and sun, first aid, and the Code of Conduct. The demonstrations were on how to build a shelter with tree limbs, vines and leaves; how to build snares and fish traps; how to skin a rabbit without a knife; and how to identify edible plants. The bottom line was, eat plants only as a last resort. In the area of resistance, we were instructed not to be heroes. Do whatever we were told to do. Do not look at our captors but look at the ground. Do not communicate with one another unless we could do it without the captors seeing it or knowing about it. The bottom line we all took away from this training was you best not get captured.

At the conclusion of the second day's training, everyone

was ushered into a briefing room. A chart board with a map was set up and one of the cadre came forward. He was wearing a black beret, black shirt and black pants. His insignia was foreign to us. He was of Asian descent.

"I am Colonel Nguyen, commander of the opposing forces, the OPFOR. Tonight you will be required to escape and evade my force. If you are captured, you will be sent to the POW camp, where you will be interrogated and reveal to my interrogator the location of your pickup point. Once you reveal that location, you will be allowed to eat and sleep. I look forward to welcoming you to my camp." With that, he left. Next up was another cadre member, this one dressed in the uniform we were familiar with.

"Tonight you will be driven to the start point for this exercise. There you will be put into four-man teams. Each team will be issued a rabbit and a chicken to prepare for dinner, since you have not eaten in the past twenty-four hours. I recommend you prepare them quickly and eat fast. At some point, and you will know when it is time, move out and head for the pickup point, which is located nine klicks[1] to the north at this location." He pulled a cover off the map, and you could hear the mumbling as we all looked at it.

"You will note that there is a major stream or river on both sides of this area. Do not cross the river or stream. Since it is December tenth, the water is about forty-five degrees and swift-moving. Across the river is out of bounds. There are several roads through the exercise area. If someone is injured, get on a road and wait. Colonel Nguyen will have vehicles on those roads looking for you. When and if you arrive at the pickup point, check in with the NCO there, and the exercise will be over for those of you that make it to there. Any questions?" Some spring-butt always had a question.

"Sir, where do we get maps and compasses?" asked Mr. Spring-Butt.

"The stars are your compass, and keep the rivers on your flanks. There are no maps. Now load the trucks, and good luck—you're going to need it."

We loaded the trucks, which were all driven by soldiers in black shirts, black pants, and black berets. As we loaded, comments such as "Be seeing you soon, Cadet" could be heard.

Each four-man team was given a live rabbit and chicken when they arrived at the start point. I broke the chicken's neck and another cadet broke the rabbit's back as they had taught us. Several campfires were already burning, so we filled metal coffee cans with water and boiled the meat. In about twenty minutes, we were eating what we could, and not having eaten in the past twenty-four hours, it tasted okay. Then all hell broke loose with gunfire, and we took off running. It was still daylight, so knowing which way to head was easy. Sun on the right and gunfire behind us sent us off in the right direction.

Soon, however, it turned into night with an overcast sky. The four of us kept moving in what we were fairly sure was the right direction. Whoever was walking point would walk ten to fifteen feet in front of the group and provide early warning if we walked into the OPFOR. That would give the other three time to escape, or so we thought. About three hours into the exercise, our point man raised his hand for us to halt and we did, going into a low crouch. He came back. There was a road ahead that was perpendicular to our line of escape. He wanted to know if we wanted him to cross it. We had not taken a break at this point and thought we would just lie there for a few minutes. As we did so, we began to hear movement off to our right. The ground cover was sparse, and we eventually saw this group moving through the trees. We didn't know who they were, but they were traveling on a parallel course. We decided to just watch them.

They didn't even stop when they got to the road, until the

headlights from the vehicle parked in the woods across the road from our position came on. The OPFOR rushed over to take them prisoner. We didn't even breathe. We lay there and watched four of our fellow cadets being tied, blindfolded and loaded into the truck and taken away. Only after we were sure that no other OPFOR were along that stretch of road did we move to the edge of the road, spread out and all at once sprint across the road. Our adrenaline was pumping as we moved on through the woods, right into a swamp.

At first we considered whether we might have bumped into the river on the left flank, but this water wasn't moving, and trees were standing. It was cold and up to our thighs, but we thought it best to keep moving. We reasoned that there would probably be no OPFOR standing in a swamp getting wet waiting for our dumb asses. We didn't consider that they might be wearing hip boots. At one point, we began to doubt our direction. Since I was the smallest guy in the group, it was decided that I would climb to the top of a tree and see if I could see anything. When I climbed to the top, the only thing I could observe was total darkness, and stars.

"Hey, guys, I see the North Star," I called down.

"Great, which way is it?" came back the whispered reply.

"That way." I pointed.

"Hey, dumbass, we can't see you or which way you're pointing," came the reply. Oh yeah, I was so far up the tree that it was difficult for them to see me or me them.

"Okay, listen up. I'm going to toss my canteen down in the direction of the star. Listen for it." The guys fanned out and I tossed it away from the tree in the direction of the star.

"Son of a bitch, you nearly hit me, pecker-head."

I got down, and we moved out. Occasionally, we could hear some commotion off in the distance as another team was caught by the OPFOR. We began to see landmarks that indicated we were focusing on the pickup point. We became more cautious, however, when we saw a campfire. Could it be a trick to lure us into the OPFOR? We decided we would move in closer and observe the activities before we approached. We were cold and wet, and that fire looked so inviting. We could see figures standing around the fire, eating hot chow and drinking coffee. After thirty minutes, we decided that this was the pickup point and we should go in. Thankfully, another team went charging in as we were getting ready to move. They were immediately captured and bound! It was a trap. The commotion we had heard earlier was another team being rounded up at this point. We moved to our left and skirted this location, continuing to move north. About a half hour later, we came upon another campfire. This one really was the pickup point, but we exercised the same precaution. Hot oatmeal, powdered eggs and bacon had never tasted so good.

The bus ride back to Hunter Army Airfield and our barracks was marked not by jubilation but by snoring. We were all dead tired but happy because that had been our last exercise. Flight training was over, and we all knew we were going to graduate. It was also the start of the Christmas holidays, and we all would be going home on leave, only to return to Hunter for three days of out-processing. Naturally we would have liked to graduate first to go home as warrant officers, but the Army had other plans for us.

One of our members was from Montana and had been sending his pay home as his parents were not well off and his pay was a big help. He wasn't planning on going home as he had no money. Before everyone left, he was handed a round-trip plane ticket home along with spending money, courtesy of everyone in the class. We were a tight bunch.

Once we returned from leave, it was a matter of three days of out-processing, which included more shots as we all had our orders to Vietnam. Of the eighty cadets in our class that had gone to Hunter for flight training, sixty-seven would be graduating, the others having quit somewhere in the sixteen weeks of training. Fortunately, we lost no members of the class due to crashes. Some of the class would go on to transition into other aircraft before departing for Vietnam, the other two aircraft being the CH-47 Chinook cargo helicopter and the AH-1G Cobra gunship, which had recently been introduced into service in 1968. We all had our orders. Bill and I were assigned to the First Cavalry Division; Bob was going to CH-47 transition and then to the 101st Airborne Division.

On graduation day, some had families attend the ceremony. The day prior, we were all appointed to warrant officers in the United States Army. My dad had flown in from Morocco and swore me in as a warrant officer. Johnson's parents were there as well and so proud of him. He had a new pair of high-priced Corfam regulation low-quarter shoes. This was probably the last time we would see our fellow classmates. We left WOC country for the last time, only to return in our memories.

## Republic of South Vietnam, 1968–1970

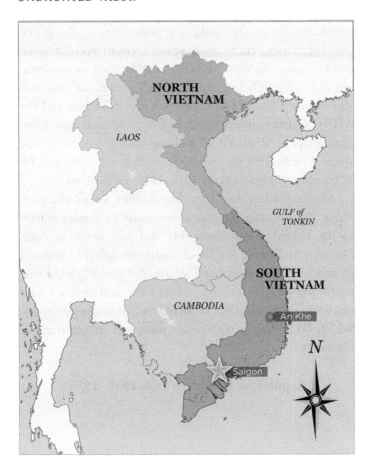

# 5

## WELCOME TO VIETNAM

THE FLIGHT FROM FORT LEWIS, WASHINGTON, TO Vietnam was fourteen hours with a two-hour stop at Yokota Air Force Base outside of Tokyo, Japan. The plane was a commercial airliner contracted by the government. Most Air Force transport aircraft were carrying cargo and not passengers. We arrived in Cam Ranh Bay, Vietnam, in the dead of night.

As the doors opened, the heat immediately penetrated the cabin, as did an NCO. "Welcome to the Republic of Vietnam. As you exit the aircraft, form two lines."

Once we were lined up, the NCO raised his bullhorn. "Once I call your name, you will proceed to that single-story building behind me and brush your teeth with the toothbrush and toothpaste provided. You will brush for a minimum of one minute. You will then exit the building and be told which bus to get on." And he started calling names.

*What! I just arrived in a combat zone and the very first thing I'm going to do is brush my teeth? You have got to be kidding*, I thought.

The toothpaste was a highly concentrated fluoride tooth-paste, as we would not see a dentist, nor want to see a dentist, for the next year. Dental service in the forward areas was primitive at best, with foot-pumped drills. As we left the building, we were directed to a bus. There were only two of us on the bus, me and Bill Michel, my flying buddy and roommate. The bus drove us across the Cam Ranh Bay base and deposited us in front of a barracks building.

"You will sleep here tonight, sir. Someone will come by tomorrow and get you. Chow is inside."

Bill and I got our bags and walked into a room that had sixty bunk beds, all made up. We were the only two people in there. Chow was waiting for us, C-rations. We skipped dinner and went to bed.

The morning heat woke us, and after a shower, I walked outside. *This place is beautiful!* I thought. Thirty feet from the front door just to the west of our building was a large lagoon probably a mile across, with white sand and swaying palm trees. I immediately thought, *We should be at a resort and not a combat zone.* The water was crystal-clear, reflecting the few white clouds in the western sky. Except for the noise of a faraway airplane engine, you wouldn't know you were on a military base as there was nothing around our barracks. About an hour later, a jeep pulled up and a young sergeant came in and asked if we were ready for the next leg.

The next leg began with a stop at the Central Issue Facility, where we were given load-bearing equipment, duffel bags, steel infantry helmets and more jungle fatigues.

"Excuse me, Sergeant, but this is infantry stuff. I'm a helicopter pilot. What is this for?" I asked.

"Sir, you are in the First Air Cavalry Division, and everyone, regardless of position, unit or rank, gets this. Welcome to the division," he said as he handed me a canteen with cup and cover. With our stateside suitcases as well as a duffel bag now, we found ourselves loading a C-123 airplane with about forty other soldiers for a flight to An Khe, First Air Cavalry Division Rear. We climbed up the back ramp and sat on the floor as the plane started up its two gas piston engines, belching black smoke, and rolled out to the runway. No seat belts, no stewardess, no bathroom and no seats. I hoped we didn't hit turbulence as this would be a really uncomfortable ride.

An Khe wasn't like Cam Ranh Bay. Located in the central highlands of Vietnam, it was a bit cooler, and instead of white sand, it was dusty red clay and everything was covered in it. Here we would spend five days "in-processing" to the division. To entertain us during this time, we had classes about Viet Cong booby traps, weapons familiarization, and rappelling from a tower. We were issued more clothing and equipment, and our civilian clothes were taken from us and placed in a box. On the outside, we had to put an address for our next of kin. I told the sergeant, "I really don't have a permanent address as my next of kin is military and will be moving again in the next year."

"Sir, you have a problem that I would not worry about. You either pick this up when you out-process, or we ship it to your next of kin if you get killed. After that, it's the US Postal Service's problem, not yours and not mine."

After our in-processing orientation week, we loaded a C-7 Caribou twin-engine plane and flew from An Khe to Phuoc Vinh, site of the First Cavalry Division forward headquarters and home to the aviation brigade that Bill and I were assigned to. Bill was going to stay at the aviation brigade's general support aviation company as he was assigned there as a pilot. I would be going on to a subordinate unit, which was located about twenty minutes southwest at Lai Khe.

Phuoc Vinh just plain sucked in my immediate opinion. It

had the same red clay dust on everything that we'd experienced at An Khe. In addition, there wasn't a tree on the entire base camp, which was all one-story hooches surrounded by sandbags about four feet high. A jeep picked Bill and me up, depositing him at his unit and me at the battalion headquarters to arrange transportation to my unit. There I was informed that it was the battalion commander's policy to see all new pilots, but that I would have to wait until the next day to see him as he was busy. That was nice that he wanted to meet and greet new pilots, but to make me sit on my ass for a whole day, let alone find a bed for the night, was rather inconsiderate, I thought. A captain that worked in the personnel shop told me to follow him and took me over to a barracks building, where he pointed out a bed that I could use for the night. The owner was on leave back in Hawaii. He showed me the mess hall and latrines and left me on my own.

"The colonel will see you at zero eight hundred in his office," he said, and that was that.

At 0800 hours, I was escorted into the colonel's office, where I came to attention and saluted. "Sir, Warrant Officer Cory reporting."

He returned my salute, told me to stand at ease, shook my hand, wished me luck and told me I was dismissed. I'd waited twenty-four hours for a less-than-two-minute "how do you do." I guessed his time was more valuable than my time. I doubted I'd ever see him again.

When I came out, the captain was waiting for me. "I notified your unit that you're here, and they're sending an aircraft to get you. A jeep will take you back to the flight line. The aircraft will have a green triangle on the door with a lightning bolt through the triangle. That's your ride. Good luck."

What was with everyone wishing me good luck? The jeep deposited me back at the airfield at about 0900 hours, and I waited, and waited, and waited. Finally at around 1630 hours, a helicopter hovered in and lands. There was a green triangle with a lightning bolt on the door. Crew chief came over and grabbed a bag as the engine was still running and told me to hurry. We got in and were out of there like a shot. I was glad to leave Phuoc Vinh.

**6**

## SETTLING IN

THE PILOT WHO DELIVERED ME TO THIS LUSH tropical rubber tree plantation said to wait and someone would come to get me. So, I waited and took in the surroundings. I was standing on the tarmac in the middle of a rubber tree plantation covered in red clay dust with everything the Army had issued me. My relatively clean jungle fatigues and steel pot with fresh new camouflage cover screamed new guy. No one else was wearing a steel pot. The flak jacket I was wearing might as well have been a sign around my neck. "Danger: New Guy. Beware." No one else was wearing a flak jacket. The tarmac had revetments for about eighty helicopters to be parked. A few of the revetments had some holes in the sides. Each revetment was about six feet high, ten feet wide and twenty feet long, just big enough to slowly ease a hovering helicopter into place and be offered some protection from rocket or mortar attack. Some revetments were empty and some held a Bell UH-1 Iroquois "Huey" or a Bell AH-1G "Cobra" gunship.

A jeep came to a stop in front of me with a hatless captain driving. "You Mr. Cory?"

"Yes, sir." I snapped to attention and saluted.

"Shit, you trying to get me shot? Damn sniper sees you doing that and I'm the one he's going to shoot. I don't have a hat on for a reason, so get your shit and let's go," he said with a disgusted tone.

"Sorry, sir." I tossed my duffel bags into the jeep and climbed in.

He extended his hand and grinned. "There are no snipers here. Just thought I'd scare the crap out of you. I'm Captain Goodnight, the operations officer for our merry band. Welcome to the Chicken Coop. The Chicken Coop is the company location, and this here parking area is the Chicken Pen. Our call sign is Chicken-man."

"Chicken-man! That's our call sign?" I responded. *That ought to instill courage in the hearts of our troops and fear in the minds of the enemy. Why couldn't it be something bold and dynamic?* I thought. *Chicken-man?*

"Sir, how did we come by that call sign?" I asked.

"The official call sign is Drumstick. There's a popular radio show in the Chicago area, and now it's on Armed Forces Radio in Vietnam, about a wicked white-winged warrior called Chicken-man. Some of the episodes are hilarious. When the unit first came to Nam, we were the Hoot Owls, and the name has changed several times over the years to Apache and Lucky Shot in 1966, Sidewinder and Swordfish in 1967 and Drumstick in 1968. Some of the warrant officers decided about six months ago to start using the Chicken-man call sign, and it's pretty much stuck. So now it's the unofficial official call sign for the unit." I was starting to like this Chicken-man call sign now.

The ride was short, but I was thankful for it with all my gear. The Chicken Coop was located in a rubber tree plantation surrounded by the First Infantry Division and owned by the Michelin tire company of France, which owned all the rubber tree plantations in this part of Vietnam. Our parent organization, 227th Assault Helicopter Battalion, was located at Phuoc Vinh, but that place was overcrowded, so our company, along with Delta Company, was located at Lai Khe. Everything except the flight line was under rubber trees, which made it cooler here than at Phuoc Vinh, and no dust. I was starting to like this place already. The only downside was the fact that our company was living in General Purpose Medium tents with wooden floors, six men to a tent. Everything was under tents except the mess hall. There were no sandbags around anything for protection from mortars or rockets. For that, there was a bunker made out of four-by-four-inch timbers for framing and dirt-filled ammunition boxes for siding, all covered with sandbags. The roof was tin, with two layers of sandbags.

"This is the operations tent. Drop your gear and come inside. I'll call your platoon leader," Captain Goodnight said as he rolled out of the jeep. As I entered, he indicated a guy with what was probably the nicest, most well-groomed handlebar mustache I had ever seen. He appeared older than most, with gray invading his once very red hair. "This is Sergeant First Class Robinson, our operations NCO," Captain Goodnight said.

"Welcome, Mr. Cory," the sergeant first class said and extended his hand.

"Glad to meet you, Sergeant." I was a bit unfamiliar with meeting NCOs in a casual manner. For the past year, sergeants had been taking bites out of my ass, and now they were so polite.

"I called your platoon leader, but he's still out flying, so one of the pilots is coming over to get you and show you where you bunk. How about a beer?" he offered.

"Yeah, thanks," I replied as I took in the operations setup. It had a counter with a map of the area under plexiglass.

Behind that were a couple of folding tables and folding metal chairs. In the rear was another bench with three radios mounted and a clerk that monitored the calls, keeping a daily log of all calls coming in and going out as well as any significant events. There was a chart on an easel with aircraft numbers, call signs, pilots' names and a mission number.

"Let me give you a quick orientation," SFC Robinson offered while handing me a very cold tin can of Carling Black Label beer with rusted seams. He pointed at the map on the counter. "This is our area of operations. It's commonly referred to as Three Corps of Vietnam, with Four Corps south of us in the Mekong Delta, and First Corps, or Eye Corps as we refer to it, along the DMZ with North Vietnam. Two Corps is between us and Eye Corps. Our actual operating area runs from Tay Ninh in the south to Song Be here in the north along the Cambodian border and back to Long Binh here to the southeast of us. Here's Phuoc Vinh, Division HQ. Operating in the region besides the First Cav are the First and Twenty-Fifth Infantry Divisions, as well as a couple of separate brigades that we'll fly for. There's a Special Forces camp here, here and here," he said, pointing at each location. "There was one here back in 1965, but it was overrun and abandoned back then. That's Bu Gia Map. Another is here at Bu Dop and it was overrun at about the same time. Song Be is the closest we've gotten to the border since then. Right now most of the stuff we fly is between Phuoc Vinh and Long Binh. The generals are worried about a major attack on Long Binh with TET coming up again next month," he added. The whole time he was talking, he was pointing at places on the map, and I still had no idea where everything was located.

"How much flying are we getting?" I asked.

"Every newbie asks that question," Captain Goodnight chimed in. "You'll get all the flying you want and more than you can handle. There'll be days when you go to bed with your butt cheeks hurting and they'll still be hurting when you wake up and you have another twelve-to-fifteen-hour day ahead of you. Some days you'll get twenty hours in before you shut the engine down. Normally when you get a hundred and forty hours for the month, you get a two-day stand-down, if I don't need you," he explained as another individual walked in. "This is Lou Price, and he's going to show you where you can set up housekeeping."

Lou was a skinny guy from California, tall, but almost everyone was taller than me. He had long blond hair for a non-military look, a thin build, and an immature mustache. His military attire was a T-shirt, OD green jungle pants and flippy-flops. Not married and no kids, that he knew about.

"Come on, newbie, let's get you settled. Where's your crap?" he asked with a beer in one hand as he reached for one of my bags with the other. We walked over two rows of tents and into one.

"Hey, guys, we have a new guy," Lou said as he tossed my bag on an empty bed.

Four other guys were present, and introductions were made, but as no one wore a shirt, I had no idea about rank or names. I could remember faces, but names were a challenge. The GP Medium tent was approximately sixteen feet by thirty feet with two fifteen-foot poles spaced twenty feet apart to hold the top up. These tents were on plywood floors that were positioned on wooden blocks. Six metal-frame beds with wafer-thin mattresses were positioned on the sides of the tent, along with six single wall lockers and six foot-lockers. All of the furniture had seen better days. In addition, it appeared that everyone had a lawn chair positioned around a homemade table. The bed that received my bag was pointed out to me, as well as a single wall locker and a footlocker.

"Don't worry. The guy that did occupy that bed just

rotated home. That lawn chair was his too, but he left it for you. Want a beer?" one of the others offered.

I was beginning to see a pattern here, and beer was it. There was one refrigerator in the tent, and it was a community beer machine. You took a beer, and when it ran dry, someone went and bought more beer. No matter how much you drank, everyone chipped in to buy the beer, and Lou could drink some beer, I was finding out. In fact, from the look of the empties, they all could drink some beer.

"Chow time. I hope you like roast beef, because that's what's for dinner. Bring a beer," said one of my new tent mates.

For what they had to work with, Army cooks did some amazing work in fixing meals. It wasn't Mom's home cooking, but it was better than most institutional food. Roast beef was for dinner that night, and almost every other night, I came to realize. If not roast beef, then spaghetti with sauce, marinara or something like that. We not only had roast beef for dinner, we had roast beef for breakfast some days too, and roast beef for lunch if you were lucky. When we were flying, we would have a case of C-rations, and they were a welcome respite from the roast beef menu.

As the four of us were eating, more flight crews came in to grab dinner. Being the "new guy," I was sort of the center of attention. Some attention was appreciated and some not. Right off the bat, the attention from the platoon leader was not appreciated.

Captain Jamison was a rather large man and not fat. "Are you Mr. Cory?" he asked.

I looked up from my tray. "Yes, sir."

"When I speak to you, mister, you will stand," he said loud enough that everyone turned and looked as I unwound from my seat.

"Sorry, sir," I mumbled and stood up.

"When you're done eating, report to my tent. Someone will show you where it is." And he walked off to sit at an empty table.

"He's an ass," Lou stated in a hushed voice. "Don't let it bother you. He's that way with every one of the warrants. Has a feather up his ass."

"Are you in his platoon too?" I asked.

"Nope, and I don't fly with him either. Not that I don't want to, but he doesn't want to fly with me. See, I'm an aircraft commander and he's still a right seater. He thinks just because he's a captain, he should be an aircraft commander. But he can't fly for shit and no one will sign him off for AC. He thinks the ACs have it out for him, and we do." Lou was digging out another beer from his cargo pockets.

"How do you get to be AC, and how long does it take?" I asked as I accepted another beer from Lou's other cargo pocket.

"First you need about four hundred hours' flight time in-country. You'll have that in four months easy, unless you're a dickhead and scare every AC. Then when the ACs think you're ready, we have a meeting and make a recommendation to Major Dickson. Have you met him yet?" Lou asked.

"No, who's he?"

"Damn, you are a newbie, aren't you? Major Dickson's the company commander, and you'll be told by the XO or by Captain Jamison when to go see him. I've been in this unit for almost a year now and still haven't reported to him. I've only seen him out of his tent maybe four times. He doesn't fly missions, he doesn't speak to warrant officers or anyone except the first sergeant and the XO. Even his meals are brought to his tent. Guy's a real hermit," Lou stated as he finished his second beer and stood to leave.

We left the mess hall and headed back to our tent with a detour to the "Officers' Club," which was another tent with a makeshift bar, refrigerator and tables. The latest Led Zeppelin song was playing on a reel-to-reel tape player. "You a poker player, Cory?"

"No, never learned. Figured if I didn't lose money gambling, then every time I passed it up, I was making money," I explained as I opened another Carling Black Label with the rusted seem. Lou introduced me to more pilots that were in the game. Hugh and Dave were both ACs and getting ready to rotate home in a month or so.

"Hi, I'm Chip. Really glad to see you here." A tall lanky fellow extended his hand.

"Thank you, I'm Dan," I responded as I shook his hand. "But why are you glad to see me?"

"Because I'm no longer the newest new guy. You are." The pecking order had just been established. It quickly became obvious that the evening would continue with jovial bantering and beer. However, I still had to go see my platoon leader, so I excused myself and went looking for his tent.

Captain Jamison had a tent all to himself. It was what the Army called a General Purpose Small, and it was the same size as the company commander's tent. In fact, the platoon leaders, XO, and first sergeant all had "single-man tents" that you could sleep ten men in if need be. After the incident in the mess hall, I thought it best to exercise proper military decorum. Announcing myself, I was told to come in, and I did so, coming to attention and saluting. Captain Jamison sat at a field desk. He smiled and stood, returning my salute.

"At ease. Nice to see a warrant with military manners, Mr. Cory. You're a first," he said, shaking my hand. I wasn't sure what to say.

"I come from a military family, sir, and manners and traditions are big in our house. My dad is Navy, submarines, so from the time I could talk, manners were ingrained in me. 'Yes, sir' and 'no, ma'am' were expected," I explained.

"So why didn't you join the Navy?" he asked.

"The Navy isn't really in this fight, is it, sir? I wanted to do more than sit off the coast doing mundane stuff on some ship. I was a merchant sailor for about five months and made good money, but I wanted to be here, doing something worthwhile," I divulged.

"Cory, you may be an idealist, but we can use you."

Surprisingly, Captain Jamison and I had a nice discussion on what I could expect in the months to come. After about thirty minutes, he wrapped up the conversation and asked if I had questions, which I did not. I was dismissed. He just wanted the warrant officers to extend military courtesy to his rank. I got along with him just fine until he rotated home.

The pilots were a mixed bag. Most of the warrant officers fell into one of three categories—either high school graduates, college dropouts, or former NCOs that had gone to flight school. Most of the warrants were bachelors with girlfriends back in the States, except the old guys, who were married with wives and two kids back in the States. The commissioned officers, Real Live Officers (RLOs) as warrants referred to them, were all college graduates, but I didn't notice any West Pointers in the unit. You could spot them by the large ring on their finger, hence the nickname, Ring Knockers. Although no one did PT, there were no overweight pilots. Most were attempting to grow mustaches, with limited success. We were all just too baby-faced.

Most of the crew chiefs and maintenance personnel were volunteers who had enlisted rather than waiting to be drafted. There were twenty-nine draftees, and most were door gunners who had volunteered to extend for door gunner duty to cut their draft time short or put more money in their pockets before going home. All were prior grunts. They were all good soldiers. There was an occasional drunk and disorderly and maybe an occasional pot case, but I couldn't recall any specific cases of a lack of discipline. If pot was being smoked, it was kept pretty quiet and infrequent.

The unit at the time of my arrival had one major, the commanding officer, plus five captains, nine first lieutenants, and twenty-nine warrant officers. Enlisted strength was ninety-six enlisted at the time. There was no such thing as racial discrimination in the unit, from what I experienced. We were all OD green in color and all bled red blood. We had two black officers and several blacks in the enlisted ranks, but from what I could see and knew, everyone was treated with respect and equality.

# 7

## WHAT AM I TO DO?

People shuffling around woke me, but it was still dark. A flashlight in the face got me to close my eyes again, and a voice asked, "Are you Mr. Runnels?"

"Not me. What are you doing?"

"Sorry, sir. I'm waking flight crews for their missions. Who are you?" the voice asked.

"Cory."

"Oh. Well, in that case, go back to sleep. You're not flying today," he said, and I followed his order.

The sound of turbine engines and beating rotor blades finally woke me again. I needed coffee, a shower and a shitter and not in that order. Showers were a four-post frame about seven feet tall with plywood sides in the middle two-thirds for privacy. The showers were mounted on wood pallets to keep your feet out of the mud that was created by the water flowing on the ground, and to keep you from stepping on a pit viper snake that liked to hang out under the showers looking for small frogs. Step lightly, my friend. Water was contained on top in a black-painted container that the maintenance shop made out of sheet metal or an old engine container box. Black absorbs heat, so during the day, the water would heat up, never hot enough to scald one, but warm enough to take a shower in the evening. Morning showers were just cold water, if there was any water. A soldier on work detail would fill the five-hundred-gallon water truck from the base water point and deliver it to the showers and mess hall. There was also a wash area for doing laundry and getting water to take back to our tents.

We also had three-hole latrines—shitters—that were designed by the Department for Defense in World War I and hadn't changed in fifty years. These were also made out of plywood, with a door positioned in front of the center hole. The top half of the sides was screened in and the roof was tin. Each hole had a toilet seat covering it. Underneath each hole was a quarter to a half of a fifty-five-gallon drum. The drum was lined with back issues of the *Stars and Stripes* newspaper, and about three inches of diesel fuel was added and then placed under the hole. Each morning, whatever soldier was on the first sergeant's shit detail removed each can and burned the contents, which would require him to stir it with a large stick as it burned. There was no escaping the smoke or the odor. Then the can was lined with paper, filled with more diesel and placed back under the hole. The odor was permanently imprinted in every soldier's senses, for their lifetime.

Breakfast proved to be rather uninviting. Powdered eggs, undercooked bacon, roast beef, bread that I had never seen before and coffee. Milk, cereal and pancakes were also offered. I started making a list of what I wanted family to send from home. Real white bread or rye was high on the list, along with a jar of peanut butter and a jar of jelly. Naturally, my Aunt Joanie's pound cake was at the top of the list. With nothing to do after breakfast, I wandered over to Flight Operations to see what I was supposed to do. During the day, one of the pilots might be there acting as the assistant operations officer. Today it was just Sergeant First Class Robertson. His nickname was "Pops" as he took care of all the pilots.

"Good morning, Mr. Cory. What can I do you for?" he asked.

"Nothing, really. I just want to see what operations does and what our missions are." I noticed that there was no assistant operations officer present.

"Well, come on back here and I'll give you a briefing. Want some decent coffee?" he asked, holding up a coffeepot. This man knew the way to my heart.

"As long as it's not from the mess hall, yes, please," I answered. As he poured me a cup, I was taking in the activity or lack thereof at this time of the morning.

"We don't have any cream, but we do have this if you want it." He raised a can of Carnation condensed milk. I loved that stuff.

"Oh yeah," I said too loud with a smile on my face.

"Boy, you must like it."

"Before my dad was commissioned, he was a chief petty officer and would stand weekend watch aboard ship. He'd take me with him on Saturdays and let me drink coffee, and he always put some of that in my coffee," I explained to him.

"So your dad's a Mustang. Where's he stationed now?"

"Morocco," I replied. "He left Japan about the time I joined the Army. Mom wasn't too happy that I quit college after two and a half worthless years, but Dad supported me on that move. Before you ask, I didn't join the Navy because the Navy isn't really in this fight unless you're a pilot, and I wanted to do more than just sit on a ship. Did that already as a merchant sailor. Here I might be able to make a difference."

For a moment, he just stared at me like maybe I was nuts. "Well, this here is Flight Ops," he said as he waved his arms around, forgetting that he had given me a brief the day before of our area of operations. He went over it again.

"What's to the northeast of us?" I asked.

"That's War Zone C, and the only people there are not friendly. Don't fly over there unless you must," warned Pops. "Now here at Quan Loi is the First Brigade; Second Brigade is here at Long Binh, and Third Brigade is at Phuoc Vinh along with Division HQ. Right now, most of our missions are between Phuoc Vinh and Bien Hoa, especially as the Vietnamese holiday of Tet is in a week or so and they're expecting it may be like last year. Bien Hoa would be the target, most likely. The Fifth NVA Division is operating around there."

"What are most of our missions that we fly?" I asked.

"Sir, it's a bit of everything. You may start the day off flying ash and trash, resupply, for a battalion, followed by being part of a six-two combat assault, followed by flying Night Hunter Killer or Chuck Chuck."

"Chuck Chuck?" I asked.

"Command and Control. A battalion commander will jump aboard with his staff, usually a fire support officer, and you fly around in a circle over a unit in contact while the battalion commander directs artillery fire," he explained. "Boring as hell for you, generally."

"What's a six-two?" I asked.

"A six-two is a flight of six Hueys and two Cobras. The Cobras will come from our Delta Company on the other side of the Chicken Pen. They refer to their area as the Snake Pit," he added.

"And Night Hunter Killer?"

"That's a fun one. Three aircraft: a Cobra flying at about a thousand feet, a Huey full of flares flying at a thousand feet, following the Cobra, and a Huey flying between the ground and five hundred feet, nice and slow with all his lights on so Charlie can see you easily and shoot at you. The low bird is equipped with a .50-caliber machine gun replacing one of the M60 machine guns, and a searchlight with a low-light-intensity night vision scope on top is mounted in the cargo door. If the low bird sees something or gets shot at, the Cobra rolls hot on it and the flare aircraft starts dropping flares so the Cobra can see the target. Want some more coffee?"

"Yeah, please. How do you get our missions?"

"During the night, and generally before twenty hundred hours, the maintenance officer will tell us how many birds we can put up for the next day. We pass that to Battalion. Some-time around zero two hundred, Battalion starts sending the missions to us. Captain Goodnight comes in about zero four hundred and assigns the pilots and the missions, and we start waking everyone up. Generally we get the birds in the air at first light. Most of the birds aren't instrument-rated, so that can be a problem in the monsoon season, which will begin in about three months. I'll let you put in your own canned milk."

He then went on to explain how our flight hours were logged and maintained by the operations section, as well as the procedure for getting aircraft logbooks in the morning before we launched. "Once you're cleared to fly, you'll be picking up the logbooks and doing the preflight before the aircraft commander gets to the aircraft," he added.

"When do I get to fly?"

"First you have to have an orientation ride with one of the instructor pilots here. Mr. Reynolds is on leave until next week, so that leaves only Mr. Baker. He'll probably get to you in the next week." *Damn*, I thought, *it's going to be a week before I even get in an aircraft.*

"I know what you're thinking, and that's good. But enjoy sitting on the ground for as long as you can, because once you're cleared, you'll get all the flying you want and then some," Pops said.

"Who's the assistant ops officer?" I asked.

"Right now there is none. Captain Goodnight doesn't feel he needs any help or advice. He's new to the job. Our previous ops officer, Captain Burbank, just left to go up to Battalion. He will be missed."

"Oh, I see." I didn't but thought that was a safe answer.

"We did have one, but he went home last month. And he was worthless. Every time he took a bird out, he'd be back in thirty minutes complaining about something being wrong with it. He'd only put himself on milk runs and never take a combat flight. Worthless! Back when he was Peter Pilot, he had no choice, but as soon as they made him an AC, he started that shit. I doubt if anyone will miss him. Most assistant ops officers fit that bill. I doubt if you'll ever make it, being assistant ops officer, though."

"Why's that?" I asked, feeling a bit offended.

"You're the first warrant that has come in here and asked what we do and how we do it. You don't strike me as a shirker. And you haven't asked the one question most new guys ask."

Curious, I had to ask, "And what would that be?"

"When did we last lose a crew? It was January, last month. They were sling loading a teeter-totter to an orphanage up Highway 13, and it flew up into the tail rotor. They spun into the trees at the end of the runway." I made a mental note to watch sling loads.

I thanked Pops and returned to my tent with nothing to do at this point but wait for someone to tell me to do something. I didn't have to wait long.

"Mr. Cory, report to the CO's tent."

I looked up from writing a letter, and there stood the company first sergeant. As a warrant officer aviator, I knew I would have few dealings with the man but was smart enough to know that he deserved a level of respect.

"Thank you, First Sergeant. Which tent is the CO's?" I asked.

He pointed it out to me, and I headed that way. It was still early in the morning, and already the humidity was taking its effect. Warm, but not stifling, outside. However, as I approached the commander's tent, I noticed that it was closed, with all the sidewalls and entrance down. I was taught that before you walk into someone's room, you knock. How do you knock on a tent? I stopped short of the tent, looking for a front tentpole, but there was none. Okay.

"Knock, knock," I called out.

"Who's there?" came a reply from inside. *You've got to be kidding me. I'm in a combat zone playing 'Knock Knock' with the company commander.*

"Sir, it's Mr. Cory. I understand you want to see me."

"Come in."

I pulled the flap back and there sat Major Dickson, behind a field desk in a totally enclosed tent with a single lightbulb on. The major was in a T-shirt and fatigue pants. He was pale and thin, with a face that reminded me of a weasel. Something was not right here. I came to attention and reported as I was taught from day one in the Army. He just sat there looking at a piece of paper on his desk. *Oh boy, power play going on here.* Finally he looked up and returned my salute.

"At ease. Are you ready to start flying, Mr. Cory?"

"Yes, sir, looking forward to it." Just violated Dad's advice and gave too much information.

"Oh, you are! What exactly are you looking forward to?" he asked as he leaned back in his chair and folded his arms across his chest. His OD green T-shirt was wet in the arm pits, and he was wearing flippy-flops. Glad he had his pants on. Now this was getting awkward.

"Sir, I'm looking forward to getting in the air to do the job I've been trained to do rather than sitting on the ground. I look forward to learning how to fly as a combat pilot, conducting resupply missions, flying formations, and improving my ability. I'm looking forward to seeing the area from Tay Ninh to Song Be to Long Binh." Thank God I had gone over to Ops and gotten a briefing from Pops. Major Dickson just glared at me. What the hell had I done?

"Mr. Cory, you are going to be the company training officer. See Mr. Leach and relieve him of those duties. See the XO when you have a plan. That is all."

I rendered a salute, did an about-face and walked out.

"Shut the damn tent flap!" he called out. *Oh, shit.* I quickly closed it and moved out. Mr. Leach was flying, so no need to hunt him down. Little did I know that this would be the only time Major Dickson ever spoke to me even though he was around for another two months. Never saw him fly a mission and only occasionally saw him walking around the company area. Took his meals in his tent. Strange man. Some said he already had done two one-year tours in-country and was burned out. Maybe so.

No one had ever told me what a company training officer was supposed to do. I was thinking that I was responsible for training this company. Hell, I was a brand-new pilot. What could I teach anyone? And what was I supposed to be training them to do anyway? I hoped Mr. Leach had his ducks in a row. You could hope all you wanted, but it didn't make it so. That evening I tracked down Mr. Leach at the Officers' Club. A short, stocky man, he could have been a double for Frodo, Bilbo Baggins's sidekick in *The Hobbit.*

"Bob, I was told by the CO to relieve you of your duties as training officer."

The look on his face told me he wasn't going to miss the extra duty. Jumping up, he motioned me to follow him to his tent and dragged a box from under his bed. Several files, a couple of regulations and lots of loose papers were in the box.

"New guy, it's all yours with my blessing." Holy shit, nothing was in order.

"Where do I start with this stuff?" I asked as I started pawing through it.

"Start with the regulations. This one. It outlines all the mandatory training that's required each quarter, semiannual and annually by the US Army," he said as he pulled out the regulation. "Then look at the division regulation and the USARV regulation. There's some overlap. If you schedule anything, go to the first sergeant and clear it with him first. Any questions?"

"Not right now. Let me look this over and get it organized and I'll get back to you," I stammered.

I'd been handed a shit sandwich, but I wasn't flying, so I might as well do something. The Department of the Army Regulation outlined what training must be done on a quarterly, semiannually and annual basis. *Chaplain's Call, quarterly; Weapons Inspection, monthly; Savings Bond Drive, annually; Hygiene Care, monthly.* The list went on and on. My job, it appeared, was to make sure each class was scheduled, an instructor designated, a location secured, and a roster signed by all in attendance. It was up to the first sergeant and the NCOs to make sure everyone was in attendance. Only one problem: no one had asked them to do it in the past, and so there was some resistance, especially as I had no authority over them. When the chaplain came to visit monthly, he would usually eat dinner and head for the Officers' Club for poker. I thought he was going to have a heart attack when I approached him about giving a class on moral conduct. Weapons inspections was easy; bring your weapon to the mess hall for chow and have the supply sergeant check the serial number. Eventually I was able to get it moving somewhat smoothly, and on paper it looked great. Maybe the next new guy could have this duty—and sure enough, he got it.

I spent the rest of the evening looking over what Bob had handed me, attempting to organize it. As my tent mates were all on the board for flying the next day, lights out was around 2100 hours, so I put everything away and lay down. Sleep came quick, and I dreamt of pleasant things as I hadn't been in-country long enough to have bad dreams. As I slumbered, I began to dream about the jet I heard coming in for a landing on our airstrip. It was getting louder and... *Holy shit, jets can't land here!*

I was on the floor of our tent with everyone else when the Katyusha rocket impacted behind our tent, followed by a second impacting the VIP landing pad behind the major's tent.

"*Incoming!*" I heard as I grabbed my flak jacket and my helmet. I was half running, half crawling to the bunker in my boxer shorts when another rocket impacted with a flash of spraying shrapnel. Diving through the door of the bunker, I plowed into someone in the total darkness of the bunker and got shoved to the other side.

"Hey, watch it, man!" someone said.

"Anyone seen the new guy?" I recognized Lou's voice.

"Over here, Lou," I answered.

"This your first rocket attack, New Guy?" he asked.

"Well, yeah, I've only been here two days. Is this common?" I asked.

"Yep, almost nightly, and since this is your first, you get to buy the beer. Be sure the refrigerator's stocked tomorrow when we come back."

In the darkness, the sounds of laughter could be heard over the sounds of impacting rockets and secondary explosions.

# 8

## IN THE AIR AT LAST, FEBRUARY 21

FINALLY, AFTER I'D BEEN SITTING ON MY ASS FOR A week, the day came for me to get my orientation ride. It was conducted by one of the two-unit instructor pilots. The day started off with a briefing in the operations tent. Since I'd been hanging out there, it went rather quickly, and then we walked to the aircraft. The crew chief and door gunner were already there, mounting the guns and doing last-minute checks.

Mr. Baker said, "Let's start the preflight." And I reached for the checklist...no, I went looking for the checklist.

"Excuse me, the checklist is missing, Mr. Baker."

"You don't have it memorized? What did they teach you in flight school?" he asked.

In flight school, you had a laminated checklist, but you used it so many times that for the most part you had it memorized. I had it memorized but assumed we would still use it. Nope, I'd just learned that "assume" stood for "make an ass of u and me."

"Cory, here we have to do it fast, and there's no time to be reading. Have it memorized and just get at it. You take the rotor head, and I'll get down here."

In about five minutes, that bird was preflighted. Before we climbed into the aircraft, the door gunner handed me a chicken plate. I noticed I was the only one wearing a flak jacket over my jungle fatigues. We didn't have flight suits at this time as Air Force and Navy pilots had; everyone wore jungle fatigues when flying. The chicken plate was a metal plate covered with ceramic tile and fiberglass. It would stop a small-arms bullet. It was normally worn over the shoulders with a belly band to hold the front and back pieces together. Here, the front of the chicken plate sat on your lap, covering your chest and stomach. It was held in place by the shoulder harness and seat belt. Where was the back plate? I wondered. The crew chief and door gunner were sitting on them, as their seats had no armor plating and the pilot seats did, at least against small-arms fire. A .50-cal or 12.7 mm antiaircraft round would punch through the seats.

As we sat in the aircraft, Mr. Baker, Tony, went over the finer points of getting the aircraft started and out of the revetment. No sloppy hovering at this point or you were going to be banging into the revetment, which would make the crew chief unhappy, the door gunner scared and the aircraft commander pissed off. Do any real damage and you'd have the maintenance officer crawling up your ass as well before the company commander got to you. The other thing to watch for was other aircraft coming out and hovering to the runway. You did not fly right out of the revetment.

As we were ready to depart, Tony said, "I'll take it out and put it back and then you do it." With the collective in his left hand and the cyclic in his right, he slowly and gently brought the bird up. On the Huey, the nose came up first when in the hover position. In a hover, the nose of the UH-1H was actually five degrees above horizontal. Tony was so smooth that you hardly noticed the movement. He was holding the cyclic with his thumb and two fingers, and the cyclic never moved. Once we cleared the revetment, he reversed the procedure and put us back in, setting us down just as gently as when he'd picked up. "Okay, Dan, your turn." Oh, wow, it was Dan and Tony now.

"I have the aircraft, Tony."

"You have the aircraft," he responded, indicating he recognized I had positive control of the aircraft.

With my left hand on the collective, right hand on the cyclic—my whole hand—I started coming up on the power. The aircraft broke ground.

"Oh, shit!" screamed the door gunner.

"We're going to die!" wailed the crew chief, and I was shitting in my pants.

"All right, knock it off, you two," Tony said to the crew. They were laughing their asses off.

"Oh, sir, can't we screw with the new guy?" asked the crew chief. *So that's the way it's going to be today?*

I got the aircraft out and over to the runway, shaking a bit, but safe. We headed north up Highway 13 towards the village of Quan Loi. Highway 13 was known as "Thunder Road" and frequently was witness to ambushes by NVA troops coming out of the Iron Triangle that bordered it on the eastern side. Highway 13 was the main road, sparsely populated, unpaved of course, from Saigon, through Lai Khe, Quan Loi, and An Loc and right into Cambodia. In the summer, it was a dusty road. In monsoon season, it was a quagmire of mud. At any one time, you would see US Army convoys, overloaded Vietnamese buses, oxcarts and bicycles. Scattered along the side of the road were young children selling Coke to GIs or fruit to the locals. Mixed in was the occasional US mechanized platoon with their armored personnel carriers, really a metal box on tank tracks.

Tony pointed out landmarks to me as we were about one thousand feet on a clear day. I was taking it all in and feeling good that I was flying again.

*BAM, BAM, BAM, BAM*, went the guns on both sides. The engine suddenly lost rpm.

"Taking fire, going down," screamed the door gunner.

Just then, the engine went quiet with engine rpm dropping quickly, and I slammed the collective down and entered into a textbook autorotation. I watched the instruments and saw nothing unusual except our low engine rpm, which was now steady but very low. Rotor rpm was looking good, and the road was a perfect landing site. I looked over at Tony, who was looking out his window. Surely he was going to take command of the aircraft and land this thing. *Oh, no, he's not!* I flared at the right altitude, sucked in some collective, let her drop some more and pulled in more to make a no-slide soft landing. Mutt and Jeff were laughing their asses off again.

Tony looked at me for a minute with a smile. "Not bad for a new guy out on his first flight. I got it."

"You have the aircraft," I responded and began to breathe.

We flew up to a Vietnamese/Special Forces base camp that had a landing strip, at Chon Thanh. Tony said, "That was a textbook autorotation. Now let's learn some combat autorotations. I'll do the first one and then you do the next one."

As we were flying out, he explained that in an autorotation, you had to have altitude, and if you didn't have that, you'd best have airspeed. He never got above one hundred feet, but we were hauling ass over the treetops at one hundred knots where normal airspeed was eighty knots. When we were about five hundred yards from the end of the runway, he cut the power and lowered the collective slightly to maintain rotor rpm while raising the nose of the aircraft to bleed off airspeed. The result was a sliding touchdown on the runway.

"Okay, your turn."

As he turned the controls over to me, I was fired up. In flight school, we never flew this low on a single-ship mission. Getting eyeball to eyeball with the monkeys in the trees was enough excitement, let alone knowing that I was going to chop the throttle as I approached the runway. Finally Tony did that for me.

"Ease back on your airspeed. Maintain rotor rpm. Lower collective. Watch your rotor rpm. Easy, easy...nice, Dan," he said as I put the aircraft down softly on the runway. Mutt and Jeff said nothing.

"Can we do that again?" I said with obvious excitement.

"First let me demonstrate a combat takeoff. In flight school, you brought the aircraft to a hover and then eased it forward, pulling power. Here you won't be able to bring it to a hover as you have only three seconds on the ground. You touch, count to three and get out of there. I've got the aircraft."

"You have it," I repeated and released the controls.

"A combat takeoff is gaining altitude and airspeed as quickly as possible, but especially airspeed. To execute, you ease forward on the cyclic—remembering that sitting at a hover, the nose is elevated five degrees, so that's five degrees you don't want in the takeoff—and come in with thirty pounds of torque quickly and smoothly. Naturally if you're in a formation, you have to key on the bird in front of you, but he'll be wanting out of there just as much as you. Do not over-torque the aircraft, which is forty-three pounds. Okay, here we go," Tony instructed.[1]

All of a sudden, the nose came over and I could just visualize the main rotor blade hitting the ground in front of me. It didn't, and the aircraft was racing over the ground and climbing fast. This was better than a Disneyland ride!

"Okay, you got it. Any questions?" Tony asked.

"I got it, and no questions."

"Let's shoot a low-level autorotation and then a combat takeoff as soon as you have power back up," Tony said while pointing forward.

"Roger," I answered.

I brought the aircraft around, and before Tony could say it, I cut the throttle and milked the aircraft back onto the runway. As soon as we stopped, I brought the engine rpm up and attempted to imitate his takeoff. *Attempted* to imitate.

"Not bad, and you'll get the hang of it after a couple of missions. Most guys are timid about pushing the nose over the first couple of times. Let's go play with the artillery now. I have the aircraft," he said as he took the controls.

We continued on our way northwest as Tony became my tour guide. "This is what we call the Iron Triangle. Chu Chi is to the west, Lai Khe to the east and Quan Loi to the north. If you fly below twenty-five hundred feet, you stand a good chance of getting shot at. This entire area is a free-fire zone, which means we can call artillery on anything we see or want to shoot at. There are no friendlies in this area," Tony pointed out. We were looking at an area of about one hundred square miles.

"How did you do on your artillery class in school?" Tony asked.

"Pretty good. I really enjoyed that one."

"Okay, you see that road crossing over there?"

"Yeah."

"What's the grid coordinates for it?"

I hadn't pulled the map out since this had started.

"Dan, don't fly without a map, and know where you are at all times on that map. If you go down, you aren't going to have a lot of time to figure that out. Take the controls."

"I got it," I said. As I took the controls, Tony opened his map and started giving me an orientation on where we were at. Once he got me situated, he showed me on the map where the artillery positions were located that could possibly fire the mission.

"Okay, you're going to call either Lai Khe Artillery, Song Be Artillery, Phuoc Vinh Artillery or Quan Loi Artillery initially, depending on where you are. If you call one, after you send the fire mission, they may come back and tell you to contact someone else that will actually fire the mission. Have pencil ready to copy. Okay, what are you going to say?"

I thought about that for a minute and gave my fire mission to Tony.

"You're good. Send it," he said after I was done.

"Lai Khe Arty, Chicken-man Two-Seven, fire mission, over."

"Chicken-man Two-Seven, Lai Khe Arty, over."

"Lai Khe Arty, fire mission, road intersection grid eight-two-three-five-seven-eight-six-one, over."

After a minute, Lai Khe Artillery came back. "Understood road intersection, grid eight-two-three-five-seven-eight-six-one."

"Affirmative, Lai Khe." A few minutes later: "Chicken-man Two-Seven, shot out." The artillery battery had just fired six rounds.

"Understood, shot out."

A few seconds later: "Chicken-man Two-Seven, splash."

"Understood, splash," I responded just as a small explosion hit about five hundred meters over the target, but along the gun target line.

"Lai Khe Artillery, drop eight hundred, over."

"Roger, drop eight hundred." A minute later: "Chicken-man Two-Seven, shot out."

"Understood, shot out."

Thirty seconds later: "Chicken-man Two-Seven, splash."

"Understood, splash." The jungle about two hundred meters south of the target exploded. The schoolhouse had taught us to bracket the target and walk the rounds in, so technically I should have had them shoot again by adding four hundred meters, but I could see the target and thought there was no point in wasting time and ammo.

"Lai Khe Artillery, add two hundred and fire for effect."

"Roger, add two hundred and fire for effect." A minute later: "Chicken-man Two-Seven, shot out."

"Understood, shot out."

"Chicken-man Two-Seven, splash."

"Roger, splash." And the road intersection disappeared in a cloud of dirt and flying underbrush as six rounds of high-explosive 155 mm impacted.

Tony looked at me and commented, "Nice shooting. I noted you skipped the bracketing."

"No need to waste time or ammo," I said, then switched from intercom to the FM1 radio. "Lai Khe Artillery, nice shooting. Mission complete."

"Roger, Chicken-man Two-Seven. Rounds complete. Mission complete."

Tony continued to fly in the direction of Tay Ninh. "We'll head up to Tay Ninh and then fly the perimeter of our area of operations. You follow on the map. Tay Ninh is the west limit of our AO. Our sister battalion, 229th Assault Helicopter Battalion, is located there. You can't miss it, as it and Song Be have the only two mountains in the entire area. That's Song Be to the northeast over there." He pointed to a lonely peak sticking above the jungle canopy by about a thousand feet.

"Are those two extinct volcanoes?" I asked.

"You think I'm a geologist or something? I have no clue.

All I know is there's an outpost on top of both Song Be Mountain—Nui Ba Ra—and Nui Ba Den, the mountain by Tay Ninh. That ridge line to the north of Nui Ba Den is called the Razorback. There's a battalion firebase on top of the Razorback, LZ Dolly. The Twenty-Fifth Infantry Division has some troops operating in that area with one of their brigades located at Tay Ninh. Their division headquarters is at Chu Chi."

As we continued to fly towards Tay Ninh, I tracked our location on the map, which wasn't easy as there were few roads and everything was flat except the two mountains and the Razorback. Under the three-hundred-foot trees that covered almost everything, I had no idea what the terrain was like and could only assume it was flat as all the trees created a flat carpet of green. However, I noticed large swaths of jungle full of craters laid in a rectangular pattern.

"What caused the craters?" I asked.

"That's where an arc light went in."

"What's that?" I asked.

"A bomb strike by three B-52 bombers flying out of Guam. They're given a box and come in at twenty or thirty thousand feet and drop. You do not want to be in that box when they do. The world literally goes up in smoke. You will see trees fly up about seven hundred to a thousand feet. I almost pity the gooks that are on the receiving end of one of those," Tony explained.

"How do you know if a strike is going in?" I asked.

"About ten minutes before, the artillery will come up on the net and issue a warning. That's another reason to know where you are at all times and to monitor the arty net. If you call Arty and tell them where you're flying to and from, they'll let you know if they're shooting across or along your flight path. They'll also give you the gun's position and impact points as well as max altitude on the shot. If you don't ask, then you're applying the 'Big Sky, Little Bullet' principle, and you take your chances."

As we approached Tay Ninh, Tony called the control tower for clearance to land and go to refueling. We'd used half our fuel as the UH-1H had about two and a half hours of flight time on a full load, but twenty minutes of that was considered reserve in case you had trouble finding fuel, so two hours was used for general planning. After two hours, everyone was ready to get out and stretch anyway. As we were in no hurry, Tony shut the aircraft down while Mutt and Jeff refueled the aircraft and we all got out.

The town of Tay Ninh was picturesque, with tile roofs and a heavy French influence as it sat on the edge of the Michelin rubber tree plantation, which covered a sizable area of Three Corps's and our AO. One problem with the rubber tree plantations, however, was that the enemy loved to hide in them, since we couldn't bomb it or shoot artillery into the place unless absolutely necessary. If we did, the US government would pay for damaged trees. *How stupid is this policy?* I wondered. As it was a slow day at the refuel point, Mutt and Jeff broke out the case of C-rations we had and distributed one to each of us.

Tony stopped them. "Okay, you two, turn the case over so you don't see what you're drawing and then pass them out. Which one did you get, Dan?"

"Lima beans and ham," I responded with a look of disgust as Mutt and Jeff put it back in the box with equal looks of disgust for being caught. They had set me up, again.

"Okay," Tony said. "I'll select and pass out the chow." With the case upside down, there were no labels to read, so it was luck of the draw. Tony pulled one out and handed it to me. Franks and beans. Okay, that was pretty good. Next he handed Mutt his, and it was spaghetti. Not bad. Out came Jeff's—oh, sweet justice, lima beans and ham—and he was not happy. Tony drew his and we dug in, except Jeff, who just took out the crackers and cheese. Inwardly, I was laughing—well, maybe smiling outwardly too.

After our pause, we cranked up, this time with me doing the start-up procedures from memory. First, scan the AC electrical panel next to my left leg. Then on to the center console. Fuel off, hydraulics on, radios off, then overhead, DC circuit breakers in, nonessential bus off, battery on. In my left hand, throttle set, press starter button with my right hand, fuel on, watch N1, fifteen percent, main rotor turning; N1, forty percent, release starter; N1, sixty-eight percent, roll throttle and slowly bring up engine rpm to 6600 and rotor rpm to 325, engine oil pressure coming up, transmission oil pressure coming up. Both engine and transmission oil temps were good. Radios on and frequencies set on UHF, VHF and FM. Transponder set to correct code. Flight controls normal. Crew chief and door gunner aboard.

Tony called the tower for takeoff instructions and told me I had the aircraft. Tower cleared us to depart from the fuel area, and Tony pointed north towards the Razorback. "This isn't a hot LZ, so no combat departure," he cautioned me. "You'll scare the crap out of the control tower. Just a nice schoolhouse departure."

"Got it," I responded. Mutt and Jeff remained quiet for once. They were learning not to screw with the new guy.

We flew past Nui Ba Den with its communications outpost on the top. Tony told me that we owned the top and the enemy owned the very steep sides. As this was the highest point in all of Three Corps, the Army Security Agency had a listening post on top of the mountain. Nui Ba Ra, Song Be Mountain, was in front of us, about forty minutes' flying time. Like Nui Ba Ra, it was only about ten miles from the Cambodian border. We passed over the Razorback, and I saw that there was a firebase on the northeast end.

Firebases were generally round fortifications where bull-dozers pushed up a berm of dirt five or six feet high, thus creating a circle about two hundred yards or more across. Concertina wire was strung completely around the outside of the berm about fifty to seventy-five feet, just far enough that someone in the wire couldn't throw a hand grenade into the berm. Tin cans and trip flares were suspended in the wire to give early warning if someone was attempting to crawl through the wire. Claymore mines were placed between the berm and wire to blow away large groups of enemy attempting to cross the wire. In addition, fifty-five-gallon drums were buried on their sides, filled with a slurry of diesel fuel and detergent. Inside the barrel at the bottom was a pound or two of C-4 plastic explosive. When detonated, it simulated a napalm bomb. Inside the perimeter, there was generally a battalion headquarters, forward supply elements, usually an artillery battery of five 105 mm howitzers, a mortar platoon of four 81 mm mortars and a rifle company. The other two or three rifle companies would be off in the jungle conducting patrols and ambushes as well as search-and-destroy missions. The rifle companies would be rotated back to the firebase on a scheduled basis. The artillery and mortars on the firebase were in direct support of that battalion, which meant that battalion had first priority on call for fire missions. However, if we called in a fire mission to the artillery, they would decide who could shoot best from a number of firebases and would direct our mission to one of those. Firebases were normally established so the artillery on one firebase could support another firebase if it became necessary, and it had several times in the past three years.

As we approached Song Be, Tony pointed out the Song Dong Nai River. "That river wanders right down to Bien Hoa, where we're mostly operating now. Charlie's moving his shit from Cambodia down the river, past here and on to the Bien Hoa area with the Fifth NVA Division. We're supporting around Bien Hoa, and SF is attempting to interdict movement on and along the river from that SF camp over there," he said, pointing to a small outpost in the middle of the jungle. "About four months ago, five of our aircraft were operating out of and supporting that SF camp." Turning south, Tony said, "Let's head to the Chicken Pen. You got it." This was a test to see if I'd been paying attention to where we were and where we needed to go.

"I got it." I turned to a heading of 180 degrees, as the Chicken Coop was due south of Song Be. I started to relax. It felt good to sit back and scan the instruments and then look outside, scan the instruments and look outside. It was pounded into us in school never to get fixated on the instruments or the outside but be scanning constantly. And listen. Listen to the sound of the aircraft. The sound of the rotor blades. The sound of the engine. The sound of the radios. Sometimes your hearing would alert you to the first indicator of trouble, like the engine suddenly becoming quiet! Or a sudden whistling sound, which generally meant you had a bullet hole in a rotor blade. Or the sudden increase in engine noise that indicated a lost throttle governor or a compressor stall. Almost every change in sound required an immediate response.

We continued on to Lai Khe, and Tony let me take the aircraft into the revetment. As we shut down the aircraft, Mutt and Jeff began the process of cleaning it, pulling guns off and removing trash. Tony started the critique. "You did okay, and I'm going to sign off your orientation ride. You'll get formation flying in soon enough with another aircraft commander, but I don't foresee any problems. Do you?"

"No, I got no problem with formation flying," I lied. I really wasn't crazy about formation flying. In fact, I was hoping to go to a medical evacuation unit, commonly referred to as a medevac unit, where it was all single-ship flying. Oh, that lie would come back to bite me in the ass.

"Okay, then let's head into Ops and get a beer," Tony said.

"Don't we need to help them get the aircraft cleaned up?" I asked. Mutt and Jeff stopped what they were doing and looked at me. *Did I just screw up again?*

"Thank you, Mr. Cory, but we got it," Mutt said. *Mr. Cory, not "New Guy."*

"Okay, thanks for a great day," I stammered and fell in alongside Tony as we carried our gear and walked to the operations office to turn in logbooks and aircraft records. Tony also suggested that we stop by maintenance and give the maintenance officer a heads-up that the bird was good for tomorrow's missions. After I dropped my gear and met Tony for a beer, for which I paid the outrageous price of fifty cents, I headed to the PX. The crew chief and door gunner appreciated the case of beer I dropped off on their bunks that evening.

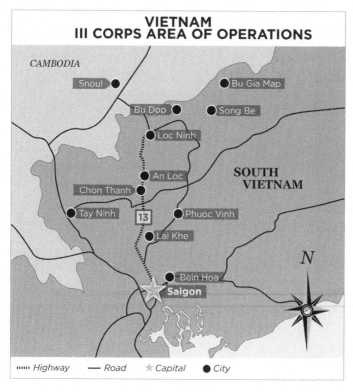

## VIETNAM
## III CORPS AREA OF OPERATIONS

*CAMBODIA*

Snoul

Bu Gia Map

Bu Dop

Song Be

Loc Ninh

**SOUTH
VIETNAM**

An Loc

Chon Thanh

Tay Ninh

13

Phuoc Vinh

Lai Khe

*N*

Bein Hoa

**Saigon**

ıııı *Highway* — *Road* ⭐ *Capital* ● *City*

*Map created by Infidium LLC for Matt Jackson Books.*

2

# 9

## FIRST MISSION

"Mr. Cory, wake up, sir," I heard as a light penetrated my dreams.

"What time is it? Why?" I asked.

"Sir, you're flying today with Mr. Leak. Launch time is zero five hundred hours. It's zero four hundred hours now. Mr. Leak said he would meet you in the mess hall," said the ops clerk. *Wonder if he ever gets cussed out for waking guys up?*

"Okay, I'm up." I'd just gotten cleared to fly yesterday. That was why I had come here, but so early? Hell, I'd been sleeping in each morning for close to a week. No need for a cold shower, so just a quick shave and brush my teeth. I was attempting not to wake anyone, and then I noticed that everyone else in our tent was getting up and moving. After dressing, I headed to the mess hall, which was the only "building" in our company area. Mr. Leak was just sitting down when I got in the line. What was on the menu? Coffee—that's good; scrambled eggs—powdered eggs, really; bacon, undercooked; and pancakes with something that resembled syrup. I settled for the pancakes with butter and jelly. Of course coffee too. Sitting down next to Mr. Leak, I started to eat and then reconsidered after the first mouthful. Pancakes were undercooked. Just coffee today.

"You awake, New Guy?" asked Mr. Leak.

"Yep, what we got for today?" I responded.

"We're flying log for First of the Seventh Cav down around Bien Hoa." He went on to explain, "A log mission is generally flying to a firebase and staying there for the day, supporting the unit however they ask. You could fly supplies into company locations in the jungle, such as water, food and ammo. You might bring someone back that's going home or on leave as well as take replacements to the unit. You might find yourself with the battalion commander in the back talking to his ground company commanders while you orbit at twenty-five hundred feet above them. Anything the battalion wants you to do, you do it. About all you don't do is medevac missions, as medevac birds are called out for that, but in desperate situations you might. You certainly backhaul bodies as the medevac wouldn't do that." As we finished up our coffee, Mr. Leak said he'd meet me at the aircraft and to start the preflight if I got there first. We parted ways.

I stopped at my tent and grabbed my gear, which consisted of a flight helmet, leather gloves, and a sidearm as well as my map. I left the flak jacket and steel pot helmet behind as no one else was wearing them. Sergeant First Class Robinson had helped me put the map together and had cautioned me, "Mr. Cory, never mark unit call signs or frequencies on the map. If that map had those locations and blew out, that would be a serious security breach." *Words to remember.*

My sidearm was a .38 Special pistol. I was a good shot with a rifle or a shotgun, but I couldn't hit my ass with that pistol. I was convinced that I was going to have to get a long gun and soon. The Army issued M-16s at this time, and I also found those difficult to shoot, having used the beautiful and accurate M-14 in basic training. Looking at the other pilots, I realized we had an assortment of weapons and none of them were Army issue. Mr. Leak carried the M-1 carbine of World War II vintage. Another pilot carried an AR-15 that the Air Force issued to ground controllers. One pilot was carrying a World War II Browning automatic rifle! Swedish K and British Sterlings were popular as well. Lastly, one pilot was toting the M-79 grenade launcher with a sandbag full of grenades. Crew chiefs and door gunners carried M-16s besides the two M60 machine guns on the aircraft.

In flight, both the crew chief and the door gunner manned the two 7.62 mm M60 machine guns that were on fixed posts. The guns could be rotated 180 degrees front to back and five degrees up and ninety degrees down. Mounted that way, the crew couldn't shoot their own aircraft, which had happened in the early days of the Vietnam War, when those guns were suspended from the ceiling of the aircraft on a cable. Ammo for the guns lay in a can strapped to the floor of the aircraft below the gun and usually had about three thousand rounds. When not flying, the crew chief was responsible for the maintenance of the aircraft and the door gunner was responsible for the maintenance and cleaning of the guns. Dirty guns didn't work. He also assisted the crew chief.

I put my stuff in the right seat of the aircraft, which in this unit was where the copilot sat even though there were more instruments for instrument flight, which was seldom done. I climbed up on the top of the aircraft and started the preflight. Jesus nut, tight, slip marks aligned, check. Pitch change horns tight, slip marks aligned, safety wires connected, check. Push-pull tubes attached and slip marks aligned, check. Every nut on the rotor head had a slippage mark that would indicate if a nut was loose, and most had a safety wire as well that should be connected and not broken. Rotor mast, no cuts or cracks, check. Attention to details. Up top was all done, so I dropped down and started on the body as Mr. Leak walked up.

"Howard, did he miss anything?" he asked the crew chief.

"No, sir, seems New Guy knows what he's doing," Howard answered.

Crap, I was back to being New Guy. I continued my walk-around, checking the engine. No disconnected hoses; no broken safety wires; no loose bolts or nuts; slippage marks all aligned. Mr. Leak climbed up top and went over the rotor head as well and then looked at the tail rotor.

"Cory, always check the rotor head and the tail rotor as well as the tail boom bolts. Almost anything else can fall off the aircraft and you'll be okay. Lose any of those three and your day is screwed. The only other thing that could give you a bad day is a frozen transmission, and there's nothing you can do about that except check the oil temperature and pressure once you start the aircraft and hope you don't get a chip detector light for either the engine or the transmission."

Once Mr. Leak was satisfied, we climbed in and I started the preflight procedures. As the engine fired up, Mr. Leak set radio frequencies and called for takeoff clearance. As soon as I had completed the flight controls check, he said he had the aircraft, and I responded, "You have it."

The door gunner and Howard came over the headsets next.

"Clear right."

"Clear left."

"Clear above."

The aircraft came to a hover and we started backing out of the revetment. Once clear of the revetment, a pedal turn to the right and we were hover-taxiing to the runway with the rest of the Chicken Pen aircraft cranking engines, hovering to take off or already heading down the runway. The unit had twenty aircraft of which about sixteen were ready for missions each day. Those on the ground were in various stages of required inspections and maintenance. Those eight pilots were also sleeping in for the day.

As we hit the runway, Mr. Leak dropped the nose and pulled in the power, climbing out above the rubber trees that covered the base. The sun was coming up in the east and the sky was clear as we turned south and headed for Bien Hoa, which was a major facility in the Three Corps area. First Cav Division Rear was located there along with major Air Force elements, to include fighter aircraft, transport aircraft and a major POW camp. People departing on or returning from R&R would travel through here, catching airline flights to such places as Hawaii, which was the destination for most married men to meet wives. Singapore, Sydney, Tokyo, Kuala Lumpur, and Bangkok were the other popular destinations. There was a large post exchange as well for support of all the people located on Bien Hoa. The Army elements generally were located on the north side and the Air Force elements on the south side of the runway.

The Air Force liked keeping the Army on the opposite side of the runway. Seems when the First Cav moved down from the central highlands, this was the first really nice place they had been and things got out of hand that first night. Someone was kicked out of the Air Force NCO club and the result was a CS riot gas grenade being tossed back into the club. The Cav was uninvited after that for some time.

As it was mid-February 1969, the memory of Tet 1968 was fresh in the minds of the powers that be, so two infantry battalions were operating about nine to twelve klicks north of the base. About seven klicks was the range of the 120 mm mortar. The Fifth NVA Division was operating in this region along with Viet Cong, the indigenous guerrilla fighters.

"Dan, call Lai Khe Arty and get us clearance to Bien Hoa," Mr. Leak said.

I switched to FM1. "Lai Khe Arty, Chickenman Two-Three, over."

"Chicken-man Two-Three, Lai Khe Arty, over," they came back to me.

"Lai Khe Arty, Chicken-man Two-Three is Lai Khe to Bien Hoa at three thousand."

"Chicken-man Two-Three, you are clear all the way." Must be a quiet day for the big guns this morning.

We left FM 1 on the Arty frequency to monitor. FM 2 was on the frequency of the unit we were going to support. UHF radio was for air-to-air communications, with the VHF radio tuned to Bien Hoa tower. At times, you would be listening to conversations on all four radios at the same time and, surprisingly, keeping up with what was important on all four.

Mr. Leak started pointing out important landmarks as we headed to the unit we were supporting for the day. "Phuoc Vinh off to the left. Highway 13 running from Lai Khe south to Saigon is over on the right. That's the Song Dong Nai River, which comes down from Song Be and runs right north of Bien Hoa. It's a major supply route for Charlie."

"Is that a Navy landing craft I see on the river?" I asked.

"Yeah. He's been there for a month now patrolling the river. They're trying to prevent Charlie from moving rockets and supplies down the river at night. Last year for TET, that was a major supply route for Charlie into Saigon," Mr. Leak offered.

"Do they move all their supplies that way?"

"No, I've heard from the guys that fly the Night Hunter missions that the gooks will chop a notch in the trees and place a candle in the notch to mark a trail to bring supplies down on bikes. I've hauled some of those bikes out when the grunts have found them. You'll be hauling all sorts of captured stuff, from bikes to rice to prisoners. You name it, you'll haul it. Call Sabre Six and let them know we're inbound."

Sabre Six was the call sign of the battalion we were supporting for the day. The firebase they were operating on was just coming into view. "Saber Six, Chicken-man Two-Three, over."

"Chicken-man Two-Three, Saber Six India[1], we've been expecting you. Come on in and shut it down," the radio squawked.

"Saber Six India, Chicken-man Two-Three, roger," I squawked back.

"Crap!" grumbled Mr. Leak. "I hope we're not going to be sitting on our asses all day. Howard, you may need to come up with a maintenance need in Bien Hoa. I'll give you the sign if necessary."

Mr. Leak was looking at the fast-approaching firebase. "I hate sitting on my ass waiting for these guys to get their shit together for our missions. Some units have got everything ready to go first thing in the morning when we arrive. This unit never has it together, and we may sit all day until late this afternoon before they have anything for us. When that happens, Howard always has a maintenance issue that we have to go into Bien Hoa to take care of, like get a hamburger or a beer."

As we circled the firebase, we could see the log pad where we were to land as all the various supplies going out that day were being positioned to load the aircraft. Cases of C-rations, water cans, mailbags and ammo cases, to name a few items. A grunt was standing at one side of the pad, raising his arms as a ground guide. Mr. Leak turned onto our final approach path and began explaining the approach to me.

"When we're at about fifteen feet, the dust is going to start coming up. Before you get to that point, you want to have your touchdown point picked out and your glide angle set and just lower your power and speed. At about ten to five feet, it'll be difficult to see below you but easier to judge your speed and rate of descent by looking with your peripheral vision. At about five feet, you'll see the ground through your chin bubble and just set it down. You do not want to be hovering around in this dust." And we touched down. "Any questions?"

"Nope," I answered.

"Good, the next approach is yours. Shut us down, then follow me over to the TOC for our briefing and let's hope they got it together today." Howard and the door gunner opened our doors and then returned to the guns and started cleaning the dust from them, using paintbrushes to get the grit out of the receivers and ammo. At this point I was fascinated with what I saw going on all around me. Shirtless grunts were going about their morning tasks, shaving, standing guard on the perimeter, writing letters, playing cards. Even the ever-present shit-burning detail was busy stirring the pot. From the looks of things, everyone was doing something different, with nothing organized but everything efficient, I would learn.

"Bring your map, Dan." *Ah, it's Dan and not New Guy.* We walked over to the TOC, or Tactical Operations Center, which was located in the center of the firebase. Five 105 mm howitzers were on one side and behind the TOC were four 81 mm mortars. All was quiet from the guns. The TOC was two metal CONEX containers with open doors facing each other, buried in the ground ten feet with corrugated metal covering the opening between them and everything topped with two layers of sandbags. This was surrounded with three rows of concertina wire. Inside this area, the operations of the battalion were tracked and directed.

When we entered, a captain greeted us. "Good morning, you must be Chicken-man Two-Three. Glad to see you this fine day," he said as he approached Mr. Leak.

"Good morning, sir. I'm Mr. Leak and this is New Guy."
*Damn, back to New Guy.*

"Good morning, sir. Mr. Cory," I said as I extended my hand, and he took it with a smile.

"So am I, Mr. Cory. Been here a week myself." *Ah, camaraderie between New Guys.*

Walking over to a map on the CONEX wall and pointing, the captain began his briefing. "First let me give you an overview of our area of operations and the enemy situation, then specifics for what we got today. The Fifth NVA Division have been moving supplies down from the north on a couple of trails that we have identified and set ambushes along last night. One comes down to the crossing point over the river as it's shallow there, maybe chest deep. Alpha Company came across what looked like a possible .51-cal position on the edge of this clearing here."

"Plot that location, Dan," Mr. Leak directed, which I did with a grease pencil on my map.

The captain continued. "Alpha's operating in this area with patrols. Bravo's in this area, and Charlie is doing the same over here along the river. Right now, scouts are on the firebase. Now Bravo's in need of a backhaul, and then they'll be moving out, so that's first thing right away. I can't give you locations for resupply yet as the companies are on the move, so we'll just have to wait until they're ready to receive you. The old man may want to go up later, so that's pretty much it for today."

Mr. Leak spoke up. "Okay, sir, I'm going to need call signs and frequencies and a location for the backhaul for Bravo, and we can get right out there. Also, we have a maintenance issue that we need to run over to Bien Hoa to take care of, which should only take about an hour."

The captain looked perplexed but smiled. "Yeah, that's not

a problem. I might have some guys to send over with you if it's okay."

"Not a problem, sir. The maintenance shop we need to stop at is close to the PX if you want to send some guys over," Mr. Leak added. The bullshit lies had been told, acknowledged and accepted with grace and joy for all involved.

I got the call signs, frequencies for all the units and the location for Bravo Company so we could backhaul some stuff. Walking back to the aircraft, Howard looked up and Mr. Leak raised his arm and moved it in a circular motion, which meant we were cranking up. Howard and the door gunner immediately got up and started getting ready. By the time we reached the aircraft, they had their helmets on and the doors open, and Howard had a small fire extinguisher in hand. Once we were strapped in, Mr. Leak gave me a nod and said, "Crank it."

As the engine was starting, Howard looked through a small inspection panel into the engine compartment to make sure we didn't have a fire on start-up. When he was satisfied, he returned the fire extinguisher and climbed into his seat.

"I have the aircraft," Mr. Leak said. "Now we know this is going to be a dust bowl as soon as we pick up, so no hovering. Also, this isn't a combat takeoff—there's too many people around us and no space for that. Here we're going to pull in max torque quickly to bring us up out of the dust, and then we'll nose over and make a normal departure."

As I sat and learned, the crew cleared us.

"Clear left."

"Clear right."

"Clear above."

This was something that the crew did every time the aircraft departed or approached a landing. Every crew, every time.

"Okay, here we go." Mr. Leak pulled on the collective to thirty-four pounds of torque. The aircraft, being empty, leaped into the air, and at about fifteen feet, he nosed over the aircraft for a smooth climb out with minimum dust over the entire firebase. I was thinking it must suck being in all that dust, all day, every day. It did. As we were climbing out to two thousand feet, Mr. Leak directed me to tune in the frequency for Bravo Company and call them.

"Bravo Six, this is Chickenman Two-Three, over."

"Chicken-man Two-Three, this is Bravo Six India, over."

"Bravo Six, Chicken-man Two-Three inbound to your location, over."

"Roger, Chicken-man Two-Three, popping smoke." Although we had plotted Bravo Company's location, we were never sure of the exact location where they wanted us, so the ground unit would toss a colored smoke grenade to mark their location. This would also provide information on wind direction and velocity. You always had the ground unit toss the colored smoke and the aircraft would identify the color.

"Bravo Six, I have Goofy Grape, over." Goofy Grape was purple smoke. Mellow Yellow was yellow smoke and Rosy Red was red.

"Roger, Chicken-man, Goofy Grape. Standing by." The smoke was drifting ever so slowly, which indicated very little wind for the landing. It also gave us an appreciation on the tree height, which in this area was not as high as those along the Cambodian border, these being only about thirty to forty feet high. Bravo was actually on the edge of a small clearing for an easy approach and landing.

As we made a pass over the intended landing point, Mr. Leak went into education mode. "Okay, the smoke tells us almost no wind, so that's not going to be a factor. The trees on the south side look lower than the north side. The unit's on the south side as well, so we'll make final approach over the south side. Never make your approach the same twice in a row if you can help it. Always make the approach from a different angle each time, turning into final at the last minute if you can. You make the approach the same each time and Charlie will fire your ass up. Got it?"

Lesson learned. "Got it," I responded.

As we dropped below five hundred feet, Howard and the door gunner brought their guns up and began scanning for enemy fire. We were ninety degrees and one hundred feet from our final approach path when Mr. Leak made a ninety-degree bank turn with a ninety-degree roll, decelerating our forward speed, dropping rapidly and flaring to a hover in front of a grunt ground guide.

"Any questions?" Mr. Leak asked. *Questions? Hell, I'm still a hundred feet in the air and ninety degrees to the final approach and we're sitting on the ground.*

"No, no questions," I lied.

The ground guide grunt hopped up on the skid next to Mr. Leak and started talking. "We have two turns for you. Those water cans and eight grunts that need to go back. Also a mailbag and six marmite cans."

"Okay, give me four guys and the water cans on this trip and the rest when I come back."

As the aircraft was being loaded, Mr. Leak resumed instructor mode. "Okay, to get out of here is pretty easy. We have a light load and probably could have taken it all in one trip, but I want to make it two. We have very little wind and the trees are the lowest on the south, which was our approach in. The friendlies are on the south as well, so we'll come to a hover, pedal turn and fly out on our final approach path, gaining speed as quick as possible and turning off the approach path as quick as we can. Get in quick and get out quick."

"You're up, Mr. Leak," Howard said as the last of the cargo and pax were loaded.

"Roger, coming up." And the crew cleared us.

I looked back and saw four dirty, smiling faces. These grunts seemed happy to be on board. They were filthy and loaded down with all their equipment. Their uniforms weren't much more than tattered rags. They looked like old men, but I would bet they were no older than me from the looks of their immature mustaches. The aircraft was rotating in its hover and slid forward with max power being applied. We cleared the tops of the trees by two feet and picked up speed quickly, flying at treetop level, eyeball to eyeball with monkeys in the treetops before suddenly entering into a power climb to two thousand feet at ninety knots.

Mr. Leak resumed instructor mode once again. "You've got to have airspeed or altitude, and preferably both. If you got both, you can survive an engine failure. If you don't have altitude, then you best have speed, and vice versa. You want to go from treetop to two thousand feet as quickly as possible as that's the prime range for small-arms fire, especially the .51-cal. If he tracks you at five hundred feet or less, you have big problems. He can touch you at twenty-five hundred feet, but not with a lot of accuracy. So the lesson is, stay fast at treetop and get to two thousand quickly with speed. When we get back tonight, check the -10$^2$ for the dead man zone. Okay, you got it. Now back to the firebase and the dust. Talk me through your approach."

As we flew back with our passengers, I described to Mr. Leak what I planned on doing for my landing in the dust. He listened and then responded, "You got the words, now show me." *Damn, this guy is Mr. Personality.*

I set up my approach and talked him through it as I was executing. We landed, not as softly as he had done, but we were safely on the ground and with no damage to the aircraft or anyone's nerves. Mr. Leak just sat there staring ahead. The pax, as we called passengers, jumped off and waved goodbye as the ground crew pulled the cans off the bird.

"You're up," said Howard, and Mr. Leak just pointed straight ahead, indicating "Let's go."

Again I talked him through what I was doing as I was doing it. At least, I thought I was talking to him as he just sat and stared straight ahead. I wondered if his intercom had gone out. Oh, maybe he was pissed at that landing I made. He continued to stare ahead. *Okay, I guess he wants me to take it in.* I called Bravo Six India and let him know I was inbound, but no need for smoke as I had his position. This time, however, I changed my approach so I was making a ninety-degree left turn into the final approach, coming in fast and low.

As I flared to decelerate, Howard came on the intercom. "Watch the tail!"

I took a bit of the deceleration out, which raised the tail so I wouldn't hit the trees, and then completed the landing. Mr. Leak said nothing. *Shit, he is pissed.*

"Howard, how close was Mr. Cory to the trees?" asked Mr. Leak.

"He wasn't, sir. I was just screwing with him." A small grin broke Mr. Leak's stoic face.

"Thanks, Howard," I said.

The aircraft was loaded and Mr. Leak said, "Let's go."

A pedal turn and out we came and headed back. My second approach, I said nothing but came in and made a much-improved landing. Sabre Six India came up on the net and told us to shut down, which we did. Howard and the door gunner began cleaning guns, Mr. Leak moved to the cabin area and pulled out a popular paperback to read: *M*A*S*H*.* He handed me the -10 and told me to look up the dead man zone.

Around noon, we had been sitting for three hours when Howard said he needed to go to maintenance to get some hydraulic fluid, or was it a hamburger instead of a C-ration? I forget. Mr. Leak walked up to the TOC and came back five minutes later with the captain. Seemed he needed to go to maintenance too. Oh, and here came a first sergeant as well. And the mail clerk needed to pick up mail in Bien Hoa too. *I think I'm beginning to see a pattern here.*

Everyone was strapped in, and Mr. Leak again pointed straight ahead without a word. I took us out and headed the fifteen klicks to the sprawling base at Bien Hoa. When we got to altitude, Mr. Leak said he had the aircraft. I tuned the VHF radio to Bien Hoa tower in anticipation of calling for landing clearance.

"Don't bother the tower. We're landing at the helipad on the north side, and there's no need to call them. They're busy with fast movers and cargo planes."

There was the helipad. In a field that separated the main runway from the combination of wooden buildings and tents that constituted the Army area was a corrugated metal pad approximately the size of a football field with a large First Cav patch painted in the center. As we shut down, Mr. Leak told our passengers that they had one hour before we headed back. Technically, the captain owned the aircraft as he represented the unit we were working for, but Mr. Leak was giving the unquestioned orders, and all agreed, in compliance.

Once the aircraft was secured, the four of us followed our noses to what was a mess hall serving hot chow. No roast beef, but hot dogs, hamburgers, spaghetti with real meat sauce, ice cream. *Shit, what world is this?* I got a hot dog and a hamburger along with French fries. And the coffee was real. It was obvious that the rear echelon lived a lot better than those closest to the front action. We lived good as aviators, certainly better than the grunts, but these rear-echelon mothers, REMFs as we called them, were living the life. There was— always had been and always would be—some animosity between those on the front lines and those in the rear. Those in the rear areas enjoyed levels of comfort only imagined by those on the front. Clean sheets, hot chow, good boots, and movies were just some of the perks, besides never getting shot at and all the while bitching how tough they had it because of the paper cuts they received. History shows that General Eisenhower wanted Paris to be an R&R center for frontline troops. Just after it was liberated, one hundred and fifty thousand REMFs took up residence, and he could do nothing to dislodge them. Some things never change.

When we had our fill, we wandered back to the aircraft to find that our passengers were there and ready to go. The ketchup on the captain's shirt told me he had gotten his maintenance taken care of—not sure where, though.

The rest of the day was more of the same. As units settled in to set up their night defensive positions, we hauled supplies out to them. Mr. Leak remained in instructor mode, pointing out things that he felt were important for a new guy to learn.

"First time into unit's location, take thirty water cans. That gives you a manageable load until you can evaluate the LZ to see if you can take more or need to take less weight. It also gives the grunts time to fill their canteens and get the empty water cans back on the bird so they're not stuck with empty water cans in case they have to move."

When we were released by Saber Six to go home, we headed straight back to the Chicken Pen, stopping only to refuel the aircraft when we got to Lai Khe.

As we slid into the revetment, Mr. Leak said, "Let's be sure and give her a good post-flight inspection. Howard, do we need to run water or walnuts tonight?"

"No, sir, we're good." To keep the engines performing at peak performance in really dusty conditions, the engine air intake filters were pulled out and cleaned off. In addition, water would be flushed through the air intake periodically to clean it out. To keep the turbine blades in the engine compressor clean, ground-up walnut shells would be tossed in to clean the blades while the engine was running.

The door gunner took both guns and started cleaning them as well as the ammo. Mr. Leak and I did a walk around the aircraft, conducting a post-flight inspection to make sure it was ready for the next day's mission. This was Mr. Leak's assigned aircraft and crew, and he wanted it all straight. Aircraft commanders had assigned aircraft and crews. The rest of us were rotated through aircraft commanders and aircraft. When done, he and I grabbed our gear and started walking back.

"Hey, Dan, you done good for a new guy today. You still have some schoolhouse hesitation in your flying, but that'll wear off quickly enough when you develop a feel for the aircraft and flying her in these conditions. These aircraft can take a lot more than what you were doing with them in flight school. Don't be afraid to stretch the boundaries with these birds, but remember, airspeed and altitude. You want both but need at least one of them. Oh, and you're buying the beer for today's lessons." I was starting to see another pattern here. Lessons cost beers.

Reaching my tent, I dropped my gear and noticed a new face talking to Lou. Grabbing a beer, I walked over and introduced myself to a very clean-shaven face. He was a new guy, which in my eyes made me an "old guy."

"Howdy, Dan Cory," I said, extending my hand.

"Bill Hess," he responded as he got out of my chair.

"Really glad to meet you."

"Oh, why's that?" he asked with a puzzled look.

"Because I'm no longer the new guy. You are," I said with a smile.

Lou cracked a smile and finished his beer. "Hey, new guys, plural, get me a beer." *Some things just don't change.*

Bill had joined the Army almost right out of high school. He was from Newburgh, New York, and had the New Yorker accent and manners to prove it. From his build I would bet money he was a football player in high school, guard or line-backer. I had been a bench warmer masquerading as a line-backer. It appeared that he might be trying to grow a mustache, or just forgot to shave his upper lip for the past two weeks.

# 10

## REALITY SETS IN

SINCE MY ORIENTATION RIDE, I HAD FLOWN FOR THE last ten days. My butt was starting to feel it too. Captain Goodnight had warned me. I was glad that I had a down day to sleep in and relax. I could get some laundry done, write some letters and go over to the PX to buy some beer. I'd heard pilots being woken up to fly today but had rolled over and gone pleasantly back to sleep. Finally the heat had gotten to be too much and I had known it was time to roll out.

Around 1400 as I was writing a letter home, I noticed a flurry of activity over at the Ops tent. Someone ran to the CO's tent, and he came out and headed to Ops. The assistant maintenance officer was even heading over there. *Wonder what's up with this?* Curiosity killed the cat, and I headed that way, as did a couple of other pilots that had the day down.

"Hey, Bob, what's going on?" I asked as I walked up. The radios in Ops were turned up loud and monitoring our battalion frequency, but the conversation was one-sided.

"Roger, Lightning Bolt Six, diverting three aircraft from Badger Six to your location. Chicken-man One-Two is off Lai Khe and en route to your location," I could hear coming from the Ops tent. I stayed out of the tent as it didn't appear that they needed anyone else in there.

Bob looked over at me with concern on his face. "It appears that Captain Pierre, who's flying Yellow One today with a six-two package, has himself a hot LZ. The LZ is only a three-ship LZ and he had eighteen sorties to get in there. He got the first three in okay when all hell broke loose. Our aviation battalion commander, Lightning Bolt Six, is up in Chuck Chuck and called for more aircraft. The maintenance officer just took off with another aircraft to replace one that was too badly shot up, and it sounds like the battalion commander is pulling other aircraft from missions to use on this mission."

Throughout the rest of the afternoon, the mission continued, but as we could only hear bits and pieces between the battalion commander and battalion headquarters, we realized that we would have to wait until crews came in that night. That evening, we were in our tent discussing the day's activity. The assistant maintenance officer came in looking for a beer.

"Hey, John, how's it going?" I asked.

"Give me a beer and I'll tell you how's it going." One of the other pilots opened the refrigerator and handed him a cold one. "We have thirteen of our twenty-one aircraft shot to shit. Two have got to be evacuated back to the States they're shot up so bad, 251 and 228. Of the remaining eleven, we have an estimated three thousand hours of work ahead of us to get them in flying condition. Tomorrow we'll have a total of six aircraft that we can put in the air, as I already had two in for periodic inspections. The first of those shot up today will be up the day after tomorrow, and that's 740 as I only—only—need twenty-four hours of maintenance to solve that one. I can tell you that maintenance platoon is not going to get any sleep for a few days," John responded. I silently thanked God I wasn't a maintenance officer.

A few minutes later, Kevin walked in and dropped his gear

on his bed. He looked tired and worn as he was flying copilot with Captain Pierre. Someone handed him a beer; no one said anything but allowed him to take a long pull. He sat down and started explaining.

"We had a six-two package for First of the Twelfth. Simple mission, eighteen sorties, three turns, in a three-ship LZ. Everything starts out fine with two groups of three separated by one minute. Before we get to the LZ on the initial lift, Chalk Six goes back to the firebase with a maintenance issue. First three birds get in and out, but Chalk Four and Five are on approach and all hell breaks loose with at least two .50-cals and a .30-cal from bunkers on three sides of the LZ. Both of them take hits. I think Chalk Four had something like fifteen holes. They never got on the ground but came back to the firebase. In the meantime, we had already picked up the grunts from Chalk Six and were taking them to the LZ. Captain Pierre heard that Four and Five couldn't get in, so he comes around to the north and makes an approach." Pausing, he took a long pull on his beer just as Lou walked in and threw his gear across the tent on to his bed. I got him a beer.

"What the hell!" Lou shouted. "I'm too short for this shit. Damn. Kevin, what the hell was he thinking? Didn't he know that me and Five got shot out of there?" Lou was Chalk Four on this mission.

Looking up at Lou, Kevin replied, "We couldn't get in on the original approach, so we set up for a different approach when we were raked good by a .50-cal. Lobo was laying down rockets and Blue Max expended everything he had. We went in again from the south and again got nailed with AK-47s and one of the .50-cals. We're so full of holes at this point that our aircraft is smoking and oil pressure is dropping." Kevin stopped long enough to finish his beer and accept another as the rest of us were listening spellbound.

"While you were changing aircraft, the grunts are calling

arty in on the bunkers on the south, east and west of the LZ," Lou added. "At this point, there are only eighteen grunts in the LZ, and God only knows how many gooks were there. We head back thinking that the arty would have opened things up for us and Lobo Six is flying cover. As we're on final, the damn .50-cal opens up again, along with a dozen or so AK-47s, and we're out of there again. This time we have a wounded grunt on board, so we get him back to the firebase and the grunts call in more arty. While we're heading back to the firebase to regroup, Chalk Three was asked by the grunt battalion S-3 to fly in with ammo and bring out wounded, and he's heading that way. Who the hell is in charge? Everyone and no one.

"Paul goes in with Lobo overhead and lands to drop the ammo and get the wounded out. Ammo goes out quick, wounded loading isn't so fast, so he's sitting there taking hits when Lobo comes over like a little bird, low and slow, putting down suppressive fire directly into the bunker openings, and he's taking hits. Paul's taking rounds through the windshield, so he picks up to a hover, does a one-eighty pedal turn and sets it back down. So now he's taking hits in the ass while the wounded are getting on.

"His door gunner, Specialist Leonard, is laying down suppressive fire and expends all his ammo, so he has to resupply off Chalk Six, as did a couple of others. When Paul gets back to the firebase, he's so shot up that he barely got back there, and that bird is done for the day."

"Done for the day, my ass. That bird is being evacuated back to the States it's so shot up. How he got it to the firebase is a miracle to me," John interrupted.

Kevin continued, "By now, a couple of aircraft that were pulled off other missions have joined us. I think one was from Bravo Company and two from Charlie. Lightning Bolt Six is in Chuck Chuck and has us load up and orbit to the east while the ground commander brings in an air strike of napalm.

Captain Pierre pulls together another flight, and again three and three, we make a run to get troops in as well as ammo and get wounded out. Some aircraft get in, some don't and everyone's taking hits. I think one of Charlie Company's aircraft had a gunner and a crew chief wounded. What should have been an easy one-hour mission took us six hours. I think the grunts had six KIA and eighteen or so wounded. Finally it just got too dark to continue the mission. I think we got fifty-eight troops on the ground before the insertion was called off."

"Where did you guys refuel and rearm?" asked someone.

"We went back to Bien Hoa. Lobo cleaned them out of rockets, fourteen hundred. The ammo resupply point people had to make a run to the ammo dump to get more rockets, 40 mm and ammo," Kevin added.

"Did we have anyone hurt?" I asked.

"No. Well, yeah, somehow by the grace of God, Kindell on Chalk Five had a .50-cal round pass between his chicken plate and his chest. Imagine, between the chicken plate and his chest. Cut him good across the chest and knocked him out. We thought he was dead, but he'll be okay. I think maybe Specialist Leonard was hit too, but nothing serious. Luckily, only our aircraft are shot to shit," Kevin added as he looked at the maintenance officer.

"That's an understatement. Well, I have work to do tonight. You ladies sleep tight. I'm not." And with that, the maintenance officer left. Kevin followed him out, hoping to find some chow. The rest of us returned to letter writing and quiet reflection on the day's events. The reality of what we did was setting in for me.

# 11

## LESSONS IN FORMATION FLYING

"Hey, Mr. Cory, wake up." This waking up at 0430 hours would be a lot easier if the ops kid could bring me a cup of coffee as well. *Ain't going to happen.*

"Okay, I'm awake and getting up. What time is it?"

"Zero four thirty," he replied as he moved to the next bed, and the next, and the next. *Shit, everyone's getting up this morning.* Once everyone was awake, he announced AC brief in the mess hall at 0530 hours and crew list was posted in Ops. It had been a week since the major firefight. Two new aircraft had come in and most of the shot-up aircraft had been repaired—most. Okay, I'd go by and check the board on my way to coffee and breakfast. As I was getting my boots on, I saw Lou sitting on his bed, smoking a cigarette and holding what looked like a cup of coffee. Looks could be deceiving.

"Hey, Lou, do you have a coffeepot stashed over here?" I asked as I walked over, sniffing the air for that aroma.

"No."

"Oh. I saw the coffee cup and thought—"

"Well, you thought wrong," he replied as he filled the cup with his morning beer. Lou had been around for about ten months when I'd arrived and was due to rotate back to the States in another month. His first mission in-country was into the A Shau Valley in 1968, and he was shot down on that mission, ending up hanging upside down in the aircraft. Welcome to Vietnam. I hadn't flown with him as yet, but he had a reputation for being an excellent pilot, according to the last new guy.

"Sorry. I'm going to get some breakfast. Can I bring anything back?"

"No. I have a mission brief. I'll get something then," he mumbled as he drained his coffee cup.

On the way to the mess hall, I passed by operations and looked to see who I was flying with. One Chief Warrant Officer Second Class Lou Price. I proceeded into the mess hall and grabbed a tray. Metal trays, just like in most federal prisons. And for breakfast today, we had powdered eggs, undercooked bacon, and potatoes. They also had something they were calling bread, but it had the feel of sawdust baked with water, and a taste to match. Of note, however, was that just about every pilot was in the mess hall this morning. Rather unusual for all of us to be up and about. Mr. Leak and Mr. Toliver were sitting together and motioned for me to join them. *Oh, this has to be a setup on the new guy.* I approached and asked if they needed anything.

"No, sit down and join us. Who you flying with today?" Mr. Toliver asked.

"I'm on the board with Lou," I replied, stirring condensed milk into my coffee.

"Good, you'll learn from him. He's good. Just remember what we discussed the other day," Mr. Leak added.

"Also, don't screw up. Lou is a short-timer double-digit midget and should be flying milk runs instead of this," said Mr. Toliver.

"Ah, what is 'this'?" I asked cautiously between mouthfuls of powdered eggs.

"It looks like we're moving two battalions today, so everyone will be flying formation all day. It's going to be a long day. One battalion will go back to Bien Hoa, and the battalion there will be inserted to replace them. Captain Goodnight will cover everything in the mission brief to the aircraft commanders. You best get with Lou and get a good preflight conducted before he comes out. Do you know which aircraft is his?"

"No," I answered. I didn't know I had to memorize the name of each aircraft commander's aircraft.

"Lou's bird is the Iron Butterfly." At this time, we had no standardized markings on the noses of our aircraft. The pilot's doors had a green triangle with a lightning bolt through the triangle, but that was all. Across the nose of each, the aircraft commanders and crew chiefs generally put their individual pet name on the nose—Iron Butterfly, Green Lantern, Devil's Advocate and Hard Luck, to name a few. We had a really good nose artist, Sergeant Scovel, who was kept busy. Some units had a bit more discipline and had a standard emblem on the noses of their aircraft, such as the unit that shared Lai Khe with us from the First Aviation Brigade. They were the Robin Hoods, and so their nose emblem was Robin Hood's hat with a feather and an arrow through it. They parked their aircraft in Sherwood Forest, as they called it.

After breakfast, I walked back to my tent to retrieve my gear, and Lou was just leaving with his stuff to attend the briefing.

"Lou, I'm with you today and thought I'd head out to preflight the bird. Want me to take your stuff out?"

Lou looked at me for a minute and slowly said, "Yeah, and thanks. Can you take my helmet?"

"Sure, your aircraft is the Iron Butterfly, right?" I asked, just to make sure I hadn't been set up for a practical joke.

"Yeah, that's her. The crew chief is Bennett and he's probably already there. You might give Brown a hand with ammo if he hasn't already got it on the bird," he called over his shoulder as he walked off to the mess hall. I went and picked up my helmet, map, pistol and turned to leave. As I did, I noticed two empty beer cans scattered around Lou's bed. *Oh boy.*

When I arrived at the aircraft, Bennett and Brown were just finishing up with their chores. I introduced myself to them and commenced the preflight, completing it as Lou arrived. I noticed all the other pilots coming out of the Chicken Coop and getting settled in their aircraft.

Lou started to brief us. "Okay, guys, this is what we got. First of the Eighth is in Bien Hoa, and we're moving them out to replace Second of the Seventh, which we're bringing back to Bien Hoa. First of the Eighth will conduct an insertion to establish a new firebase here," he said, pointing at the map spread out on the cabin floor. "We'll be a twelve-ship formation, making three turns to get the whole battalion in. After they're inserted, we'll refuel at Bien Hoa and then break into a six-ship formation and start extracting elements of Second of the Seventh, taking them back to Bien Hoa. We're Chalk Six today. Any questions?"

Bennett straightened up. "We expecting any enemy, Mr. Price?"

"Nothing more than the usual. If these guys are the same bunch as last week, no telling. If they're VC and not the hardcore NVA, they can't hit their ass with both hands let alone hit us in flight. If we are going to get hit, it'll be on the approach going in or coming out. Okay, let's saddle up."

As we settled into our seats, the crew came forward and closed and secured our doors. Bennett grabbed the fire extinguisher and took his position next to the engine. I went through the start procedures and pressed and held the starter button. Slowly the turbine started turning, and at sixty-eight percent N1 I rolled the throttle open. Lou was tuning radios. Other aircraft were calling Flight Leader that they were up.

"Chalk Six is up," Lou announced with a corresponding response from Lead. Finally all twelve aircraft were up and ready to depart. Flight Lead, Yellow One, announced leaving the revetment, followed by Chalk Two and so forth until Chalk Twelve announced he was in position.

Flight Lead announced, "Yellow One on the go," and twelve aircraft started down the runway, following the leader.

"Flight, come up staggered right," ordered Yellow One.

We flew different formations depending on several factors. Staggered right was Chalk Two flying behind and to the right of Chalk One, with Chalk Three behind Chalk One and to the left and back from Chalk Two, and so on for all twelve ships. To land such a formation, you needed a long landing zone, and we could fly staggered left or right. Another formation was wedge, which looked like a flock of geese in flight. Trail was one aircraft following the other. An echelon right or echelon left formation was all aircraft slightly behind and off to the side of the aircraft in front, with Flight Leader the very first aircraft. Switching between formations once in the air was done only if necessary.

"Yellow One, Chalk Two, over."

"Chalk Two, go ahead."

"Yellow One, we are clear of arty all the way to Bien Hoa, over."

As Lou was bringing us up into our position as Chalk Six, he asked, "How much formation time do you have?"

"Just what we got in flight school and a couple of hours the other day," I replied without looking in his direction.

"Don't tell me this is your first combat assault."

"Okay, I won't, but it is."

"Oh, it's going to be a long day, I see." He took a deep breath. "Okay, formation flying here isn't like flight school," he said as he moved closer to the right side of Chalk Five. "In Mother Rucker, they wanted two-rotor-blade width between aircraft. Here we fly at one to one-half rotor from the other."

He was going for the half-rotor-blade distance, and my pucker factor was starting to suck the seat up my ass. I looked back at Chalk Seven. *Oh shit, he's going for the half-rotor distance as well.* Lou was calmly smoking his cigarette and continuing with his lecture while he held the cyclic in his thumb, index and middle fingers.

"The one thing you don't want to do is overlap rotor blades." *Oh, trust me, that ain't happening.* "Okay, you got it," he said.

I responded, "I got it," and wished I hadn't. Immediately we started sliding back to a two-rotor-blade distance.

Chalk Seven called us. "Hey, Chalk Six, did the new guy just take it?" Great, now the entire formation knew I had it.

"Yeah, and he's shitting in his pants." Now that wasn't true, but it wasn't far from the truth.

"Okay, let's close it back up and get with the formation." I pulled in some more power and eased the aircraft forward. "Good, now just hold it here," Lou said, and I immediately started drifting back. "No, get back up there."

Lou hadn't raised his voice or hit me yet but coached me back into position each time. However, every aircraft behind us was giving Lou a raft of shit about the speeding up and slowing down, which was causing an accordion effect on those behind us. After about thirty minutes, I had a death grip on the cyclic and white knuckles on the collective, with sweat just pouring off me.

"Okay, I got it," Lou said as we approached the PZ in Bien Hoa to pick up the grunts. Stretched out before us were twelve groups of grunts, with seven grunts in each group, in the same formation as our flight. In addition, one grunt was out front in each group with his weapon above his head in both hands. Lou picked out group number six and eased the aircraft to a stop with us at a hover and the nose of the aircraft touching the nose of the soldier ground-guiding us to our spot. Lou touched his nose with the hovering aircraft and the grunt hardly felt it. Talk about a confidence builder for the grunts to see that kind of aircraft control. Good thing for that soldier it wasn't me. As the soldiers climbed aboard, Yellow One came up and told us to "roll them back." This meant we weren't taking off right away as he was talking to the ground commander.

"Do you like formation flying?" Lou asked.

"To be honest, I'm uncomfortable in formation flights."

"It shows. Look, no new guy does well in formation flying over here right out of school. They teach the basics, which you have. Now it's a matter of taking what you know and applying it to combat. Why do we fly close together? Two reasons. First, if you're two or more rotor blades away, the other aircraft can make some major attitude adjustments before you notice them, and then you're playing catchup, which is no fun. Second, the closer we are to each other, the more concentrated our firepower is with all guns firing. At night in formation flying, close is much safer than two rotor blades apart. People flying formations at night will either be crawling up your ass or so far away you'll wonder if they're in the same formation. I'll take the guy flying up my ass any day as he's the safer aircraft."

As we talked, we saw the ground commander walk over to his jeep and grab his gear. "Flight one minute," Yellow One announced.

Lou rolled the throttle back to full power. "Okay. I'll take this one and you get the next one." Brown and Bennett cleared us to come up. The grunts were sitting on the floor and there were no smiles. They knew what was in store for them. No hot shower tonight, or hot food. Flight Lead lifted into the air and we followed, but Lou picked up at the same time as Chalk Four and ever so slightly before Chalk Five.

"You notice that I didn't wait for Five to move his ass."

"Yeah, why?" I asked.

"The last thing you want is to get caught in the downward rotor wash of an aircraft in front or alongside you. That'll cause you to use a lot more power to take off, and you'll be struggling on a warm day to get back in the formation, with everyone behind you cussing you out. And that can happen on takeoff or once you're in formation and we're getting buffeted by updrafts and downdrafts."

All twelve aircraft were in the air when, off in the distance, the earth erupted in small dirty explosions.

"We're six minutes out now as the artillery will shoot from H minus six to H minus two. At H minus two, the gunships will roll in when they see a white smoke round hit the LZ, and at H minus one, we will commence firing. Got it?"

"Understood." I was about to enter into my first combat assault. My pucker factor was now really sucking my shorts up my ass. I didn't feel scared but anxious in anticipation of what was coming. This was nothing like flight school, but I felt confident in what I was about to do. We continued to move towards the impacting artillery, and at H minus two, a white phosphorous round hit the LZ.

"Tubes clear," Lou said, "which means the artillery isn't shooting any more. There go the Cobras." Four AH-1G Cobra gunships from Second of the Twentieth Aerial Rocket Artillery Battalion, call sign "Blue Max" and carrying the "Blue Max" emblem on the side of their aircraft, moved out ahead of us in a dive and started firing 2.75-inch rockets from their tubes. Each aircraft carried forty-eight rockets and was laying them into the tree line. On one pass, those aircraft would expend all their rockets.

"H minus one. Gunners open up." And Bennett and Brown went to town firing their guns into the tree line. More Cobra gunships from our own Delta Company, call sign "El Lobo," who normally escorted us, were adding to the destruction. Lou was steady on the controls, watching the aircraft in front, as well as Chalk Five off to the left front, and the small trees and bushes in the LZ, careful not to hit one with the tail rotor. I was sitting there trying to absorb it all.

"Yellow One coming out." Oh hell, we were on the ground maybe three seconds and this aircraft was empty. As the aircraft lifted up in order, Lou asked, "Any questions?"

"No. It gets a bit intense for those two minutes, doesn't it?" I responded.

"You'll get used to it pretty quick. Okay, you want to take it?" It wasn't so much a question as a statement. Lou was in need of a cigarette.

"I have the aircraft," I said as I settled into concentrating on Chalk Five and maintaining position off him.

As the day was getting warmer, some turbulence was felt, with updrafts and downdrafts that started a seesaw motion in the entire flight as each respective aircraft hit an updraft or a downdraft. Yellow One might be rising one hundred feet in an updraft and yet Chalk Four might be dropping one hundred feet in a downdraft. This ripple effect through the entire flight was making it increasingly difficult for me to maintain that one-rotor-blade staggered formation off Chalk Five. Then the inevitable happened. Chalk Five was in an updraft, I was in a downdraft and slipped into the downward rotor wash of Chalk Five, or so I thought. In order to maintain formation, I was pulling a lot more power to get back in formation, so much so that I was on the edge of forty percent N1, which was a red line. Exceeding it could over-torque the aircraft. I was struggling and Lou just sat there.

"I got it," he finally said. I was crushed. Sliding the aircraft to the right, he took us out of the rotor wash and brought us back up into the formation, although the flight was still experiencing the updrafts and downdrafts. Next he slid the aircraft back to one-rotor-blade distance but took up a position slightly above Chalk Five so I was looking to my left and down slightly at the roof of Chalk Five.

"When in formation, make the other guy work for it. You should position yourself to be slightly above him so that you're looking literally into his cockpit. Then you won't get caught in his rotor wash and have to use too much power. A proper formation should have each succeeding aircraft slight above the aircraft in front of it. At night, we fly trail, and you're going to want to line up the tail rotor hub of the aircraft in front of you with the exhaust housing of that aircraft. That'll keep you above him and out of his rotor wash. Okay, we're back in position, now take it."

"I have the aircraft," I said, thinking this was going to be a long day. We were turning to final and the grunts were positioned to receive us as they had done on the first lift. I wasn't about to attempt to get nose to nose with the ground guide but selected an appropriate touchdown point a few feet back from him. I think he was disappointed that I didn't nose him.

The crew cleared us, sounding off as I was about a foot up and settling down. Clearing the ground by the crew was important. Landing on a log would bend the skid of the aircraft, and landing on a stump could penetrate a fuel cell. Hitting a small sapling with the tail rotor would do damage ranging from a damaged blade to losing the entire tail rotor system, which would cause a serious and possibly explosive accident. In addition to watching below the aircraft, they were also watching the main rotor for possible tree strikes, which again could just damage the rotor blade or rip off the entire rotor head. The crew chief and door gunner were two more important sets of eyes. As the grunts piled on, Lou went over the takeoff with me again. Once everyone was on, the crew gave me a verbal thumbs-up, and as Lou had told me, I started pulling in power just to get us light on the skids as Chalk Five was still loading. I watched Chalk Three lift off, followed by Chalk Four, and saw Chalk Five getting light on his skids as I pulled in power and broke ground just enough not to get caught in the rotor wash that was already coming off Chalk Four in front of me. As Chalk Five moved forward, so did I, and I remained slightly above him.

Lou said, "Slide to the right a bit to stay out of Four's rotor wash. That's it, good. Okay, now get back into position again slightly above Five. See how being slightly above Five keeps you above Four's rotor wash? Chalk Four's rotor wash is the one you have to worry about, not Chalk Five. Rotor wash goes down and behind the aircraft, not much of a factor off to the side."

Damn, I was concentrating on Chalk Five's rotor wash and should have been looking at Chalk Four's as he was the aircraft in front of me. Talk about feeling stupid. Lou could see I was a bit upset at myself.

"Don't beat yourself up. They don't teach that in flight school because they have you two rotor blades apart, and at that distance rotor wash is seldom a factor. Here we can't afford the luxury of two rotor blades apart."

Yellow One was turning onto his final approach. Unlike the initial insertion, there was no artillery fire or attack helicopters rolling hot as the LZ was secured by the infantry that we'd inserted on the first lift. What was different was, while we were picking up the second lift, CH-47s had brought in a small bulldozer in two pieces, and it was now pushing dirt to create a berm for the firebase perimeter. In addition, a backhoe was digging a hole for the two CONEX containers that would constitute the TOC when the firebase was finished. What had been a peaceful meadow in the middle of the jungle was now a beehive of construction activity.

Picking my touchdown point while maintaining formation, I was cleared by the crew. Even before I touched the ground, the grunts, who at this point were standing on the skids, started jumping off. This time I was on the ground maybe two seconds and Yellow One was already lifting off with everyone else in hot pursuit. As we were coming up, Lou took the controls.

"Lou, may I have one of your cigarettes?" I asked.

"I thought you didn't smoke," he said while handing me his lighter. I already had the pack in my hand.

"I don't." I inhaled, wishing it was a cold beer instead. Lou took us in for the next and last turn on this mission, and as before, the troops were waiting. All were grunts, but some were mortar men with their equipment, and it appeared that all these grunts had some heavier equipment than just a pack and rifle. Ammo and C-rations were being tossed on the aircraft too. Again the crew cleared us for takeoff, and Lou took us out. As we came back to the LZ, construction of the firebase was still underway, but in our absence, a battery of five 105 mm howitzers had been added to the firebase and was receiving ammo from a sling under a CH-47. Although it was only 1000 hours, this firebase would be operational by sundown.

"Flight, this is Yellow One. Heading to Bien Hoa for refuel. Aircraft commanders, meet me when done for mission briefs on extraction."

"Yellow One, you are arty clear to Bien Hoa," Chalk Two responded.

"Roger, Two."

"Yellow One, Chalk Three, over."

"Yellow One, Bien Hoa Tower says you are cleared to land if we stay on the north side."

"Roger, Three."

Lou gave the aircraft back to me and we had an uneventful flight back to the refuel point at Bien Hoa. Well, uneventful for Lou and the crew. I was still trying to get this formation flying thing. Lou was still in instructor mode.

"In a staggered formation, a good way to hold your position off the other aircraft is to line up his navigation light with the towel rack on top. That'll position you so you're actually looking across the pilot's shoulder at the oil pressure gauges in his cockpit." The towel rack was a UHF antenna on top of the aircraft that looked like a towel rack in a bathroom. On top of the aircraft and slightly behind the towel rack on each side of the aircraft were navigation lights. Oil pressure gauges were located in the center of the instrument panel, so looking over a pilot's shoulder from a position slightly behind and above would show those instruments.

I was attempting to process all this. *Maintain one-rotor-blade distance; stay slightly above the aircraft in front of me; avoid rotor wash; line up towel rack with pilot's shoulder—no, no, with navigation lights; don't over-torque engine. Oh, yeah, and breathe!*

After all the birds were refueled, we hovered to a parking area and shut down while the aircraft commanders went for their briefing for the next mission. Bennett and Brown right away went to cleaning the guns and checking the fluid levels on the aircraft. I sat in my seat and breathed.

I sensed someone was beside me. "Mr. Cory, you look dehydrated," said Bennett as he handed me a frosty cold soda.

"Thanks, Bennett. Where'd you get this?" I asked.

"We keep half a dozen in the marmite can under Brown's seat. Got water too. Mr. Price buys it and we pack it. Just don't make it too obvious, especially if some RLO comes around. We don't share."

"I fully understand." I closed my eyes and relaxed for a minute.

After about twenty minutes, I saw Lou walking back and he did not look happy, talking to himself and shaking his head. "Hey, Bennett, here comes Mr. Price," I said.

Bennett jumped up and retrieved a cold soda for Lou. After a long pull, Lou briefed us on the next mission.

"Okay, we're going to start extracting units to come back here. We are Chalk Six of a six-ship flight and will be making three turns on this first mission. It's a rifle company located here"—he pointed to the map—"and we're bringing them back to here. Flight leader will be Captain Bullock." The name Bullock did not flow from Lou's lips easily. Bennett groaned; Brown cussed. I had met Captain Bullock, as he was a platoon leader in another platoon. Seemed like a nice guy.

"What's so bad about Captain Bullock being flight leader?" I asked.

"Watch and learn," Lou responded.

Something told me this wasn't going to be fun. We started getting ready, donning our chicken plates and flight helmets once seated. Doors were closed and secured and engine was cranked. Lou took the controls. By now all six aircraft were turning blades. Other aircraft from the original eighteen were also cranking but going to other locations in flights of six to extract rifle companies as well. Our original flight leader was taking one of those groups. Lou was not happy.

"Flight, this is Lead. We will come up echelon right on departure. Chalk Three, get us departure clearance. Chalk Two, arty clearance."

"He doesn't need to tell Two and Three to get clearances. It's SOP for them to do that, and they've probably already done it," Lou grumbled. I kept quiet.

Yellow One received clearance from Chalk Three, and Chalk Two told him we were cleared of arty fire. The rest of the aircraft were to our left as we joined the end of the formation on the far-right side and staggered back, creating half of a V with Flight Lead at the front. We climbed to about one thousand feet.

"Bennett, Brown, stay alert. He's going to fly it at a thousand feet so every damn kid with a gun can get some practice," Lou said.

Bennett and Brown already had their guns up and were scanning the ground for possible fire. The vegetation we were passing over was mostly low brush and bamboo about ten to fifteen feet high with the occasional taller hardwood tree. As we passed over the Song Dong Nai River, Yellow One began a descent to the PZ, which was a small meadow off in the distance. At about a quarter mile from the PZ, Yellow One began a deceleration, slowing the flight from ninety knots and holding at an altitude of three hundred feet as we continued to the PZ.

"Perfect damn targets, you asshole!" came over the radio. Someone was not happy.

"Flight, this is One. Come up staggered left." As it was obvious that a right echelon formation wouldn't fit in the PZ and the troops were lined up for a staggered left formation, several disparaging remarks were made on the radio as six slow-moving, very low aircraft switched formation right over the approach into the PZ.

"This is why you don't want Captain Bullock to be flight leader. We're sitting ducks right now. If some gook opened fire on us, this would turn into a real goat rope," Lou grumbled as we passed over the last trees and lowered into the PZ to a ground guide waiting for us. As soon as the skids touched, the six grunts were on board and ready to go. And we sat and we sat.

"What the hell are we doing?" Lou growled. "Yellow One, this is Six. All aircraft are loaded," Lou said on the UHF frequency.

"Roger. Wait one," came back from Flight Lead.

"Wait one! We've been waiting for two already," Lou screamed at no one. "This is another reason why you don't want him as lead. You get into a PZ fast and out fast. Sitting here does only one thing, and that's drawing mortar fire as Charlie has time to locate you and set his guns."

Flight Lead must have heard him and started moving forward and up, and we all followed. Once we reached Bien Hoa, the troops got out and Lou turned the controls over to me. Flight Lead didn't change the formation, but we still came into the PZ slow and low. Our ground time was less but still too long for Lou's liking. Lou took us into the PZ on the third turn and nothing changed. Coming out, all door gunners opened fire on the tree line, as Charlie was known to wait for the last flight out before opening fire on the last aircraft, which in this case was us. We took no fire on this day, however, and returned to Bien Hoa, only to shut down and wait for another mission. After sitting for three hours, we were released to return to the Chicken Coop, but some of the other aircraft were sent on log missions.

"Take us home, Dan," Lou said.

That night, sitting in our tent along with Mr. Toliver, an old guy, and Mr. Jones, I asked who the designated flight leaders were.

Mr. Spivey answered that one. "Captain Goodnight, Captain Pierre and Captain Bullock."

"What about the CO?" I inquired.

"Have you ever seen him in the cockpit, or on the flight line, or out of his tent? When you do, please let us know. It'll be a first," said Mr. Toliver. The others seconded that comment.

"How come?" I asked.

"The CO's on his third tour over here. His first was as an advisor in the early sixties, and his second was in sixty-five as an aviator. Pretty tough assignment, and he took a couple of hits in the aircraft and on his body. He's paid his dues. He only has another couple of months in command and then he'll probably move up to battalion or brigade staff. He's all right, just doesn't care to fly anymore," responded Mr. Toliver.

"Well, what makes a good flight leader?" I asked as I opened another beer for myself and the others.

Mr. Reynolds fielded that question. He had been in the unit for about seven months and was considering extending, but not for our unit. No one seemed to do that. Extending your tour was a rare occasion in Vietnam, even in those units that appeared to have high morale and good leadership.

"A good flight leader must first be a good pilot and know his aircraft. Know what its limitations are and how far he can stretch them. He must be a good aircraft commander, taking care of his aircraft and his crew. Just because we're officers doesn't mean we can't help the crew take care of the aircraft. Did you notice when Captain Bullock landed, the first thing he did was leave the aircraft to his crew and beat feet to the club for a beer instead of stay behind and help them sweep it out and post-flight it? No, he left that to Hess, his copilot for today, and the crew. Self-centered bastard. Just because he's an RLO, he thinks he's too good to get his hands dirty. Do you think he helped fill sandbags to build the bunker? Not him or any of the RLOs for that matter. Jamison stood there that day and 'supervised' while everyone else did the digging and stacking."

"Okay, Reynolds, that's enough venting," interjected Mr. Toliver. "Besides being a good pilot and aircraft commander, a flight leader must plan, coordinate and anticipate the mission. Once he gets his brief from the ground commander, he needs to do a recon flight over or by the LZ or PZ. He needs to judge how many aircraft will fit and what formation will work so we're not doing the last minute dick dance like we did today. Bullock never did a recon, and that's why we were dick dancing in the kill zone. Once he's done his recon, he needs to coordinate with the ground commander on what the formation will be so they can plan accordingly. He needs to coordinate with the attack helicopters if it's going to be an insertion. He needs to coordinate with the aircraft commanders and let us know what's what. And he needs to anticipate what all can go wrong and have a plan for that as well, be it an aircraft breaking down before the mission or ground fire on the LZ/PZ. Today was an example of what not to do on an extraction. One time, Bullock was flight lead on an insertion. He had twelve aircraft in that one, and instead of using the entire length of the LZ to get everyone on the ground, he landed short, getting only eight birds on the ground. The last four had to break off, do a go-around and wait for him to get out so they could come in. The ground commander was pissed. Our battalion commander was in the C&C above, and he was pissed. The CO caught shit for that one, and Bullock will never lead a flight bigger than six ships again."

"With all the time you guys have, why aren't you flight leaders?" I asked.

"Because we're not RLOs," sneered Lou. "Aviation brigade policy from the almighty brigade commander is that only RLOs will be flight leaders. Warrants are pilots and not leaders according to him. He should know. It's his first tour flying in Vietnam."

"Where did he come from?" I quizzed.

"He was a transportation guy stationed in Europe and Korea for most of his time. Went to flight school for the 'short course' and came over. The CG made him the aviation brigade commander because we're transportation and he's a pilot," Mr. Toliver interjected.

"What's the short course?" I asked after a long pull on my beer.

"General officers and full colonels get to go through an abbreviated flight school, which is a condensed primary course and a Huey transition course. Basically it teaches them to hover, fly straight and level and land in a Huey. They get no instrument training at all. And they get wings just like ours and think they know it all," Mr. Toliver said. With that, Lou turned off the light and rolled into his rack, mumbling something about the motherhood of full colonels.

# 12

## SNIFFER

After the usual breakfast at the usual time of 0430 hours, I got my gear and went by Ops to see who I was flying with and what ship. I had been flying about a month now in the unit and was becoming proficient at formation flying—well, getting used to it at least. Today it was with Mr. Bob Lucus and his aircraft Whispering Wind. Bob had just been promoted to chief warrant officer second class. He'd been in-country for about eleven months and was due to rotate home next month. A quiet man, he wasn't in the nightly poker games, drank little and stayed to himself most of the time. I really hadn't had a chance to talk to him much. When I arrived at the aircraft, Sergeant Scovel, the crew chief, and Specialist Mackintyre were already getting things squared away. I put my stuff in my seat and began the preflight, climbing up on the roof to inspect the rotor head and specifically the Jesus nut. As I was finishing the preflight, Mr. Lucus walked up.

"Good morning, everyone. How's it look, Dan?" he asked, tossing his gear on his seat.

I returned his salutation. "Morning, Bob. She looks really

good. Got to admit, that engine compartment is the cleanest I've seen yet."

Sergeant Scovel smiled and nodded to say thank you.

Bob climbed up on the roof and checked the rotor head after preflighting the lower half of the aircraft, and I certainly didn't take offense. He was just double-checking, and that was fine with me. Coming down, he said, "Let's get going."

We all climbed in and I went through the start-up procedures as Bob tuned the radios to the correct frequencies. Sergeant Scovel and Specialist Mackintyre went about their duties of closing doors, getting fire extinguishers and strapping in. Both Scovel and Mackintyre wore monkey harnesses, which allowed the maximum freedom of movement without letting them fall out of the aircraft. Once we were at full power, Bob told me to take us out. Coming to a hover, I was cleared by the crew and I hovered backwards out of the revetment, pedal turning to the runway. Bob told me we were cleared to depart, and so I came to a fast hover forward and, upon reaching the runway, pulled in collective power and nosed it over to achieve maximum airspeed quickly and began the climb to twenty-five hundred feet.

"Your heading is Quan Loi. We'll just follow Highway 13 right up to there," Bob directed me. "Have you been up to Quan Loi?"

"No. Just the area down by Bien Hoa," I replied.

"Quan Loi is a village that houses workers in the Michelin rubber plantation. The Third Brigade is headquartered up there and works that area. The base is in the rubber trees just like us, so it's pretty nice. At the end of the runway, which is laid out northeast to southwest, there's a two-story stucco home with a tile roof, and in the back is the most inviting swimming pool. Especially nice is the blonde Caucasian woman that sunbathes next to the pool with no top on. Kind of reminds some of us of home. You married, Dan?"

"No, not married, and no one waiting back there for me either," I replied.

"Well, flying up here is a bit different than down at Bien Hoa. First, unlike Bien Hoa, there are few open meadows to land in. Second, the trees in this area are either rubber trees or three-hundred-foot hardwood trees with triple canopy. Makes for fun times trying to resupply or insert. Once we get to Quan Loi, we're working for the brigade, so there's no telling what they're going to want us to do. Just wait and see after the brief. Where you from?"

"Nowhere in particular and everywhere. Dad's career Navy, currently stationed in Morocco. Grew up around every submarine base on the East Coast. Lived in Naples, Italy, for a couple of years and graduated from high school in Yokohama, Japan. I went to college in La Grande, Oregon, for a couple of years and decided that college wasn't for me. My first job out of high school was working on a logging crew setting chokers in Oregon. Not going back to that. Had spent a summer working on an oil tanker from Okinawa to Saudi Arabia and thought about going back to sea, but Dad talked me out of that. Convinced me to join the Army and try out for warrant officer flight, and here I am," I explained.

"Had you done any flying before flight school?" he asked.

"Yeah, I got a private pilot's license working one summer as a line boy in Coos Bay, Oregon. Instead of cash, I got paid in flying lessons. One of my instructors even went into the warrant officer program. Last I heard, he was flying Caribous. Are you married?" I inquired.

"Yep. Just saw my wife in Hawaii two months ago. She's already moved our stuff to Fort Rucker, which is my next assignment. We're going to be having our first when I get there. Well, six months after I get there," he added.

"Well, congratulations, Mr. Lucus," chimed in Sergeant Scovel. As I continued to fly the aircraft, Bob worked the radios, getting arty clearance as we proceeded up Highway 13 at twenty-five hundred feet. Another cloudless day, but hazy due to forest fires. Below, large swaths of jungle were leveled and large bulldozers were busy cutting the swaths.

"What are they doing?" I asked, nodding in the direction of the bulldozers.

"Those are called Rome plows. Big damn bulldozers with a special blade on the front. They're clearing the jungle to expose Charlie's holes and bunkers down there. This area is loaded with tunnels and that's the quickest way to find them. The First Infantry Division operates in this area. You can see their mark over there. I guess since they're going home soon, they wanted to leave something for this place to remember them by," Bob pointed out. Carved into the jungle was a replica of the Big Red One shoulder patch approximately a thousand meters long and appropriately wide. Actually a well-laid-out piece of work.

"When are they leaving, and is anyone coming into Lai Khe to replace them?" My curiosity was piqued. Lai Khe was a large area with a four-thousand-foot runway down the middle, a small village, and several units that weren't part of the First Infantry Division. Besides our unit, as well as our sister company, which had all the Cobra gunships, there was a medevac unit and MASH unit; an artillery battery; an aviation company, the Robin Hoods; and an engineer brigade head-quarters. That wasn't a lot of people to maintain security of the entire perimeter when the First ID departed.

"Not sure when they're leaving. In a couple of months, I believe. I don't think anyone is replacing them. They're the first of the drawdowns, I think. No, come to think of it, the Ninth in the delta has already gone home. I guess the president was serious when he said that the Vietnamese would be taking the fight now and we were cutting back. The Vietnamese Army should be cleaning up." Bob continued to watch the jungle-clearing activity on the ground. In the distance, Highway 13 entered another rubber tree plantation. Bob called for landing clearance as there was also a runway about the size of ours at Lai Khe. "I got it," he said.

"You have the aircraft," I responded as he took the controls and began our slow descent, turning to final over a beautiful two-story tile-roofed home with a very inviting swimming pool in the backyard, but no sunbather. "Why does this guy stay here in the middle of this war?" I asked.

"He's a Frenchman, and the manager of this plantation. He knows where the enemy is located but won't tell us. So as long as he keeps his mouth shut, they don't mess with him. We can't shoot artillery into the rubber tree plantations, so we don't often send troops into the plantations, and the enemy lives in relative peace. I guess you'd call that a symbiotic relationship."

"Wow, you using them big words again, Mr. Lucus. What does symbiotic mean?" Mackintyre asked.

"I'll lend you my dictionary and you can look it up when we get back," Bob answered.

After we refueled, we parked the aircraft and a jeep with driver was waiting for us. While the crew looked after the aircraft, Bob and I jumped in and headed to the TOC for our mission brief. The TOC was two hooches. The brigade S-3 air was a captain and met us as we came in.

"Mr. Lucus, good to see you. How was your R&R in Hawaii?" asked the captain.

"It was good, sir. Sir, this is Mr. Cory, a new guy," Bob explained.

"Morning, sir," I said, extending my hand, which he took.

"Welcome. Now let's get started. Two missions for you today. First is a sniffer mission. The sniffer team is at your aircraft now loading the equipment. El Lobo just called me with a flight of two and will be here to refuel shortly. We would like you to fly this area along the river from this bridge north to where Highway 13 intersects the river. Report anything you find right away as it'll be a day before the intel guys decipher anything the sniffer picks up. Based on what you tell me, we have a psyops mission for you for this afternoon. The old man also wants to get up sometime today, so you'll be flying him around. Any questions?" the captain asked.

"Where are the friendlies located?" Bob asked.

"We have companies here, here, and here right now," he said as he pointed out locations on the map, and I started plotting those locations on my map. Call signs and frequencies I wrote on a separate piece of paper.

"What's the enemy situation? Must be something in this area if you're having us fly a sniffer," Bob pointed out.

"Actually, that picture is a bit vague in this area. Around An Loc it's a different story, but here we've had ground sensors indicate a lot of activity and that's why we want to use the sniffer to confirm locations along the Song Be River. We haven't pushed any recon elements into that area, so it's pretty virgin territory. There's been some activity southeast of An Loc, where we found that large cache site and that NVA hospital and base camp. We're going into this area, the area you're flying, for the first time."

"Okay, we'll head back and get in the air as soon as the sniffer guys are ready. Can we get a ride back?" Bob inquired.

"Sure. Harris is waiting for you in the jeep outside. When you get back, I'll have him give you a ride to the chow hall for lunch," the captain offered.

Arriving back at the aircraft, I saw a black box about the size of a footlocker sitting in the cabin with two four-inch tubes coming out of the sides and snaking down to the skids, where they were tied facing forward and down like large wind scoops. Sergeant Scovel spoke up.

"The sniffer guys went to get their gear and will be back shortly. The Cobra jocks went over to the PX and will be back in a minute."

"Okay. Here's what we got." I motioned over Scovel and Mackintyre while Bob spread my map on the cabin floor and commenced his briefing. "We're flying along the river on this one. We'll make about four passes, two on each side, one pass close to this side of the river going up and one further over coming back and then up again, but further out and back down close to the river. Anytime you hear 'Max Mark,' you open fire." Scovel and Mackintyre looked at each other with smiles and fist bumps. "Any questions?"

"No, sir." And both started brushing the clean guns again as well as the ammo that each had, about three thousand rounds.

"What's a sniffer mission, and what's this box?" I asked.

"This machine picks up ammonia, which bodies give off in this heat in the form of perspiration. When the machine gives a reading of max, the operator will call out 'Max Mark,' which means he has a large group giving off a lot of perspiration and we should engage. First problem is, not only do humans give off ammonia, but so do monkeys, so we'll be probably shooting a lot of monkeys. Second problem is, in order for this to work, we'll be flying at treetop level and sixty knots. The two Cobras from El Lobo will be one thousand feet and following us and will engage if we call for fire or are taking fire," Bob informed me.

"You're shitting me, right? We're really going to fly at treetop and only sixty knots?" My eyes must have been as large as saucers.

"I shit you not," Bob said with a grin. "Truthfully, as short as I am, I'm not thrilled about flying this one, but we play the hand we're dealt. Let's get ready. I see the Lobo pilots are strapping in, and here come the sniffer grunts."

Two sniffer operators climbed aboard and one briefly talked to Bob about the mission. Bob showed them how he was going to fly the mission and they seemed happy about it. One was carrying an M79 grenade launcher with a sandbag full of grenades and the other his M16 with ten magazines. I had to get something besides my .38 pistol, I thought. The only thing it was good for was blowing my own brains out.

As we ran up the engine, Bob took the controls. "I'll make the first pass, and you have it for the second."

"Okay," I answered as the crew cleared us.

"Call Lobos and see if they're ready. Then get clearance for all three of us," Bob instructed me once we were at a hover.

After we had clearance and Lobos were up, Bob took us down the runway heading northeast. This route took us out of the rubber tree plantation and out over the jungle. This was my first up-close look at this vegetation, and it was amazing. A very dense forest was below us, with hardwood trees reaching up three hundred feet. So dense was the foliage that I couldn't see the ground. Occasionally we saw an opening in the jungle where a bomb crater had exposed the ground. An engine failure over this would not end well, I concluded, especially once we dropped down to treetop level and only sixty knots. That was just above the dead man zone.

After twenty minutes, Bob started a slow descent and decelerated our speed to sixty knots. Lobo called and confirmed they were in position, one thousand feet and behind us on both sides. We approached the river at a ninety-degree angle and Bob slowly turned us over the bank of the river. "Scovel, watch that far bank for activity. If we're going to take it, it'll come from there."

"Roger that, sir," Sergeant Scovel confirmed.

"Lobo Six-Eight, this is Chicken-man One-Six, over," Bob called out.

"Chicken-man, go ahead," Lobo came back.

"Yeah, Lobo, keep an eye on the far bank. If we're going to take fire, I think it'll come from over there as it's the only clear sight they have of me," Bob explained.

"Roger, Chicken-man. We're thinking alike. Got you covered," Lobo confirmed.

As we were over the bank, Bob said, "If we have an engine out at this speed and altitude, the river's our best bet for a landing spot. Going down in these trees will make it impossible for any of us to get out, so if necessary, land in the river. Everyone got that?" We all confirmed we understood. The river was just outside my door, the right side of the aircraft. I was thankful for the armor-plated seat I was sitting in and the chicken plate covering my chest. Sergeant Scovel had a chicken plate as well but no armored seat except the back of my chicken plate. *Sucks to be you*, I thought.

"Max Mark." And all hell broke loose. Mackintyre's gun was hosing the area under the aircraft on his side, and the sniffer grunt with the M79 tossed a round into the trees, which really did no good as the canopy was three hundred feet high and the round exploded as soon as it hit a tree limb, but I guess it made him feel good. Sergeant Scovel never engaged, since there was no one on the river and he didn't see anything on the other bank, which was about one hundred yards away. We didn't take any fire from the ground. Lobo continued to orbit above us, providing cover if need be. After the first pass, Bob told me to take it, and we headed back down the path with the river off to the left about four hundred yards away. Sergeant Scovel engaged anytime we hit a Max Mark indicator this time.

"Follow the contour of the jungle and stay about fifty feet above the tops. Watch for any branches that may be sticking up above the rest. Tree strike we do not want," Bob instructed me.

As planned, he flew the next leg and I the last leg. As we

completed the leg, Bob said to head to Quan Loi and get some airspeed and altitude, which I immediately did.

As I made my turn to the west and reached ninety knots, Sergeant Scovel screamed, "Taking fire!"

He opened up. Mackintyre immediately did the same, and as quickly as it started, it was over.

"Chicken-man, Lobo Six-Eight. Over."

"Lobo, I think we just took fire," Bob reported.

"Roger, I saw it. Are we cleared to roll hot?" Lobo questioned.

"Affirmative, as there are no friendlies around here. I'll report this to higher," Bob indicated.

"Roger, Lobo's hot." And rockets began impacting in the area where we'd taken fire, which was a small clearing. We continued on to Quan Loi with a brief look back as Lobo unloaded all their rockets and some miniguns. Sergeant Scovel said he thought it was small arms, AK-47 most likely, from a couple of guys. They must not have seen the Cobras following us. It happened so fast I was unaware that we were even shot at.

"Is that your first time, Mr. Cory?" Mackintyre asked me.

"Getting shot at? Yeah," I answered.

"Yahoo, Mr. Cory buys the beer tonight!" Sergeant Scovel chimed in. "*Yes!*"

"What?" I shout.

"First-timers buy the beer for the crew," Mackintyre explained. "Thanks, Mr. Cory." Bob just sat there smiling at me. I was definitely seeing a pattern here about lessons and beer. Returning to Quan Loi, we refueled the aircraft and bade farewell to Lobo, who had been released from our mission, parking the aircraft. Our ride showed up and we headed back to the TOC and the S-3 air.

"I understand you did better than expected out there, giving me a real no-shit position. Where were they and how many?" the captain asked.

Bob pointed out on the map where we had taken the fire, stating that we thought it was a couple of guys as it was light fire and only from AK-47s. Bob also told him that the Cobras had rolled in hot on the location.

"I'll get a request in to get a scout team from First of the Ninth to go up and check it out," the captain mumbled thoughtfully as he reached for a radio. The First of the Ninth was the air cavalry squadron for the First Cav Division. Their aircraft consisted of mostly OH-6 scout helicopters and Cobra gunships. They also had one platoon of UH-1H aircraft and grunts, referred to as the Blues Platoon, in each of their cavalry troops. Each troop had a platoon of OH-6s, a platoon of Cobras and the Blues Platoon. On a scout mission, two OH-6s would fly at treetop level in circles, covering each other, with a Cobra watching over them. Frequently, one OH-6 would come to a hover to blow the vegetation back so they could see the ground. OH-6 crews were shot down on a frequent basis. Seldom did an OH-6 survive to receive its first three-hundred-hour inspection, although since the VC were less active after TET of '68, their survival rate had improved for a short period of time.

After the captain completed his mission request for a scout team, he said our next mission would be at 1330 hours and we should get some chow at the brigade headquarters mess hall. He would see us back at 1245 hours and would send the jeep to get our crew. This captain was okay in my book.

When we returned to the TOC at 1245 hours, the captain told us there had been a change in mission. "The old man has canceled the psyops mission. He, along with the S-2, the S-3 and the brigade engineer captain, want to have a look at where you took fire this morning. Between the readings from the sniffer and you taking fire, which is a confirmation that someone is out there, the old man's looking at moving a firebase into that area to interdict the river. Takeoff will be thirteen thirty."

Bob said that was fine and we would be at the aircraft waiting for them. When we got to the aircraft, Sergeant Scovel was hanging under the tail boom in a hammock and Mackintyre was lying in the cabin, trying to go to sleep.

Time waits for no man, but pilots do wait for colonels. Thirty minutes late to us, but not to the colonel, he arrived with his staff in tow. This guy looked like a warrior. Tall, well built with a square jaw, he introduced himself to me and Bob. New to the division and having just taken command, he was out to make a name for himself but had a reputation already of taking care of his people and doing the right thing by them.

Colonel Irons spread out his map and briefed Bob on what he wanted to do as I climbed into my seat. Basically, he wanted to find a clearing that was close to where we had taken fire, and along the river so he might move a battalion in quickly and put a firebase in place to interdict the river and cover the area from Quan Loi to the river, as this was an area that some rockets had been coming out of and hitting the base. The 130 mm Katyusha rocket was a Soviet rocket used in World War II and Korea which the enemy had acquired and used mostly to harass us, as they were not very accurate.

As everyone settled in, I started the aircraft. Bob got our clearance and a thumbs-up from the colonel and told me to take us out.

"Head for the river at three thousand and ninety knots. I want to stay well above any possible .51-cal fire," Bob said. "An old trick of Charlie's is to fire at an aircraft with AK-47s, and when a flight returns or the scout aircraft shows up, they open up with three .51-cals in a triangle to trap you. If you're low and that happens, you're going to have a miserable day."

The colonel asked what altitude we were going to hold and Bob explained the situation to him. No argument from the colonel. He told Bob he could see everything he needed from three thousand feet. *Yeah, I like this guy.*

Once over the area, we started circling, making the circle ever so slightly wider with each turn. The staff in the back were huddled together, comparing what they were seeing on the ground with what was on their maps. After about thirty minutes and further to the northeast, a clearing was noted. The colonel asked, "Mr. Lucus, how many aircraft do you think we could put in that clearing at a time?" *Wow—a colonel asking us warrant officers for our opinion?* Well, asking Bob, but...I really liked this guy now.

After a minute or so, Bob came back. "Sir, I think we could get twelve aircraft in there. That tree in the middle is going to cause a problem, but a flight in staggered formation could fit on both sides. The problem for you is going to be the separation for the ground forces once we unload as they'll be on opposite sides of the LZ. Approach would have to be along the northeast-southwest axis. Also, that's the largest clearing around, so Charlie may have it targeted as well. Not a lot of options in this area for an LZ."

"My sentiments exactly, but it's going to have to do. Okay, take us home." And with that, the colonel went into a huddle with his staff and we turned back to Quan Loi. The S-3 air was waiting at the pad with the colonel's jeep. Once the colonel was loaded up and out of there, the captain jumped on the skid to talk to Bob.

"That's it for today. You're released to go home. Thanks for your help today. Be safe," he said, shaking Bob's hand.

Bob turned to me and directed me to move us to refuel and then head home to buy beer for the crew. As we were flying back, Bob asked, "What are your plans after this?"

"What, after Vietnam?"

"Yeah, you going to stay in or what?"

"I intend to go back to college and get a job flying helicopters and maybe attend law school. Not really sure what I want to do at this point. Just flying here right now is as far ahead as I'm thinking. What about you?" I asked.

"I don't know. My wife and I talked about it a bit when I was on R&R and we're just going to play it by ear for now. With a kid on the way, that sort of changes my options."

"That's one thing I don't have to worry about right now, and no plans either for the immediate or foreseeable future. No one back home waiting for me, so I'm a bit free to do as I want."

"Hey, Mr. Cory, I have two sisters back home," Sergeant Scovel chimed in.

Mackintyre, imitating a New Jersey shore accent, said, "Mr. Cory, I have seen his sisters. Forget about it." With that, Bob and I had to listen to a running exchange all the way back to Lai Khe about the appealing qualities or lack thereof of Sergeant Scovel's sisters.

# 13

## HOVER HOLES

WO1 MIKE ROBERTS DREW THE LUCKY STRAW FOR this day and met me at his aircraft after he got a mission brief. We were going back up to Quan Loi to fly resupply for one of the infantry battalions, and any other missions they had for us. Start-up and departure were typical and routine for me at this point. Mike got our clearances and let me handle the aircraft. We went into Quan Loi just long enough to refuel the aircraft and fly out to the firebase that had been inserted two days before in the location that Mr. Lucus and I had reconned with the brigade commander.

Since that recon, the Fifth of the Seventh Cavalry had been inserted and was finding trails, cache sites and some activity. It was reported that there were .51-cal antiaircraft guns in the area. So it was NVA forces and not the VC. That changed things a bit. The NVA knew how to shoot at helicopters.

Arriving at the firebase, we were directed to the log pad and shut down to get a brief from the battalion S-3 air. When we entered the TOC, the battalion commander was waiting for us.

"Good morning, gentlemen. Ready for some work?" he asked.

"Yes, sir," Mr. Roberts answered. "Beats sitting on our asses all day."

"I don't think you're going to have to worry about that today. Each of our companies needs a backhaul this morning and a resupply this afternoon. I may want to take up about midday and have a look-see. That okay?" the battalion commander asked.

"Sir, we work for you until you release us. What you want, we will attempt to accommodate."

"Good. The S-3 air will give you the locations and frequencies for each unit. They should be loading your aircraft with the first load now, so the sooner you get started, the better. If you need anything, call us."

"Thank you, sir." And he was out the door. The S-3 air gave us the unit locations and call signs, which I plotted and wrote down on a separate piece of paper. As he was wrapping up friendly information, Mike asked the enemy situation.

"Oh, yeah. As of two days ago, a chopper took fire at this location from AK-47s." David looked at me as the S-3 air continued. I just nodded. "We caught four gooks coming down a trail here yesterday and found a cache site here. Last night, one of our ambushes blew Claymores on some people, but no bodies were found, only blood trails and scattered equipment. They estimated the group to be fifty people. Don't know if they were NVA or VC. We have found some .51-cal antiaircraft guns southeast of An Loc, but nothing in this area so far. That's about it."

"Okay, then, we'll get out and cranked. We'll do the companies in order starting with A Company, if that's okay," Mike indicated.

"Yeah, that'll work. I'll let them know you're coming so

they'll be ready for you." The S-3 air picked up a radio handset.

Mike and I walked back to the aircraft and saw that it had a light load of some ammo. Morning missions usually meant picking up empty water and marmite cans from the night before and taking ammo in for the day ahead. As we started the aircraft, Dave asked, "Have you done any hover holes yet?"

"Just down around Long Binh, which I understand isn't much compared to this area," I replied.

"You're about to experience the scariest thing about flying in Vietnam," Mike said with a resigned voice.

"Scarier than formation flying?" I asked. I would come to regret that comment.

"What, you don't like formation flying?" Mike shot me a look.

"I'm just not that comfortable with it," I offered. I was unknowingly digging myself a hole.

"Who have you flown with in formation?" he asked.

"With Lou a couple of times and Bob Leach a couple of times."

"Lou's one of the best to learn from for formations. How did it go?" he asked as picked up to a hover, checking his power.

"Okay, I guess. Learned a lot."

"Well, you're about to get another lesson. Always check your hover power when going into hover holes. On this one with only a light load, it's no problem, but this afternoon it'll be hot and we'll be loaded to the max. You don't want to be over a hole and run out of power and pedal at the same time. I'll take us in the first time and you have it the second time," Mike said.

Our crew responded accordingly.

"Clear left."

"Clear right."

"Guns up."

Since the Third Brigade had arrived in this province, a healthy respect for what the enemy could do had been developed. As soon as we were airborne, our crew chief and door gunner were looking of telltale tracer fire, especially the .51-cal rounds. Unlike US ammo, which used a red tracer round, the NVA used a green tracer round. Both were easy to spot, especially when it was heading for you. It sort of looked like a ping-pong ball on fire in daylight and a basketball on fire at night; at least, that was what your mind's eye saw. Flying at ninety knots, if the enemy was shooting directly at you, they were probably going to miss as you would be past the point of aim. However, if they were aiming in front of you, then you were going to fly right into the round and your day would be ruined.

As we gained altitude over the firebase, Mike had me crank in the frequency for the first unit on the FM radio, and I gave them a call.

"Alpha Six, Chicken-man One-Seven, over."

"Chicken-man One-Seven, Alpha Six India, go ahead."

"Alpha Six, Chicken-man inbound to your location. Pop smoke."

"Chicken-man, smoke out."

Slowly out of the jungle, a small yellow cloud began to form, but I saw no landing zone or place to set down.

"Alpha Six, I have Mellow Yellow smoke."

"Roger, Chicken-man, we're ready for you. Empty water cans and two pax."

"Roger, Alpha Six."

I was really wondering where we were going to land this thing when, passing over the smoke directly, I saw a hole in the jungle with a soldier standing in the middle of it. It wasn't really a hole in the ground but a circular area devoid of any trees or vegetation and a few stumps indicating that at one time it had looked like the rest of the jungle. It wasn't much bigger than the rotor width of the aircraft, however.

"I have the PZ, and from the looks of the smoke, the wind is coming from the east, so we'll circle around and make final to the east," Mike said as he took the aircraft around twice, each time coming lower and lower but never cutting back on speed until he made his final turn to the east and heading to the PZ. He came to a deceleration and hovered over the hole at three hundred feet and maybe ten feet above the trees.

I looked down through the chin bubble, and this grunt was standing right below us with his arms out to his sides and waving us to come down. At this point, the crew started clearing our tail rotor, and we started down. I was watching the main rotor on my side to see that we didn't hit a tree limb.

"Hold," came the crew chief. "Tail right. Hold. Clear down. Clear left." This conversation continued as we slowly lowered the aircraft three hundred feet to the bottom. Whoever had the controls concentrated on maintaining his position and following the commands of the other three crew members, who were attempting to watch the tail rotor and main rotor, preventing a tree strike. We were all hoping that the grunts were watching to make sure we didn't take any fire, because at this point, we were sitting ducks! As we touched down, the ammo was kicked off and exchanged for thirty empty water cans and two soldiers that had all their equipment and huge smiles. They were going home, it appeared, as they were waving to those left behind.

When ready, the crew gave us the all clear to ascend, and the entire process was repeated in reverse. As we broke over the top of the trees, Mike lowered the nose and pulled in maximum power to accelerate as quickly as possible while staying at treetop level in a contour flight mode. Contour flight was flying as fast as you could while flying just above and following the folds of the terrain. We would be doing a lot of that in the future, especially on single-ship missions. Not so much on formations, I would come to find out. Once we had our speed, Mike turned the aircraft over to me and called Alpha Six.

"Alpha Six, Chicken-man One-Seven."

"Roger, Chicken-man, that's all we got for you today."

"Roger, Chicken-man's back to higher. Have a good day. Out."

When we arrived back at the log pad, the next load was waiting to go out, and it was about the same except it had a major and a staff sergeant who did not look happy. The major told the staff sergeant to pick up his gear and get on the aircraft, which he was reluctant to do, finally throwing his rucksack on the aircraft.

"Hey, Mr. Roberts, this staff sergeant isn't real happy about getting on this aircraft. He's giving the major a raft of shit," the crew chief indicated.

"Is his weapon loaded?" Roberts asked, turning around to see what was going on.

"No magazine in it, no, sir," came the response.

"Okay, just keep an eye on him and let me know if he's starting something," Mike said.

"What's going on?" I asked.

"Don't worry about it. You just fly the aircraft. Let's go as soon as that NCO is on," Mike directed me.

"He's on, Mr. Cory," said the crew chief.

I pulled up to a hover. The NCO started to move to the door, but the major grabbed him by the back of his load-bearing equipment harness and put his ass on the floor. I pulled in the rest of the power and we headed out to Bravo Company's location. Mike made the calls, and soon we saw a puff of yellow smoke slowly and gently drifting from the trees. But this time, there was no neatly cut hole in the jungle canopy but an honest-to-goodness bomb crater. As we passed over it, another soldier was standing in the middle with his arms raised. I started assessing the conditions. With the light wind, almost none, really, I was thinking of making my approach to the east and told Mike that.

"Look at the trees around that hole. Note how the ones on the north side are lower than the ones on the west side. There's probably a ridge that they're on, making the north side lower than the western side. We have almost no wind, so that won't be a factor. Make your approach north to south over the lower trees, and when you come to a hover, pedal turn to the east. We have plenty of power with this light of a load," he instructed me, and I obeyed.

As I came in over the northern edge of the PZ, I had decelerated all forward motion to a slow walk and came to a stop as I executed a slow pedal turn to the east. All the while, I was watching my power and the tip of the rotor blade in front. I wasn't looking down, nor was I looking sideways. My eyes were glued to the front of that rotor tip and I couldn't really tell how close I was to the tips of tree limbs. We were at two hundred and forty feet, and I had a death grip on the controls.

"Clear to come down right."

"Clear left."

"Clear front."

"Stop. Bring the tail right. Stop," I was instructed.

"Clear down right."

"Clear down left."

"Clear front."

I started easing off the power again.

"Stop. Slide right," came the command. I eased the controls to inch the aircraft to the right.

"Stop. Clear down right."

"Clear down left."

"Clear down front."

This continued until I felt the skids touch the ground.

Immediately the ammo was kicked out, but the staff sergeant wasn't moving. The major was talking to him, but he just sat there with a pissed-off look.

"Mr. Roberts, I think we have a no-go with this staff sergeant. He's refusing to get off the aircraft," the crew chief said.

Sure enough, the major pulled out a card and started reading him his rights. Somebody was going to be facing a court-martial. The major took his weapon and made him put on a seat belt as the empty water cans and mail sacks were tossed on board. Once everything was on, the ground guide gave a thumbs-up.

As in our descent, I had to stop and move the aircraft to clear some tree limbs before I could continue. As we cleared the last of the trees, I pulled in full power and nosed the aircraft over to build speed and stay at contour level. I liked this contour flying, recalling someone telling me to watch out for the occasional limb that would be higher than all the others and attempt to smack the aircraft. Mike finally reached over and took the controls. I pried my fingers from their death grip on the controls.

"You need to relax," he told me. "For your first hover hole, you did good, but that was an easy one. You're going to get some that, when you get to the bottom, you won't be able to see much of the sky above you through the overlapping canopy. You have to trust your crew to keep you cleared."

"Mr. Cory, was that your first hover hole?" asked the gunner. I knew what was coming.

"Yeah, and I'm buying the beer tonight."

"All right, you're learning fast, Mr. C," chimed in the crew chief. Maybe I needed to take more than fifty dollars a month in pay and put less in the bank, I thought.

When we reached the log pad, a first sergeant was standing there and took the staff sergeant and weapon from the major.

Together they escorted the staff sergeant to the TOC as we were loaded for our next run. Mike was taking us in and I was working the radios. This wasn't bad, as it was a small clearing about twice the size of the aircraft with about two feet of water covering it. We kicked off the ammo and they tossed in what needed to go back and we departed.

We had been flying for about an hour and a half, so Mike asked that we go back to Quan Loi to refuel. They wanted us to stop at the log pad before we went as they had pax to get back. Mike gave me the controls, and as I made the approach, I saw the two homeward-bound soldiers standing there, along with one major, one first sergeant and one staff sergeant with no weapon. As they loaded, the major talked to Mike. He wanted to go to the brigade pad before we went into refuel and have us pick them up when we were done.

When we landed at the brigade pad, there were two MPs with a pickup truck waiting and a jeep. The homeward-bound grunts were loaded into the jeep. The major and NCOs climbed into the truck with the MPs. We moved to refuel and were told to shut down when we got back to the pad. It was getting along towards lunch, so no tears from us.

We arrived back at the aircraft from lunch, and the major and first sergeant were just walking up. Loading the aircraft, we returned to the firebase and shut down, waiting for the afternoon missions. With nothing to do, the crew chief and door gunner decided to amuse themselves. Ant mounds were very plentiful, as well as ant holes, with an army of ants going and coming into each. The crew chief began pulling the heads off bullets and pouring the powder down the holes. After the hole was sufficiently full of powder, a cigarette was placed next to the hole. At first, nothing happened. Then the powder caught and began burning. In the confined space of the hole, it spewed forth like the tail end of a rocket, kicking burnt ants out. The bigger the hole, the more crispy ants came forth. It became a game of how many ants you could cook. Boredom has a way of making the mind creative. Finally word came that the units were ready for resupply, and supplies that had been sitting next to the pad were loaded. The first load was thirty full water cans. I started the aircraft while Mike worked the radios. He took the controls once we were at full power and I took over the comms.

Mike brought us to a three-foot hover and checked his power. Once he was satisfied, we accelerated forward and headed for the first location. As the units had moved during the day, each PZ was new and the location was passed to us over the radio as we were airborne. Coming up on Charlie Company's location, we called for smoke and it came drifting up through the canopy. No wind was indicated, and Mike took us in, coming to a hover over the bomb crater clearing. Again, the crew cleared him down, careful not to tap any tree limbs.

Coming out was a reverse of going in. Flying back, he gave me the controls for the next return trip. We would be going back into the same hole. Once loaded and returning, I went over what I was going to do as I was going to make a different approach to a final, but as we were heavy, I had to use what wind we had. As I came to a hover over the hole, the crew went into overdrive and talked me down. At times like this, you just thought about moving a control because you were moving the aircraft inches in many cases or pivoting the aircraft several degrees to move the tail boom away from a potential tree strike. By the time I came out and cleared the trees, my fatigues were soaked with perspiration. This would keep up for another three hours, with a break to Quan Loi for fuel. When we were finally released, it was getting dark as we headed back to the Chicken Coop. I was mentally drained and physically worn out.

"Mike, can I have one of your cigarettes?" I asked, reaching for the pack before he could answer.

"I thought you didn't smoke," he said.

"I don't," I responded as I inhaled and started to relax.

Arriving back at the company area, Mike and I headed to the mess hall for some chow. Taking a table with Lou and another warrant, we were discussing the day's activities when Captain Bullock came in with another RLO, a first lieutenant. Approaching the table next to us, where two other RLOs were already seated, Captain Bullock began with introductions.

"This is Lieutenant Weed," he said, indicating the new pilot.

LT Weed was tall and lanky, with long blond hair reminding me of a California surfer, which he claimed he was during his introduction. We didn't pay much attention until someone asked him for his first name. "Richard," was his response.

Lou couldn't let that one go. Looking at the four of us, he said, probably loud enough to be heard by the group, "Lieutenant Dick Weed."

We couldn't keep it in—all three of us were in hysterics. Lou maintained a straight face, standing up and turning to Lieutenant Dick Weed to introduce himself.

"Welcome, sir, I'm Lou Price. DEROSing back to the States next month," he said and left the mess hall.

Lieutenant Dick Weed was in Vietnam on his first tour, and he would prove to be a cocky guy. If he wasn't in charge of something, he tried to make himself in charge and on more than one occasion was put in his place by a flight leader or an aircraft commander. He arrived in the unit before I made aircraft commander, so I was fortunate enough never to fly with him.

That night, with a beer in hand, I went to find someplace to be alone and think. I went to the most secluded spot we had, the top of the bunker. Except I found I wasn't alone for very long. As I was sitting there contemplating life, Bill Hess dragged himself up but stopped as soon as he realized that this seat was already taken.

"Come on up, Bill. Hope you brought your own beer. I'm not sharing," I told him.

"Brought my own. How's your day?" he asked.

"A lot better than yours, evidently. I understand you and Lou had an active day," I stated.

"It got a bit tense. Have you seen anything like this since you've been here?" he asked.

"Hell no. I only got here a couple of days ahead of you— what, two weeks? And then sat on my ass for a week, waiting to get a check ride," I said with disappointment in my voice. "I feel like I haven't done shit here," I added.

"Well, I hope this isn't the norm. Lou said it wasn't." He took a long pull.

"What happened? Lou didn't say much when he came in."

"We had a log mission today, and en route to the battalion, they call us and tell us they have a unit in serious contact and need us there ASAP. When we land, they inform us that the company is in heavy contact, needs an ammo resupply, but they have no LZ. They want us to take it in by sling load! Lou agrees and they get it ready." Pausing, he took another drink.

"When it's ready, Lou moves over the load and they hook it up and we start up and up and up. The sling is a hundred feet long. When it's taut, we stop because it's too heavy and we had a full load of fuel. Lou's pulling the guts out of the bird, but we aren't going any higher, so he starts dragging the load over the ground. At first, we're going so slow with this thing banging along on the ground. Finally we get up enough speed with this anchor that transitional lift kicks in and we start rising. But as we get higher and the load is swinging wildly under us at about a forty-five-degree angle, we can see it swinging past the damn chin bubbles! The aircraft's getting pulled all over the place, and Lou says to release it. We have got to drop this thing before it drags us down. He can't, because his electronic release isn't working. I step on the manual release and it isn't working either. What the fuck!" He took another drink and pulled out a cigarette.

After a puff, he continued. "This thing isn't going to release and is only getting worse. Lou finally gets this thing under control, and I still don't know how he did it." I made a mental note to ask Lou about this.

Bill continued, "As we get close to the unit, I call for smoke, because at this point I'm only a radio operator with Lou flying. When we see the smoke, we also see that there's no LZ, not even a bomb crater. As we make our approach, the load is snapping tree limbs and steadies pretty much, which is good, but here we are two hundred feet in the air with this load hanging under us as Lou starts lowering us down to the point where I'm eyeball to eyeball with a damn monkey in the treetop. Lou tells me to release the load, and it ain't going anywhere. The grunts want to cut the load down on the bottom, but that would leave us with the sling flying up into the main or tail rotor. The gooks have started shooting at us and they're on my side. I tell Lou and he tells me not to worry, right seaters are expendable! I'm attempting to hide behind my seat and the door gunner, Leonard, is shooting. The solution —the crew chief, Grossman, climbs out and hangs under the aircraft in his monkey harness and cuts the sling with a machete. He's still hanging there when Lou pulls up and out of there. Lou is putting him in for an Air Medal for Valor. He saved our asses."

As I took another drink, I told Bill he was lucky he was flying with Lou. I hoped I would be as lucky. I was; I never flew a sling load mission my whole time in-country.

# 14

## NIGHT HUNTER

THE JUNGLE ABSORBED ALL LIGHT AT NIGHT. WITH no major cities, there was no artificial light. What villages there were had little or no electricity, so what light they emitted was minimal. On the other hand, if you saw a light along a river or in the jungle, you found Charlie, because only Charlie used light at night. And we were looking for Charlie.

The mission was unique to the 227th and 229th Aviation Battalions. Each battalion put up a Night Hunter Killer team. The teams had two ways of finding the enemy. A large starlight scope was mounted on top of a searchlight, allowing the operator to see clearly at night, but with a green tinge to everything. Any artificial light, such as a candle, was instantly seen as the starlight scope was very sensitive and powerful. If the operator sighted something, he turned on the searchlight and the gunner sitting next to him engaged with a M2, .50-caliber machine gun. Upon engaging, the flare ship, which was flying at one thousand feet or higher, dropped a one-million-candle-powered flare, and an AH-1G Cobra gunship attacked the target with rockets and 7.62 minigun and/or a 40 mm grenade launcher while the low bird continued to engage the target to cover the Cobra. The second way to find the enemy was for the low bird to fly at sixty knots and only five hundred feet, low and slow to draw fire. If the low bird drew fire, the Cobra immediately engaged, giving the low bird an opportunity to clear the area. This night, I was copiloting the low bird with WO Mike Driscoll as AC. Mike had been in-country for about eight months and normally flew this mission when the unit received it.

Our mission for the night was to recon along the Song Dong Nai River for possible sampans moving supplies south towards Bien Hoa. Our mission brief was conducted at the Brigade TOC in Bien Hoa, followed by Mike conducting a briefing on how we would proceed. Mike had flown this mission for the past two weeks. Generally once the company received the mission, the same crews flew the mission for a month as they would sleep in the day and fly all night, opposite cycle from the rest of the crews. To add a bit more firepower to the low bird, the pilot's doors had been removed and both pilots had M79 grenade launchers on our laps.

"Dan, be sure that thing's on safe, and when you fire it, be sure it's not pointed at anything on this aircraft, such as the rotor blades," Mike warned me. Two bags of 40 mm grenades were on the back of our chairs in case they were needed. In addition, there was a thermite grenade on the back of the center console, in case the aircraft went down and we had to destroy it and especially the M2 .50-cal machine gun. Charlie would love to get his hands on that weapon.

Flying north out of Bien Hoa, we reached the river and then started following the bank northeast. As we descended from one thousand feet, we lost all reference to a horizon on this moonless overcast night. *Damn, it's dark.*

"Flying low-level at night presents its own issues. First, you're going to lose the horizon the lower you go." *Tell me something I'm not seeing*, I thought. "You know the elevation and you know the height of the vegetation, so you continue a slow descent to an altitude that will give you a hundred-foot buffer above the vegetation," Mike pointed out.

As we descended, I felt like I was going down a well as all references started to disappear into blackness. Just my luck that tonight would be a moonless overcast night. Even our instrument lights were turned down to minimum intensity, but the navigation lights were full bright.

"Why do we have the navigation lights on and the instrument lights so low?" I asked.

"The nav lights are on so Charlie can see us, all the better to shoot at us. The instrument lights are down low, all the better for us to see outside."

Mike continued our descent and instruction. "As we approach that buffer, you'll start to see the treetops, and that's when you continue to descend. But slow it down until you're about fifty feet above the trees, and then you won't have a problem seeing the trees." Damn, he was right! Once we reached fifty feet above the trees, the navigation lights were providing enough ambient light for us to see the tops fairly well even on a night as dark as this one.

"Jones, are you on the scope?" Mike asked the searchlight operator.

"Yes, sir. She's operating okay. If you want to put us over the river and lower, I can get a look under the trees," Jones replied. Jones actually worked in the vehicle motor pool as a wheel vehicle mechanic but always volunteered for this mission when it came along. Said it made him feel like he was in the fight.

*Lower? Are you shitting me?*

Mike slid the aircraft over the river and dropped another fifty feet. We were now flying at sixty knots and about two hundred feet above the river. Trees on the banks were higher than us. An engine failure at this altitude and we were going into the river, which, considering the denseness of the jungle, was a preferable alternative to landing in the jungle. As we continued up the river, Mike was chatting with the Cobra and watching the river. I was watching the shoreline on my side of the aircraft along with the door gunner manning the 7.62 machine gun on the aircraft. We continued for an hour and saw nothing, and we didn't draw any fire. The return trip was equally uneventful, except I was flying this leg. When we completed the leg, we returned to Bien Hoa for fuel and a powwow between the crews.

Mike laid his map out in the TOC and we huddled around with the intelligence officer from the brigade. Pointing at locations on the map, the S-2 indicated possible enemy locations off the river but close by. "We have a trail network in this area, all moving towards the river, with a crossing point here, here and here. Since last night, Mr. Driscoll, First of the Seventh found another crossing point north of their location about here." I had done a couple of days resupplying First of the Seventh and was somewhat familiar with the area. They were located on a firebase at a bend in a smaller river that fed into the Song Dong Nai. We hadn't gone into their area as of yet tonight.

"We'd rather not get into an area where friendlies are operating as we don't want to light up any of our guys. What about this area here, along the river?" Mike asked.

"Down here, the Navy has a patrol boat, but they're aboard tonight and there are no friendlies operating in that area. There are some supposed friendlies living south along the river, so you'll have to get clearance to engage unless engaged. We have the call sign and frequency for the Navy, and I'm sure they'd be happy to have you working the area."

"Okay, we'll wait a couple of hours and then go into this box," Mike said, and we headed back to the aircraft.

"Why are we waiting to go back out?" I asked.

"Jones needs some time to rest his eyes. Looking through that scope in a moving aircraft will get him airsick if he doesn't get a break after two hours. Also, the later we go out, the better the chance we'll catch someone on the water. They saw us working the area earlier. Right now they're moving their boats to the river and loading them and will shove off, staying close to the shore to hide in the overhang, if we come back. Last two nights I worked up north, so they've probably set up some ambush in that area, thinking we'd be back tonight. Wrong. Never fly the same pattern three times in a row. If you do, you're just asking for trouble. If the ground commander wants you to work the same area a third night, try to talk your way out of it, or certainly change how you work it. Fly two nights north to south, the third night northeast to southwest or east to west. Change it up somehow, but change it up."

Arriving back at the aircraft, the crew was into a case of C-rations. No one offered me the lima beans this time but asked what I would like. Then it came. "Hey, Mr. Cory, is this your first Night Hunter mission?"

"Yeah. And I'm buying the beer in the morning," I added with a smile.

"Just glad you know, sir," Jones interjected with a smile to the crew chief and door gunner.

After a couple of hours, Mike conferred with the other crews and we prepared to head out. As the power came up, Mike said, "I got it," and I turned the controls over to him. The crew gave a positive "clear" and we departed towards the river. This time, Mike took us to the vicinity of the Navy patrol boat. Since we had to call for clearance to engage anything on the south side of the river, we positioned the aircraft so the starlight scope was on the free-fire side of the river.

As we approached the river, however, Mike told me to take it. I started down from one thousand feet. *Damn, it's still dark out*. I felt like I was in a pitch-black basement and going down-stairs very carefully, putting out my foot and reaching for the next step, without a banister to keep me from falling. *Okay, two hundred feet above the trees; one hundred feet; wait one. Okay, I can see the tops now. Ease down another fifty feet. Yes. I didn't fall down the stairs.* As we reached the river, I turned south and reduced airspeed. Jones was watching the bank. The vegetation in this region wasn't as dense as in the Quan Loi area, so the scope was more effective.

"I got a light!" Jones bellowed and turned on the search-light, but we saw nothing and commenced shooting, hoping to draw some fire. A flare ignited from the flare ship above, and the Cobra was poised to attack, but nothing. We continued on our way up the river. This scenario played out several more times in the next hour.

After about an hour and forty-five minutes, Mike said, "We'll make one more pass southbound and then call it a night." I had the controls and was about a hundred feet over the river. The south side of the river was on the side with the starlight scope, and we had to get clearance to shoot in this area. Dawn would be in about thirty minutes. As we rounded a bend in the river, Mike and I simultaneously spotted a dim light on the southern bank even before Jones called it.

"Jonesy, light ten o'clock on the bank!" Mike yelled. The searchlight came on, and son of a bitch—two sampans with four guys and rockets in the sampans were sitting there. They knew they were cooked and scampered up the side of the bank into a house. "Hold your fire while I get clearance," Mike instructed the gunners.

"Badger Six, this is Chicken-man One-Six, over." Mike was calling the Brigade S-3 air.

"Chicken-man One-Six, this is Badger Six India, go ahead."

"Badger Six, enemy sighted with two sampans, four pax

and several Katyusha rockets." Mike gave the coordinates. "Request clearance to engage, over."

"Chicken-man One-Six, wait one." After a minute or two, "Chicken-man One-Six, are you taking fire?"

"Badger Six, that's a negative. The pax ran up the bank into a house. The boats are on the water. Are we cleared to engage the boats?"

"Chicken-man One-Six, wait one." Again we wait. "Chicken-man One-Six, this is Badger Six India. You are not, repeat not, cleared to engage."

"Badger Six, the damn boats are on the water. Let me sink the damn things."

"Chicken-man One-Six, I repeat, you are not cleared to engage."

"Hey, Badger Six, if I ain't cleared to engage, then what the hell am I doing out here all night? You can eat these damn rockets tomorrow night. Chicken-man One-Six is end of mission and returning to the Chicken Coop. Out!"

Mike was pissed. I was pissed. The crew was pissed. The Cobra jockeys were pissed. No one said much as we headed back to Lai Khe. As we pulled into our assigned revetment, other aircraft were cranking up and departing on their missions for the day.

"After we get the aircraft serviced and cleaned up," Mike said, "let's meet at the mess hall for breakfast and a mission debrief."

Over powdered eggs and coffee, we discussed the night's events and how we could change our game for tonight to maybe catch the sampans before they got to the south shore. One of our pilots who had the day off strolled by.

"Good morning, ladies." Bob was a big guy with a shaved head and a handlebar mustache that would make a walrus envious. He was dressed in flip-flops and pants, no shirt. An unlit cigar of fine quality was in one hand, along with the latest *Stars and Stripes* newspaper, a cup of coffee in the other.

"Hi, Bob. I take it you're not flying today," Mike said.

"Nope, got a down day. This head cold has me all stopped up. Just heading to the library for some reading. See you later." And he strolled off toward the latrines, which we referred to as the library, about seventy-five yards away. I noticed Bob going into one and the door closed.

Mike continued with the debrief. "Tonight, let's first work the area around the Navy—"

*KABOOM!*

The sound of an explosion cut him off in mid-sentence. I looked up to see the door of the latrine Bob had just entered fly off its hinges as Bob was propelled through the screen with a fireball launching him. We were all up and moving to get out of the mess hall, not sure if we were under attack. And we were heading towards Bob.

"Medic! Medic!" called others that were closer and attempting to help Bob. Our medical officer, Doc, arrived and started assessing the burns on Bob's back, ass and genitals. Two medics arrived, and we gently picked Bob up and placed him facedown on a stretcher.

"Get the ambulance. We need to get him to the MASH unit now," Doc said to one of the medics, who sprinted off to get the jeep that was used as an ambulance. When it arrived, six of us picked up Bob, who wasn't hurting as bad now since Doc had administered a shot of morphine. Bob's burns were already starting to blister.

The first sergeant asked, "Doc, how bad is it?"

"I would say it's bad. Looks like second-degree burns, maybe third. Might have someone start packing his stuff as he's probably going to be medivacked back to the States," Doc stated. About then, the XO arrived. *Better late than never.*

"What happened?" he asked no one and everyone.

One of the soldiers who'd been in a tent close to the latrine area spoke up first. "Sir, the latrine just blew up."

"Latrines just don't blow up. What happened?" the XO fired off. No one wanted to answer now for fear of getting their ass chewed out for answering. Finally the first sergeant spoke up.

"Sir, let me look into this and I'll get back to you as soon as we have it figured out." It appeared that a cooler head was prevailing here.

"You do that, First Sergeant, but I want some answers." And with that, the XO walked off. He never bothered to ask how Bob was doing. The XO was still sporting the rash on his neck from the other night's mortar attack. Seemed he had run out of his tent, heading for our one bunker, and plowed right into a tent rope holding the sides of one of the GP Medium tents. Nearly hung himself on the rope. He put himself in for a Purple Heart, but no one would sign as a corroborating witness, not even Doc.

The latrine that had exploded was destroyed, but there were two others available for use and the first sergeant started his investigation there. It didn't take long for him to determine the cause of the explosion. Instead of putting diesel fuel in the cans under the latrine, the village idiot on shit detail had apparently used JP-4 aviation fuel, which was highly explosive. Bob must have lit the cigar after he'd sat on the toilet and it ignited the fumes from the JP-4. Diesel fuel and JP-4 had distinctly different odors, but with his head cold, he'd probably never smelled the difference. The other two latrines also had JP-4 fuel in the cans as well. Immediately, all the latrines were closed and the first sergeant went looking for the kid who was on shit detail. So did some of the other soldiers.

## 15

## ATTENTION TO ORDERS

It was early May and I was sitting in a refuel point when one of the aircraft commanders approached me.

"Hey, Dan. Two newbies arrived today."

"Damn, that makes me feel good. Any idea what their names are?"

"One I don't know, but the other is Major Anthony, our new company commander," he replied. Well, I guessed I wouldn't be jerking his chain anytime soon. I hoped the other was a warrant officer.

"What's the rank on the other guy?" I asked.

"He's a warrant too," he said. *I might be able to pass off some shit details to him*, I was thinking. For the rest of the day, I concentrated on my flying, especially getting better at this formation flying, as we were still moving the Second and Third Brigade around.

Arriving back at the Chicken Coop, I was thinking of one thing—a cold beer. I dropped my flight gear in my tent and headed to the club. It was closed. *What's up with this?* I returned to my tent to find Lou sitting there on his bunk. "Hey, Lou, why is the club closed?"

"We got a new CO and he wants to see all the pilots in the mess hall after chow. The club's closed until after that meeting. You want a beer? I have a couple here, but not very cold."

"Hell yeah, and I don't care how cold they are. I heard we got a new warrant in today."

"Yeah, he's in the next tent over. His name is Hanna."

"Dave Hanna?" I asked.

"Yeah, I think that's it. Why, you know him?"

"Yeah, we were together at Fort Polk. I'm going to find him." As I got up to walk out, who walked in but Dave.

"Dave, how the hell are you?"

Dave had started basic training with me at Fort Polk and was supposed to start in my flight class but had to drop out for two weeks to go home on emergency leave. It put him in a class behind me in flight school. He was married and a baby was on the way. This guy was amazing when it came to musical instruments. Piano, guitar, you name it, he played it.

Sitting down, we proceeded to drink the rest of Lou's beer —actually, it was probably my beer that I'd had to buy since I'd screwed something up, but who was counting? Most of the pilots waited until the end of chow to wander over to the mess hall as we were going to have to stay anyway. Little did we know that the entire company was going to be there too. As the place wasn't that big, it was crowded with the whole company in there.

"Attention to orders," bellowed the first sergeant. Everyone stood, and some even remembered what the position of attention was. Up front stood the first sergeant and our new commanding officer.

"By order of the President, Major... blah, blah,... signed... blah, blah," the first sergeant announced, reading the orders.

Major Anthony, now the new company commander, just stood there looking over us, and we at him. No one said anything until he finally told us to take our seats. He then went on to give us his philosophy on command and how he expected the unit to operate.

An hour later in the club, some discussions took place about what had been said. Mike asked me, "Dan, what did you get out of the major's speech? I'm wondering if I heard wrong."

"What I heard was, 'Don't do anything that's going to jeopardize my success in command, and we'll get along fine. Do so and I will be unmerciful upon you.'"

"Yeah. That's about what I heard too," Mr. Hess agreed.

I continued, "You know, I've seen commanders like this when I was a kid with some of my dad's skippers. Having a command is mandatory for a successful career, especially the higher up you go. However, managing and leading that command effectively and efficiently is what's important. Some officers view it as a threat if their subordinates do anything that would reflect badly on them. Major Anthony strikes me as that type. We'll just have to wait and see, I guess."

Shortly thereafter, Major Anthony walked into the place. Okay, good time to get to know the man.

"Gentlemen, I believe you're all flying tomorrow. Why are you here at twenty-one hundred hours drinking? There will be no drinking in the club twelve hours before launch time. Good night." And he stood there waiting for us to leave. Slowly, those on the board for the next day got up and moved out.

*Holy shit*, I thought. *We all fly off at 0500, so that means we have to stop drinking at 1700 hours the night before. Hell, we aren't done flying until 1800 or 1900 hours. This shit is not going to work.* After that, we had no club. The Warrant Officer Protection Association concluded that he was covering his ass. If we had no club, and someone screwed up, the screw up couldn't be blamed on him as he had demonstrated that he didn't promote drinking but enforced Army policy of no drinking twenty-four hours before flight. What we did on our own was okay as the blame would just fall back on us. Even the RLOs and first sergeant were taking objection to this one.

Other small stuff began to appear as well.

Major Anthony moved his tent out of the Chicken Coop to the edge of the Chicken Pen. That way he could see and mark off each aircraft as we departed. Woe betide the aircraft commander that got off late, because he and the copilot would hear about it when they got back that night. And God help anyone who was unlucky enough to have a blade strike or a chin bubble knocked out.

One morning just after I made aircraft commander and about the second month into his six-month command, I was woken up and told to get out to the flight line right away. It was a down day for me. When I got there, Major Anthony was standing under the tail rotor of the aircraft I had flown the day before with my copilot and the crew chief as well as the two pilots who were taking that aircraft out that day. As I approached the group, he turned to face me and took a couple of steps towards me.

"Mr. Cory! Did you do a post-flight last night?" I could tell he was pissed.

"Yes, sir, we did."

"I told him we did," said the crew chief.

Turning towards the crew chief, the major said, "You will speak when asked, Specialist. Now shut up."

*Wow*, I thought. *Officers do not speak to soldiers that way. NCOs might, but not officers.*

Turning back to me and pointing at the tail rotor, he asked, "Well, if you post-flighted this aircraft last night, why didn't you report that tail rotor strike?"

The tail rotor was in a vertical position with one blade pointing skyward and the other pointing straight at the ground. There was a crease on the lower blade that ran from the tip to the hub. No marks on the top blade. Normally, on a tail rotor strike, both blades will have a crease and maybe a tear on one or both, and the damage will be horizontal to the blade, not vertical. As he was another non-flying CO, he probably didn't realize that. He flew milk runs, not combat assaults or log missions.

I stood there and studied the blade. Finally, I said, "Sir, I did not report that because that was not there last night."

"What? Well, Mr. Cory, if it was not there last night, did anyone else fly this aircraft last night? And if not, how did it get there?"

"Sir, I can't tell you if anyone flew this aircraft last night. But if they did, they didn't have a tail rotor strike either. That isn't the mark of a tail rotor strike. I would say that is the mark of a whip antenna on a jeep that was driving around the Chicken Pen in the dark and smacked the tail rotor, as the revetment doesn't cover the end of the aircraft and the tail rotors stick out." Leaning slightly forward and pressing my luck, I added, "But that wasn't there when I post-flighted last night. Anything else, sir?"

Everyone was looking around, attempting to avoid eye contact with the major, who was showing signs of possibly exploding. "You're dismissed."

"Thank you, sir, and good morning. I'm going back to bed." I turned and walked away.

That night, the other AC came to me and said that after I left, he tore into those still standing there to get that tail rotor replaced and get in the air. He never said another word to me after that but showed his disdain later.

On April 16, 1969, I was flying with Mr. Driscoll, returning from a long day in the Quan Loi area flying resupply of one of the infantry battalions. It was late in the afternoon and the sun was setting. We were monitoring the four radios when we heard the mayday call.

"Mayday, mayday, Lobo One-Three is going down."

"Mr. Driscoll, a Cobra just went into the bamboo at three o'clock," said our crew chief, Specialist Grossman.

Lobo One-Three got off one call before he plowed into the bamboo. He was in a dive on a gun run and pulled out too late, only being able to get the nose of the aircraft up but not enough to stop his downward motion. He crashed into ten-foot-high bamboo and put the aircraft over on its side. He was on top of an NVA bunker complex.

Quickly, Mr. Driscoll took the controls from me and told me to plot our location and get out an additional mayday call, which I did, alerting everyone where we were. While I did that, Mr. Driscoll made an approach into a small clearing he'd spotted close to the downed aircraft and landed. It was just big enough for us to fit into. The first thing I noticed was the NVA bunker opening not ten feet from my door. I drew my .38 and pointed it at that opening, expecting someone to open fire at any moment. The downed crew was struggling to get the miniguns off the front of the Cobra when they began taking small-arms fire.

Specialist Grossman opened with the M60 machine gun, shooting at nothing specific but in the direction of the enemy fire, as did Specialist Leonard, our door gunner. I cocked my .38 and waited. As soon as the downed pilots got the miniguns off the downed Cobra, they ran to our aircraft and Mr. Driscoll pulled power to get us out of there as both gunners were firing and I emptied my .38 at the bamboo. *Worthless weapon.* The downed pilots thanked us profusely for saving their butts. As they occupied the other side of the Chicken Pen, their CO came over that night and bought drinks for us at his club since we no longer had one. He invited Major Anthony, who declined to drink with us but made sure we didn't fly the next day.

A few months later, I came in from my flight and lying on

my bed were orders for an Air Medal with "V." The downed crew had put our crew in for the award. There was nothing our CO could do about it, but instead of presenting the awards to us in front of the entire company, he simply put them on our beds, or at least had the orderly room clerk do it. He did that as well for the crew chief and door gunner's awards. The man held grudges. His last words to anyone when he departed the unit after his six months were something to the effect of he wouldn't have us around to ruin his career. I think he may have done that on his own.

Lou left us in late April to go back to the States. He was headed to Fort Rucker to be an instructor. He had been in the unit for a year, and it was time. We also were losing several other pilots whose time was up. Replacements were coming in, and there were enough of them that I was no longer considered a newbie. Included in the replacements were both warrant officers and RLOs. These RLOs, however, were different. They were all new pilots and hadn't served previous tours in Vietnam. They struck me as leaders.

Our new XO was a special breath of fresh air, exercising common sense that had been absent before. A new assistant maintenance officer arrived as well, and I was glad to see him. He was a staff sergeant when he joined us that first day at flight school. Dee could always be counted on and would prove to be a wonderful assistant maintenance officer.

# 16

## DIVISION

THE DIVISION HAD MOVED INTO THE AREA NORTH OF Saigon in the fall of 1968 and operated throughout 1969 and 1970 in the Three Corps region and along the Cambodian border. As a result, numerous rice cache sites were seized, weapons cache sites were destroyed, and a major base camp outside of An Loc and northwest of Quan Loi was captured. With these successes came a decrease in the enemy's ability to attack Bien Hoa or Long Binh. In addition, the division moved Second Battalion, Seventh Cavalry and First Battalion, Twelfth Cavalry with the Third Brigade to conduct interdiction operations along enemy infiltration routes north of Bien Hoa. Firebase[1] Cindy and Firebase Liz were put into position to accomplish those missions. From the start, both units were in contact with enemy forces. By April 19, the mission was complete and the Third Brigade returned to the Cambodia border region.

Throughout the spring and summer of 1969, enemy forces attacked firebases along the border. Their tactics were always the same. Waiting until after midnight, the enemy would commence their attack with a mortar and rocket barrage in concert with sappers attempting to penetrate the wire, followed by infantry waves attempting to penetrate the perimeter. LZ Grant was a favorite target of these attacks. Several times between February and May, LZ Grant experienced major attacks. The first, in February, saw the battalion commander, Lieutenant Colonel Gorvad, killed when a round hit the TOC. He was seriously wounded but refused to leave the battle.[2] The enemy managed to penetrate the perimeter wire, and fighting was fierce, to include the artillery lowering the tubes and firing point-blank into the charging enemy with antipersonnel shot. Blue Max gunships were called in and engaged the follow-on enemy as well as pursuing those attempting to retreat.

In May, LZ Grant was under attack again. Simultaneously, Quan Loi, LZ Jamie, and LZ Phyllis also came under ground assaults that night. The enemy wanted the First Cavalry Division out of the Three Corps region, which was not going to happen. Again the enemy attempted to move against Bien Hoa and Long Binh with the Fifth VC Division moving from War Zone D towards this target. The Third Brigade was once again moved to the area to block this move and required helicopter support to put soldiers in the field.

While Third Brigade bounced between Quan Loi and Bien Hoa-Long Binh, Second Brigade remained in the north along the border. In addition, with the First Infantry Division leaving Lai Khe, Second Brigade was given responsibility for the security of that installation. The solution was to create the "Rat Patrol." This unit was devoted to the security of Lai Khe and operated out of gun jeeps that patrolled the perimeter of the base, augmented by units that were permanently stationed at Lai Khe.

The First Brigade was focused on the southern end of War

Zone C and the Ninety-Fifth VC Regiment. In a major engagement supported by B-52s, the First Brigade cornered the Ninety-Fifth along the Saigon River and the area known as the Crescent. An infantry company was inserted after the first bomb strike, only to meet stiff resistance. Four more bomb strikes were made, and then six infantry companies were air-assaulted by helicopters into the area. Tanks from the Eleventh Armored Cavalry Regiment supported the air assault with a ground attack, driving the enemy deeper into War Zone C and across the Saigon River.

In June, LZ Joy and LZ Ike were both attacked in the usual manner with the usual results, which were many enemy dead. In all of these actions, lift helicopters were actively involved, flying resupply missions, troop displacements, Night Hunter Killer missions, command-and-control missions and medevac missions when called upon as well as psyops missions to encourage the enemy to surrender. Some did. In the area of Phuoc Long Province, a total of 546 Vietnamese deserted the enemy by the end of November. The division would continue to establish firebases where intelligence said the enemy was moving or establishing base camps. The division was constantly on the move, as was the enemy.

In order to avoid the division, the enemy continued to move eastward along the Cambodian border. The division did likewise, moving eastward to Song Be. Here the division discovered a trail network different from what had been found before. Bamboo had been cut and laid to create a roadbed along the boundary between Two Corps and Three Corps. This would provide good roadbeds during the monsoon season instead of mud trails. This trail network was approximately four feet wide and had bunkers established every one hundred meters or so. First Battalion, Ninth Cavalry found the network and immediately went to work destroying it with air strikes and cavalry helicopters, while Night Hunter Killers patrolled the area to restrict movement. This trail complex was named the Jolley Trail after the commander of the cavalry troop who had found it.

## 17

## WALKING ON THE MOON

It was July, and I was back on Night Hunter missions. We were working in the Quan Loi area, the only road being Thunder Road. There was a small Special Forces outpost in the area along with a firebase, but aside from those two, there was nothing. No roads, no rivers, just the black hole of the jungle that night. After a couple of hours, we returned to Quan Loi to refuel and reconsider what we wanted to do.

"Chicken-man One-Niner, Cherokee Six, over." It was the actual brigade commander on the radio and not his radio operator or the S-3, and he did not sound happy.

"Cherokee Six, Chicken-man One-Niner, over."

"Chicken-man One-Niner, what the hell are you doing up around Loc Ninh lighting up our elements with your search-light? Get the hell out of there!" My copilot looked at me like *What's he talking about!*

The Lobo aircraft commander, who was standing on my skid and heard the conversation, verbalized my copilot's thoughts.

"Ah, Cherokee Six, Chicken-man, we have not been north of Quan Loi tonight, over."

"Chicken-man One-Niner, where are you right now?"

"Cherokee Six, we are in the refuel point here at Quan Loi. Over."

"Chicken-man One-Niner, wait one." Cherokee Six was still not happy and a bit anxious.

A few minutes later, "Chicken-man, are you still in the refuel point?"

"Roger, Cherokee Six."

"Chicken-man, here's the situation. There's an aircraft flying over our positions north of Loc Ninh and covering each with a landing light or a searchlight. We have no idea who it is. Get up there and see if you can see them and get back to me. Understood?"

"Cherokee Six, understood. We're launching now." All three aircraft came to full power and we were off.

"Lobo Two-Four, Chicken-man One-Niner, over."

"Go ahead, Chicken-man."

"Lobo, I will contact GCA and see if they have this aircraft on radar."

"Roger, keep me posted."

I switched frequencies on the VHF radio from Quan Loi Tower to Approach Control. "Quan Loi Approach Control, Chicken-man One-Niner, over."

"Chicken-man One-Nine, Quan Loi Approach Control, over."

"Approach Control, Chicken-man is a flight of three off Quan Loi, en route to Loc Ninh. Have you got any other traffic in that vicinity?" Quan Loi Approach Control was the only radar in the region and capable of tracking low-flying aircraft. Capital Center in the Saigon area could track high fliers but not low-flying aircraft this far north.

"Chicken-man One-Niner, there's one aircraft approximately twenty miles north of your location, but I have negative contact with him."

"Roger. Can you keep me posted on his location? We're heading in his direction." I switched back to the brigade net on the FM radio. "Cherokee Six, Chicken-man One-Niner, over."

"Chicken-man One-Niner, Cherokee Six, over." Still the brigade commander was on the radio.

"Cherokee Six, I have Quan Loi Approach Control tracking an aircraft in the vicinity of Loc Ninh. We're proceeding to its location."

"Chicken-man One-Niner, roger. If you can, identify who it is."

"Cherokee Six, roger."

After a pause: "Chicken-man One-Niner, if it's not a friendly, you are cleared to engage." *Holy shit*, I thought. We were liable to find ourselves in an aerial dogfight. With our .50-cal and two M60 machine guns, I was willing to take this on and add Lobo to this.

Switching to the UHF radio, "Lobo Two-Four, Chicken-man One-Niner, over."

"Go ahead, Chicken-man One-Niner."

"Lobo Two-Four, Cherokee Six wants us to identify that aircraft and if necessary engage."

Silence from Lobo Two-Four. Finally he responded, "Chicken-man One-Niner, I understand and am standing by. I'll stay high, you go low."

And we proceeded with all the speed I could milk out of the aircraft. Lobo was a faster aircraft but wanted to stay with me so we could work together. As we continued flying north, we were ever watchful for another aircraft. No one aboard said anything.

"Chicken-man One-Niner, Quan Loi Approach."

"Quan Loi Approach, Chicken-man One-Niner."

"Chicken-man One-Niner, that aircraft is slowly moving north and will be over the border in about ten mikes if he continues his current speed and direction."

"Roger, what is his heading?"

"Chicken-man One-Niner, he's on a heading of three-two-zero degrees at ten miles at this time."

I immediately corrected our heading a bit and milked another ten knots airspeed, which now had us at one hundred knots. The aircraft was shaking more than usual, and, conscious of retreating blade stall, I didn't want to push it much faster. We continued on and kept looking. Finally, Approach Control called me.

"Chicken-man One-Niner, Quan Loi Approach Control."

"Go ahead, Quan Loi."

"Chicken-man One-Niner, he has crossed over to the other side and is climbing to altitude. His airspeed is one hundred and twenty knots on a heading of three-five-zero degrees." *Damn*.

"Cherokee Six, Chicken-man One-Niner, over."

"Chicken-man One-Niner, Cherokee Six, go ahead."

"Cherokee Six, Quan Loi has that aircraft crossing over the border. What are your instructions?" Again a long pause.

"Chicken-man One-Niner, roger, understood. Break off your pursuit and resume normal mission. When you get a chance, come to my location when you refuel. Cherokee Six out."

I relayed Cherokee Six's instructions to the flight and could tell there was disappointment in the tone of the response I received. We were all hoping to be the first helicopters to be engaged in aerial combat in Vietnam, but it was not to be.

Back at the TOC, we were met by the brigade commander as well as the NCOIC from Approach Control with a map showing the track of the other aircraft. He had tracked it out of Cambodia to a location north of Loc Ninh and then back across the border. He hadn't bothered to notify anyone of that aircraft coming out of Cambodia since there was a special operations helicopter unit at Quan Loi and he thought it was one of their aircraft returning for a mission.

Cherokee Six released us from our mission and we started home. The moon had come up and it was a full moon night. A bright full moon. The black jungle terrain was bathed in gray and black, almost as if it was day. There was no turbulence. An absolutely beautiful night to be flying, and so I thought a little music from AFN would be appropriate and tuned it in. We didn't get music but something better. The announcer was giving a running commentary on the landing of Apollo 11, commanded by Neil Armstrong. We listened intently, not realizing that this was the night of the scheduled landing.

And then we heard the words,

"One small step for a man; one giant leap for mankind."

Instantly, every firebase on that black-and-gray landscape exploded with gunfire and tracer rounds as well as star clusters and parachute flares. Even our flare ship dropped every flare he had on board, making a trail of our flight path. From Tay Ninh to Lai Khe to Song Be to Quan Loi, it was as if, out of the darkness, every weapon in Three Corps was fired on a single command, all against the backdrop of a full moon. As stupid as it sounds, we all strained to see if we could see Neil Armstrong up there taking that first step.

Arriving back at the Chicken Pen after sunrise, we noticed all our aircraft still in the revetments. That was odd as normally everyone would be gone by now. As we walked into the company area, the place was a beehive of activity.

Grabbing one of the other pilots, I asked, "What's going on?"

"Oh, you just got in. We're moving across the Chicken Pen, taking over the hooches that were occupied by the

Quarter Cav. Best be packing your stuff and find out where you're moving to. The warrant hooches are the last two next to the mess hall. I think Dave Hanna's tagged a room for you and him." And he was off with an armload of personal items.

We spent the rest of the day moving our worldly possessions from the tents across the flight line to hooches. A definite improvement in our living conditions, we quickly came to realize.

To make things even better, we had a new commander arrive in August who was a major improvement, Major Robert Saunders. He was a leader, and we recognized it almost immediately. One of his first actions was to allow us to hire hooch maids. Previous commanders wouldn't hear of it, so we cleaned our own tents. Now we had hooch maids that would come over from the village and clean our rooms, do our laundry, shine our boots. Mine even insisted on cooking Vietnamese food for us one day, which we bought and she cooked. She was a good lady. Major Saunders made it very clear from the beginning that no sexual activity would be tolerated with the hooch maids, and none was.

In an effort to raise morale, Major Saunders directed that one hooch would be turned into a club for the enlisted members of the unit. There wasn't another empty hooch available, so he directed that the officers should build our own club. We had an engineer RLO pilot, and he drew up a design for the commander's approval. With a design, we then began a scavenger hunt throughout Lai Khe for building material, and before long we had an officers' club. The engineer brigade headquarters collocated at Lai Khe with us poured a concrete floor for us in return for some flight time for their projects.

## 18

## NIGHT FORMATION

"Everyone, wake up!" shouted the operations clerk as he ran through our hooch. "Get your flight gear and meet the CO in the mess hall in fifteen minutes."

"What? What's going on?" someone shouted.

"CO wants all pilots in the mess hall now with your flight gear. Briefing in fifteen minutes," he hollered and was out the door to raise the next hooch. People were scrambling now to wake up, get dressed and find their gear.

Someone asked, "What time is it?"

"One thirty," someone else answered. Expletives were muttered as we hurried out the door and noticed all the crews' hooches had lights on and movement as well. At the mess hall, Major Saunders and the ops officer had the mission board and crew assignments posted as we all grabbed seats.

"Here's the deal," Major Saunders started off. "Intel says we're going to get hit hard tonight in about an hour. We have to get all the aircraft out of here now. Yellow One is Captain Bechtold, and crew assignments are listed here. We have sixteen aircraft that need to launch, and quick. The flight will be trail formation, and we're going to Bear Cat. Get to your aircraft and get them cranked ASAP. Maintenance platoon and company ground personnel will be your passengers. Get as many as you can on board as they'll be without equipment, so maximize your loads. Now go!"

And with that, there was a mad dash out the door and through the company area to the aircraft. People from the maintenance platoon and company support were already getting to the aircraft in groups of eight to ten, which, without equipment, the aircraft should be able to handle. My crew chief was already at the aircraft and had the blades untied and passengers ready to load. My copilot and I were the last to arrive and conducted a very quick preflight, being assured by the crew chief that he had already done it. Good thing we had done a post-flight when we had come in only a couple of hours earlier. Not going to be much sleep tonight.

I had been flying Night Hunter, so I had night formation flying under my belt, but some of the aircraft commanders had not. *Oh, this is going to be fun*, I thought. The last time most of these guys had flown night formations was back at flight school, and that was a gaggle. Sarcastic bastard I was. As each aircraft came up to full power, each contacted Yellow One and reported ready. When the last was up, Yellow One notified everyone he was coming out and started moving. At the same time, each aircraft fell into place behind him, hovering to the runway. Lobo was also cranking, as were the Robin Hoods. That was about sixty aircraft all moving to the runway, and surprisingly it was done in a rather orderly fashion. Robin Hood was located along the runway, so they were the first to take the runway and were off, followed by us and then the Lobos. As each flight was off, we separated and headed for our respective destinations.

"Yellow One, Chalk Sixteen, all aircraft are up."

"Roger, Flight, come up trail formation."

And the formation began to take shape. My copilot, WO1 Fender, had not flown night formations, so I went into instructor mode and initially had the controls.

"Okay, Ron, we're going to position ourselves slightly above the aircraft in front and maintain our one-rotor-blade distance."

"Okay, but how do you know we're only one rotor blade and not overlapping?" he asked. I could hear some apprehension in his voice.

"Notice his tail rotor hub and his exhaust?" I asked.

"Yeah."

"What we want to do is line up his tail rotor hub in the exhaust stack, and that'll give us our position slightly above him. You don't want to focus on his taillight, as that will put you on the same level as him and subject you to his rotor wash. The trick is to stay slightly above him. The guys behind us will be doing the same," I said.

"Okay, but what about the distance?" he asked. I could still hear some apprehension in his voice. He was a new guy, and in flight school you did night formation flying, sort of, with at least two-rotor-blade separation but more like three.

"To judge your distance, watch his exhaust flame. If you can barely see it, you're about the right distance. If you lose it, then you're back too far, and if it's bright, you're too close. Just watch," I added as I eased us into position above and behind the aircraft in front.

"Hey, Specialist Posey, what does it look like behind us?" I asked my crew chief.

"Sir, some are hanging close and others might as well be in another formation. The aircraft behind us is looking good, but there's a gap between him and the next aircraft. Some of our passengers don't look real happy, however. They best not puke in here or they're cleaning it up," he added.

"Yellow One, Chalk Sixteen, Flight is up, sort of."

"Chalk Sixteen, what do you mean sort of?"

"Yellow One, we have a couple of gaps of three to four rotor separation, it looks like. But everyone except one is in position above the next. Someone is having problems, it appears," Chalk Sixteen added.

"Yellow One, Chalk Twelve."

"Go ahead, Twelve."

"Yellow One, that's me. I put my newbie on the controls and he's learning. We'll get there."

"Roger, Twelve."

Chalk Twelve had a very old aircraft commander who was about to rotate home. To his credit, it was very good of him to let the newbie take the controls. We didn't fly night formations very often, but when the opportunity to learn came along, we took it. The night was calm, so turbulence didn't play havoc with us, and the weather was good, so no rain showers. In the distance, we could see the lights of Bear Cat, and Yellow One set us up for a long final approach.

"Flight, Yellow One. We will land and hover off the runway to the right. There's an open field there and we'll occupy it for the night. Shut down and get some sleep. We'll refuel in the morning before we head home."

Coming into the field, each aircraft came to a hover and set down. Specialist Posey got out and opened my door while Specialist Quillin, my door gunner, opened Ron's door. As soon as the main rotor stopped, Specialist Posey had it tied down, and out came his hammock, which he proceeded to string up under the tail boom and climb in. *Damn, I have to get one of those for myself*, I thought, but he was the crew chief and staked out his sleeping area first. Our passengers just lay down on the ground or inside the aircraft. Chicken plates made horrible pillows, but I staked out a spot on the ground under the aircraft.

Intel didn't get it right, as Lai Khe didn't get hit that night. Instead, it got pounded with rockets and mortars the next night, once we returned. Some aircraft were hit and one was lost completely with a direct hit. One of Lobo's aircraft took a direct hit as well. We'd suspected as much, as all the hooch maids had left that day at about 1500. They'd said nothing directly but had given plenty of indications that we'd best be on our toes for what was coming. We were used to receiving a couple of rockets or mortar rounds three or four times a week at night, but not like this.

In hindsight, this exercise prepared us for upcoming events.

"Wake up! Mission brief in thirty minutes in the mess hall," screamed the ops clerk as he ran through the hooch. As we were all light sleepers now because of the rocket attacks, everyone was up immediately and scrambling to get dressed.

"What time is it?" someone asked.

"Zero two thirty. What the hell now?" responded Mike George as we were all heading out the door. Over in the crew chief and door gunner hooches, lights were on and everyone was moving with a lot of hollering. Entering the mess hall, Major Saunders and the ops officer were posting crew assignments and tail numbers.

"Okay, get in and get seated," directed the major. Once we settled down, he began the mission brief.

"Firebases Jamie, Grant, and Joy all got hit about an hour ago by at least a regiment-size force at each one." Worried looks were exchanged amongst the pilots. "Division has ordered an operation to place two companies in a blocking position north of Grant to foil a withdrawal of the remnants of the regiment in that area or to reinforce Grant if necessary. Our mission is to pick up one rifle company at this location" —he pointed at the map—"and insert them three klicks north of Grant in this location. I will be Yellow One and this will be a twelve-ship lift with two turns. Those of you not in the lift will go to Quan Loi and fly resupply to each firebase and backhaul wounded." He paused while we absorbed his words.

"Now the bad news—there will be no artillery fire on the insertion. Division does not want the gooks to know we've landed in this location, so artillery support will be on call but not fired unless absolutely necessary. In addition, there was concern that an artillery prep would obscure the LZ with smoke and make it more difficult for us to land. The good news is that a recon team is at the LZ and reports no activity. I will be in contact with them on our approach. It is now zero three hundred and we launch in twenty minutes. Get your crew assignments and get out there. Crew chiefs and gunners are at the aircraft now." With that, we all departed as ACs already knew which aircraft they were flying and right seaters had studied the board while the major was talking.

Arriving at the aircraft, we saw that the guns had been mounted and preflight was complete. Posey and Quillin were on top of their game. Mr. Fender was my copilot again for this mission, and he began his start-up procedure as soon as we were all strapped in. We were flying Chalk Four of the twelve-ship lift.

"Flight, this is Yellow One, coming out." And with that, he picked up and moved to the runway, followed by each chalk in sequence. Over in the Snake Pit, Lobo was also cranking up four aircraft that would escort us. As each aircraft came out, they called Yellow One to let him know his flight was up.

"One, this is Two, you are clear to take off."

"Flight, this is One, come up trail." We had assumed this would be the formation as it was the easiest to fly at night. As most things in a lift were done by standard operating procedures, SOP, little communications and directions were necessary. As we departed, Chalk Three provided artillery clearance.

As we attained our altitude of two thousand feet, we could see three separate fire fights in the distance even though all three firebases were ten to twenty klicks to the north, and about nine klicks apart. Tracer rounds in green and red criss-crossed the night sky, along with flares being dropped from an unseen helicopter from our sister company, lighting up the firebases and impacting artillery on the perimeter of each base, either from our guns or the NVA mortars. I thought it must be hell right now on those firebases.

Mr. Fender had learned well the other night and was holding a good position on the aircraft in front of us. Our navigation lights were on but we had turned them down to low intensity, not wishing to give someone on the ground a target.

"Flight, this is One. Starting our approach to the PZ." With that, Yellow One began our descent. On our previous night formation, we were landing on a lighted airfield; this time we were landing to a black hole.

"I got it," I said as I reached for the controls.

"You have the aircraft," Mr. Fender said with some enthusiasm. "Dan, do you have a cigarette?" he asked.

"Afraid not. I don't smoke."

"Hey, I got some smokes, Mr. Fender," Quillin said as he moved up and handed his pack of cigarettes to him along with a lighter. "Keep them up here." Sitting in the door gunner or crew chief position made it difficult for them to smoke due to the wind, so they only smoked in the cargo area out of the wind. Mr. Fender lit up right away.

As we approached the PZ, we slowed our airspeed based on the aircraft in front of us and reduced our altitude. Crossing over the trees into the PZ we began to see small lights marking the position of each group of soldiers to pick up. We quickly loaded and with a call from Chalk Twelve were lifting off.

Almost as soon as we lifted off, Yellow One came up on the net. "Flight, this is One. The recon elements say that there's no activity around the LZ so there will be no artillery prep and no suppressive fire going in unless we take fire. Be sure your crews know this. We do not want to tip our hand on this. Eight minutes to touchdown."

"Mr. Cory, did I just hear the major correctly? No suppressive fire or artillery prep?" asked Posey.

"Yeah, I sort of forgot to tell you guys that. He's talking to a recon team in the LZ and we don't want the gooks to know we're putting these guys in there. So unless we're taking fire, there will be no shooting. Understood? Pass that on to the grunts so they understand as well," I instructed Posey. He was not smiling.

As our altitude decreased into the darkness below, I said, "Okay, guys, heads up. Watch for small saplings in the LZ as well as stumps and logs. Last thing we need is a tail rotor strike." Clearing the trees surrounding the LZ, we decelerated and touched down in a large clearing. The grunts were out in record time and we were out of there.

The insertions went off almost perfectly. It became obvious that everyone's night formation flying ability had improved considerably with these two hours of additional practice. We took no fire and arrived back at Lai Khe just in time for breakfast and received our missions for the day. The fact that we were off at 0300 hours made no difference. Missions still had to be executed. It was going to be a long day. This made me start to wonder. We were over here attempting to help the Vietnamese people maintain their freedoms, and the best they could do for us was to leave work early. Several small things had happened in the past couple of months that were making me reconsider why I was here. Cambodia and Laos had fallen to the Communists, and South Vietnam appeared to be next. How much further could they go in taking over Southeast Asia? But why should I care, as it appeared the local populace didn't care? Of what value was Vietnam to US interests? These questions began to eat at me, and the lack of appreciation I was seeing from the locals didn't help me reach any answers.

# 19

## DARK DAYS BEGIN, SEPTEMBER 1969

RALPH WAS A GOOD AIRCRAFT COMMANDER. A QUIET man, he was the youngest pilot in the outfit as he'd joined the Army right out of high school. He was not a drinker and spent his evenings working on college correspondence courses. His mission for the day was flying C&C for the division's engineer battalion commander. The engineer battalion commander wanted to fly out to where his engineers were working on various projects in the AO and see their progress. Not unreasonable, as they were scattered all over the AO improving roads, building a school in Quan Loi and supporting projects on the various firebases. The day started off normal, and they were visiting the various locations. However, just after lunch, things changed.

The colonel wanted to go on a recon of some areas. Ralph agreed to fly to those areas and proceeded to fly between Quan Loi and Song Be. The colonel was focused on looking for clearings. Finally he asked Ralph to take them down and land in one. Ralph asked for the frequency and call sign of the unit in the clearing so he could contact them prior to landing, especially as he didn't see anyone in the clearing. The colonel came up with an excuse for why he couldn't provide the information and told Ralph just to land. Ralph insisted on a call sign and frequency before he would take the aircraft down. The colonel became irate, but when he accused Ralph of being a coward, that was when things exploded. Ralph reached up and disconnected his helmet from the intercom system, took the controls from the copilot and headed back to Camp Gorvad. The colonel was livid. Ralph didn't care.

Reaching Camp Gorvad, Ralph landed at the engineer pad and told the colonel politely but firmly to get out of his aircraft. He then called our battalion headquarters on the radio, which was being monitored by almost every pilot from the battalion, and told them that he had just tossed Engineer Six out of his aircraft and was returning to Lai Khe. To say the least, shit was about to hit the fan. Making that call on the radio alerted every aircraft on the frequency as to what had happened. However, someone saw Ralph's position in this, and nothing came of it, at least on Ralph.

At this time, we had a new aviation group commander, Colonel Leo F. Soucek, and he looked out for his aviators' best interest. More than one officer attempted to order an aircraft commander to do something dumb and paid a dear price for it when Colonel Soucek was done with them. Days later, while flying with another unit, Engineer Six did the same thing, and the aircraft managed to clear the supposedly safe LZ with only a few bullet holes in the tail. A few days later, Dave Hanna got the mission to fly him.

When I returned from my mission that evening, Major Saunders approached my aircraft as I was shutting down in the revetment.

"Mr. Cory, a word please," he said as Posey opened my door. The major was standing in front of my aircraft and hadn't approached me.

"Yes, sir." I unstrapped, climbed out and came over to

him. *It's Mr. Cory now instead of Dan. What did I do wrong now?*

"Let's walk. Mr. Cooper!" he called over his shoulder, addressing my copilot.

"Sir?" Cooper answered.

"Would you grab Dan's gear and put it in his room, please?"

"Yes, sir," he called back with a question mark look.

We walked halfway back to the Chicken Coop with nothing said between us, but were angling towards his hooch. Finally, he said, "Dan, I have some bad news. Dave and YA were shot down today. I'm afraid the entire crew was killed." YA was Dave's copilot for the day and fairly new to the unit. I felt like I had just been gut-punched.

"What happened, sir?"

"As best as anyone could tell, while supposedly flying from Quan Loi to Bu Dop, the engineer colonel had again gone on a recon and convinced Dave to land in a clearing. A scout team happened to find the aircraft sitting there. It was obvious that someone had landed the aircraft before the enemy opened fire with some heavy weapons, as the only damage to the aircraft was in the cockpit and transmission and none in the engine or belly. The skids indicated a normal landing. Dave and YA were still strapped in their seats, and Sergeant Alford, the door gunner was in his as well. The crew chief, however, was found about a hundred yards from the downed aircraft. It appeared that Specialist Collins fought, as empty 5.56 shell casings were around him but not a weapon. The aircraft was booby-trapped. The colonel and his staff were dead in the back of it. There had been no friendly soldiers at that location," the CO explained as he opened the door to his hooch and motioned me inside.

"Damn! That son of a bitch has gotten more aircraft shot up than anyone. Damn his sorry ass. And now he's gotten people killed. At least his sorry ass was one of them. Bastard," I exploded. Major Saunders just let me rant as he opened a cabinet and pulled out a bottle of Johnnie Walker scotch. Filling two glasses, he handed one to me and raised his own.

"To absent comrades. To Dave, YA, Alford and Collins."

And we chugged it down, then sat in silence. Finally he suggested that he and I go to the club and have a drink, bringing his bottle with us. In the club, everyone was initially looking someplace other than at me and the CO. Finally, some of the old-timers came over and offered condolences.

As word spread that the crew had been lost, other pilots came over to my room and offered condolences as well as something stronger than beer. We didn't have formal ceremonies for lost comrades at this time, but we drank to their memories. This crew would be the first of our losses, but not the last.

A few days later, I was sitting in my room writing a letter when my new roommate, Owen Richie, came in from flying. He looked troubled as he grabbed a beer and tossed his flight gear on the bed.

"What's up, Richie?" I asked.

Owen was a bit older than most pilots. He had been a cop in Las Cruces, New Mexico, from the time he got out of high school until he joined the Army. He didn't have gray hair but we would accuse him at times of dyeing it, which he flat denied.

"Just a bad day. Saw my first crash and it was not pretty," he said, finishing off the first beer and opening the second.

"Hey, what happened? Was it one of ours?" I asked.

"No, it was a Charlie Company bird, and one of the pilots was in my flight class. I'd just been talking to him before we launched, and now him and his crew are dead. Hit a tree."

"Damn. Were you under fire?"

"No, we were coming out of an LZ, which we'd been in

four times already, and the blade on the right side hit a tree about seventy-five feet up. Rotor blade just came apart and they crashed and burned. No one got out."

"Damn, sorry, Owen. Who were the pilots?"

"Let's see, WO1 Thomas Brown was in flight school with me. A WO1 Dennis Varney was the AC. Specialist Marcene Shelby was door gunner, and the crew chief was Specialist Robert Lazarus. I had just met them, not an hour before, when I went over to talk to Tom."

Opening another beer for myself, I raised it and tapped Richie's beer in a toast. "To absent comrades."

A few nights later, our platoon leader came walking down the hall. "The CO wants to see everyone in the club," he said. We all started heading that way. The CO did not look happy.

"Gentlemen, take a seat, after you get a beer." He didn't have to say it twice. After everyone was seated and holding a cold one, the major raised his beer. "To absent comrades!" The look of shock and dread was on everyone's face.

We all stood and raised our drinks. "To absent comrades," we all repeated and chugged our beers, still wondering who we'd lost.

Motioning us to sit down, the major looked over everyone before he started to speak.

"Charlie Company lost a crew last night. They were on a night mission out of LZ Buttons and ran into bad weather. At about zero two hundred hours, they attempted to take off in fog. The grunts on the perimeter said they had all their lights on so they could see them in the soup. The aircraft got about two hundred feet up, and as it crossed the perimeter wire, it appeared to roll ninety degrees and crashed into the trees on the perimeter. The whole crew was lost.

"Guys"—he paused—"make sure you're practicing instrument takeoffs and instrument landings, and don't attempt it if your aircraft isn't one hundred percent on its instruments.

Spend the night or however long on the firebase. It's just not worth it. The weather is going to continue to get shitty, and I do not want to lose a crew to it," he went on to say. "I expect you all to practice one instrument approach and one instrument takeoff every day. Get some hood time while moving from here to Song Be or wherever you're going. Practice some partial instrument failure flying as well, especially with no artificial horizon flying as that's the most likely instrument to fail.

"Hey, sir, do you know who the crew was?" asked Roy Moore, a new pilot to the unit.

"It was WO1 Ralph Tadevic, the AC; 1LT James Spencer, copilot; Specialist FW Smith, crew chief; Specialist George Avala, door gunner; and a Corporal Terrence Connoll, an observer, for what I don't know. You know any of them?" the major asked.

"No, sir, I don't think they were in my flight class. The lieutenant might have been, but I don't know," Roy explained.

"Just let's be careful, guys. That's all I've got," he added as he walked to the door.

The next month would start off no better.

On November 5, two months after Dave went down, we lost another crew, not to enemy action but to maintenance. I had been high-time pilot for this month. The company policy brought in by Major Saunders was, if you were high-time pilot, you would be the standby aircraft. You had no assigned mission but would wait in your aircraft, and if another aircraft couldn't start its mission because of maintenance issues, the standby bird would take the mission. If all the birds got off, you got a day off. My aircraft had been in maintenance, getting a new rotor head installed. The assistant maintenance officer had taken the aircraft out the night before on a test flight once the work was complete. He had come back, conducted a post flight and signed it off.

The next morning, my crew and I arrived at the aircraft and conducted our preflight.

"Good morning, Posey. How's she look?" I asked my crew chief.

"All's good, Mr. C," he answered as he closed the engine cowling.

"Quillin, how's the guns and ammo?" I asked my gunner.

"Fresh cans of ammo this morning, Mr. Cory. We good," he responded. I climbed up and looked over the rotor head while my copilot for the day, WO1 Ron Fender, did the walk-around inspection and tail rotor. All appeared to be good. We strapped in, started the engine and waited, ready to assume a mission if called upon.

"Chicken-man One-Niner, Chicken-man Three India, over," the radio crackled. It was Flight Operations.

"Chicken-man Three India, Chicken-man One-Niner, go ahead."

"Hey, One-Niner, Two-Seven is down. Assume his mission, and contact Badger Six when you reach Quan Loi for further instructions," Flight Operations instructed.

"Roger, Three India, One-Niner has it."

I started pulling power. "Okay, guys, coming out." About this time, I saw "Chip" Rumble, Chicken-man Two-Seven, along with his copilot, WO1 McCartney, waving to me and running over. I set the aircraft back down.

Jumping up on the skid next to my door, Chip asked, "Hey, Dan, I'm low-time pilot for the month. Let me take the mission." He had just returned from a seven-day R&R trip to Hawaii and hadn't flown much for the past month.

"You got it," I said as Ron and I unstrapped and climbed out, turning the aircraft over to Chip and McCartney. We watched as they hovered out of the Chicken Pen and on to the runway. We were walking back to Flight Operations when they started down the runway and disappeared behind the trees.

Reaching Flight Operations, we went in. Sergeant First Class Robinson was crying. He saw us and immediately got this shocked look on his face.

"Oh my God. Who's flying your aircraft?" he asked.

I told him. "Why, what's the problem?"

"They got off the runway and were climbing out when the rotor head came off. They're all dead."

I was stunned and suddenly sick to my stomach. Outside, I threw up. Ron dropped to his knees and stared at the ground. I went back to my room and just sat on the bed. Thirty minutes later, Major Saunders stopped by.

"You okay, Dan?" he asked.

"I don't know, sir. I checked that head and all looked good. What happened?"

"Don't know, but the accident investigation board will figure it out. You just take it easy." He left, but about an hour later, he was back.

"Dan, I hate to ask, but can you take a mission? It seems Lieutenant Weed is too upset to fly his mission and has brought his aircraft back." Lieutenant Weed was close to Chip, the aircraft commander.

"Yes, sir. I got it." I picked up my gear.

"I'll walk out with you. I want to see just how upset he is."

The major and I walked together to the flight line. We didn't say much as there wasn't a lot to say. I didn't expect what came at me. As soon as Lieutenant Weed saw me, he threw his helmet on the ground and came at me. "You son of a bitch, Cory! This is your damn fault."

Major Saunders stepped between us. "Lieutenant, stop right there. Get your shit and go to your room. Not another word. Do you hear me? Now go!" Turning to me, the CO said, "Dan, forget this and get on with the mission."

This wasn't over, however.

That night at the club, Lieutenant Weed proceeded to

loudly badmouth me. I let it go, as he was a lieutenant and I was just a warrant, but finally I'd had enough.

"Hey, Lieutenant Dick Weed, with all due respect for your rank, go to hell!"

I knew using his full name, as modified by the warrant officers, would piss him off, and it did. With that, he was up and heading straight for me. I was off my barstool and eager to get it on with him, looking forward to hurting him. I was not a brawler but could hold my own in a fight. Just before he got to me, Captain Armstrong, a platoon leader, stepped behind him and jerked him off his feet.

"Don't you dare move, Lieutenant." Captain Armstrong was an infantry officer of considerable size. Very tall and very muscular, he was a no-nonsense man. "Mr. Cory, I think you should retire for the night. *Now!*" he told me.

"Yes, sir." And I departed back to my room in the warrant officers' hooch.

"Lieutenant Weed, you will go to your room, and don't leave until the major calls you. Understood?"

Lieutenant Weed wasn't happy, but he wasn't about to have it out with Captain Armstrong in front of witnesses. He waited until he was outside and decided to challenge the captain. Bad mistake. I wasn't privy to the conversation, but I was told that the CO had a very one-sided discussion with Lieutenant Dick Weed that night.

After any aircraft accident, an accident investigation is held. My copilot was interviewed, as were the assistant maintenance officer and myself. The crash site was examined as well. The rotor head was flown to a general aviation support facility at Vung Tu and examined. The results were posted and indicated that the rotor head had not come off but had failed. The rotor head that had been put on the aircraft the night before was a rebuilt one. During the rebuilding, the bolt holes for the bolts that held the pitch change horn had been cleaned and resized one millimeter. However the same original bolt sizes were installed aboard the USNS *Corpus Christi*, a floating aircraft overhaul facility. Those original bolts were one millimeter too small. Between the test flight and the takeoff, the bolts holding the pitch change horn had failed due to the stress, and the result was loss of control over the blades, making the aircraft unstable in flight. The investigation board found that there was no way the assistant maintenance officer or I could have found the problem, as the bolts hadn't twisted out but had simply, and instantly, torn out. The bolts were never found, but the condition of the bolt holes told the story. Easy for them to say, but this would haunt me every day. I couldn't help but think that it was something I should have caught on the preflight. It could have been me and my copilot. We had come that close.

About this time, we began losing pilots and crew chiefs. Rocket and mortar attacks targeted the Chicken Coop at night. Several crew chiefs were wounded as well as a pilot when shrapnel ripped through the night from exploding rounds. One pilot was wounded by small-arms fire. An entire crew was wounded from a "short" round fired from the 81 mm mortars on a firebase. The unit hadn't lost a single crew member since January 1969, and now that was changing.

## 20

## NIGHT HUNTER ON THE JOLLEY TRAIL, NOVEMBER 1969

I WAS BACK ON NIGHT HUNTER KILLER MISSIONS and we were flying in the vicinity of the newly discovered Jolley Trail. We were flying with a flare ship and a Cobra, and I had been an aircraft commander for about five months now. In the copilot seat was Major Saunders. He had taken command and right away was flying missions. Not milk runs, but real missions. He wanted to see what this Night Hunter Killer mission was, as his last aviation unit didn't have that mission. It was with the First Aviation Brigade, which supported those divisions that didn't have dedicated aircraft as the First Cavalry Division and the 101st Airborne Division had.

We had been working along the Song Be River when we received a call from the brigade we were flying for.

"Chicken-man One-Niner, this is Comanche Six India, over."

"Comanche Six, Chicken-man One-Niner, over."

"One-Nine, Six India, we have a unit that needs your assistance. They're a long-range recon patrol and are reporting that they're surrounded and need assistance. Over."

"Roger, Comanche Six. What's their location, call sign and frequency?"

Comanche Six India passed the information to me. The major plotted the location, and we changed course to go directly to the patrol's location. I briefed the crew en route and informed the Cobra and flare ship as well. As I closed in on the patrol's location, I contacted them on the radio.

"Delta Six, this is Chicken-man One-Niner, over."

In a whisper, a response came back. "Chicken-man One-Niner, this is Delta Six, over."

"Delta Six, I understand your situation. What's enemy estimate of strength?"

"One-Niner, we are surrounded. Estimate one hundred. We can hear them talking, and they're attempting to get us to reveal our position. Over."

"Roger, understand one hundred. How are they attempting to get you to reveal your position? Over."

"One-Niner, they're tossing sticks and rocks in the brush around us."

"Roger, understand. But they have not engaged you, is that correct?"

"Affirmative. I can hear you approaching, Chicken-man."

"Roger, tell me when I pass over you." To my crew, I said, "Heads up, we have about a hundred gooks down there, and they won't like us low and slow over them. I'm taking us over at ninety knots initially and will slow it down for a second pass."

"Chicken-man, you're passing me to the south."

*Damn*, I thought, *the jungle is thick around these parts*.

I asked my starlight scope operator, Specialist Brewster, "Are you getting anything?" Brewster worked in supply and had traded off with Jones for the fun of doing something different.

"Nothing, sir."

"Delta Six, is there a way you can mark your position?"

"Roger, I'll put a flashlight in the barrel of an M-79. You should be able to see that without them seeing it. Wait one." He was still whispering.

"Okay, crew, I'm slowing us down on this pass. They have a flashlight in the barrel of an M-79, so we should be able to pick that up pretty easily."

As we came around for another pass, this time at sixty knots, Specialist Brewster said he had the light. "Oh, shit, sir, they're surrounded." And then he started laughing.

"What's so funny?" I asked, slightly annoyed that he was taking this dangerous, tense mission so lightly.

"Sir, they're surrounded, by a herd of monkeys! The damn things are all over the place. The only people down there are four guys in the patrol," Brewster said.

"Are you sure?" the major asked as he and I exchanged puzzled looks.

"Yes, sir, I'm positive," Brewster replied. Vietnam had gibbon monkeys, and they moved in herds. If they felt threatened, they would throw sticks and rocks at the threat. They were big and noisy critters.

"Delta Six, One-Niner. What do you want me to do? We have your position." I didn't have the heart to tell him who his enemy was.

"Chicken-man, if you can lay down some suppressive fire to the south, we'll break to the north while you keep them down."

"Roger, wait one," I replied.

Switching radios from FM to UHF, I contacted Lobo and Chicken-man One-Four, who had been monitoring my conversation with Delta Six on the FM radio. Enlightening them on the true nature of the enemy, I said, "Okay, here's what we're going to do. On this next pass, lay down fire on the south side of the trail. Chicken-man One-Four, hold off dropping flares. Lobo, do you copy?"

"Roger, One-Nine, will make a run on your mark. One pass sufficient?"

"Lobo, yeah, that should be enough," I chuckled. "I don't think we will take a lot of fire from the monkeys." As we came around, my guns opened fire and the Cobra rolled hot with minigun and rockets. The patrol successfully avoided the enemy monkeys and lived to fight another day. We laughed our asses off back at the base while refueling. In the TOC that night, we found out that it was a new patrol leader. I was glad that I hadn't divulged the true enemy situation to him, but I did tell the brigade intel officer that the enemy situation reported might not be quite correct. He should get a scout bird out in the morning to see if there were any bodies.

After refueling, we returned to our original plan on the Song Be River. I had run this route the night before with another copilot and had run it the night before that as well. In both cases, I had run it from south to north. Tonight I would change it up and run north to south. We were about five hundred feet and sixty knots. There was a known crossing site over the river, which in this particular area was only about fifty feet wide. As we approached, out of the far bank, what appeared to be a string of green basketballs came arching towards us. Our door gunner opened fire with our 50-cal, engaging the .51-cal that initially engaged us. As I executed a left turn, Lobo called me.

"Chicken-man, you're taking fire."

"Roger, we're engaging."

Suddenly, my crew chief opened fire with the M60 onto the near bank. "Taking fire!" he shouted.

"Negative, Chicken-man, you're taking it from behind. Lobo rolling hot." *What the hell?* And then it dawned on me. We had flown into a trap, but as we had approached from a direction they weren't expecting, they were out of position. As we continued our left turn, I heard Lobo's rockets impacting. The major was on the radio calling Song Be Artillery with a fire mission. Suddenly it was as bright as day as the flare ship was dropping flares, and now we could see what was shooting at us. Three gun emplacements had been set up, with two on one side of the river and one on the other side. One gun on the near side was out of position for our flying north to south and still hadn't engaged us but was out in the open. Lobo had completed his first pass and was about to engage this target when it opened up on him. That really pissed Lobo off, and he punched off the remaining seven rockets he had. The gun never answered his challenge. As for the two guns engaging me, the one that Lobo fired on didn't answer, and the initial gun fell silent. As we climbed to altitude, the major took over directing artillery fire on the crossing.

The next morning, a scout team from First Battalion, Ninth Cavalry was out and found three destroyed guns and indications that someone had died with the guns and that the bodies had been removed.

The NVA didn't like leaving their dead for us to find.

Major Saunders was okay in my book, and he would prove to be better than just okay.

Several nights later, the mission was given to Charlie Company. They were flying the same area and route. The same trap was laid for him, but they engaged before the NVA could. The next day, a scout helicopter team found twenty-one bodies and three guns left behind by the NVA.

# 21

## OTHER MISSIONS

BESIDES COMBAT ASSAULT, RESUPPLY AND NIGHT Hunter Killer missions, we flew other missions, but not as frequently. Being lift ships or slicks, as we were referred to, we could be asked to haul anything and everything from one point to another. Some days we might find ourselves in support of a Vietnamese unit that was attached to the division, and then you could expect chickens, ducks, women, children and only God knew what else in your aircraft. Several times I was asked to fly psyops missions.

Generally for a psyops mission, a very large loudspeaker would be placed in the door of the aircraft—barely, it was so big. It would be connected to the aircraft's electrical power supply, and a microphone or tape player was added with a US soldier and a Vietnamese soldier. We would then fly out to a predetermined location, and the tape player would start, or the Vietnamese guy would start talking. I would fly at twenty-five hundred feet. Thank God we were wearing flight helmets as the noise was tremendous. Wouldn't have been so bad if we were playing music, but we never did.

"Good morning, Mr. Cory. Ready for some flying today?" asked the captain in charge of the division psyops program.

"Yes, sir. Beats sitting around waiting all day," I responded.

"Good. Well, here's what we have today. Need you to fly out to this intersection south of An Loc and orbit while Captain Ngnan operates the player and talks. Sergeant Davidson will be dropping leaflets as well," he explained as he pointed out the location on his map.

The leaflets were small pieces of paper with Vietnamese writing and pictures. They were basically a free pass to "Chieu Hoi," the Vietnamese term for surrendering. The Chieu Hoi Program allowed an enemy soldier to surrender and start working for us as a scout. Some of these scouts worked out; others came in long enough to get a hot meal and a rest period and then melted back into the jungle, returning to their units.

We loaded the aircraft and took off on a forty-minute flight to the road intersection. The division had been operating in the area for some time and was using the existing road network more often now, relying on helicopters to do all the heavy lifting in less accessible areas. This area wasn't as heavily vegetated as other areas around An Loc but was covered in bamboo. As I entered an orbit, Captain Ngnan turned on the loudspeaker and began talking in the singsong language of Vietnam. It was going to be a long couple of hours.

"Hey, Mr. Cory, I can see some guys down there in the bamboo," indicated Specialist Linam, my crew chief, who was sitting next to the loudspeaker.

"Where and how many?" I asked.

"Over on the north side of the road in the bamboo. Must be fifty guys, and they're digging, it looks like," he indicated.

I refocused my eyes and sure enough, there these guys were.

"Hey, Sergeant Davidson, do you see those guys down there?" I asked the psyops soldier.

"Yes, sir. That's an NVA unit we're attempting to Chieu Hoi," he replied.

"The hell with this. Instead of talking them out, let's hit them with some artillery to convince them," I said.

"Sir, we can't do that. We have to talk them out." Sergeant Davison sounded stressed.

Now this was the third time I was clearly seeing the enemy, the first being back on the river flying Night Hunter Killer, and I couldn't shoot at those guys from some bullshit reason. Dave had been recently killed, in part by these guys and in part by the engineer battalion commander. It reminded me of a popular cartoon at the time of two vultures sitting on a tree limb; one says to the other, "Patience my ass, I want to kill something." I wanted to kill something.

"Sergeant Davidson, I don't think they can really hear what he's saying flying up here. I'm going to take us down a bit so they can better hear him. Also, a lower altitude will let you concentrate your leaflet drop better," I informed him.

"Damn, that would be great, Mr. Cory. None of the other pilots will go below twenty-five hundred feet. The best altitude is fifteen hundred."

"Fifteen hundred, you say. Yeah, I can do that. These guys want to surrender." And I lowered the power and switched my communications so only my copilot could hear what I was saying.

"Pete, tune in Quan Loi Artillery. Plot this location and give them a 'be prepared' fire mission." He looked at me with a question but said nothing.

"Hey, Sergeant Davidson, we're at fifteen hundred. How's this?" I asked.

"This is great, sir. Although Captain Ngnan is a bit nervous at being this low," he replied. Sergeant Davidson and Captain Ngnan were having a vigorous conversation in the back with Captain Ngnan pointing out the aircraft, shouting at Sergeant Davidson and looking at me. I didn't speak Vietnamese, so I had no idea what his problem was. I just flew my aircraft, but I had my suspicions.

"Mr. Cory," Sergeant Davidson said, "Captain Ngnan is worried that they may start shooting at us as we're lower than he likes. He wants you to fly higher."

"Tell Captain Ngnan that these guys want to Chieu Hoi and he just needs to talk a bit more convincing. I'm sure he can talk them out onto the road," I replied. Sergeant Davidson went back to a conversation with Captain Ngnan, who was really looking upset.

"Taking fire!" screamed Specialist Francis, my door gunner. I banked hard out of the orbit but held altitude. Sure enough, about four or five green tracers were coming up at us, but none were accurate enough to hit us. Before I could say anything, Francis, who was now looking straight down as I made the hard right turn out of the orbit, opened up with his M60 machine gun into the group of guys on the ground. More fire came up towards us. I pulled in some more power and took a wider orbit.

"Quan Loi Arty, Chicken-man One-Niner, fire mission," my copilot called into the radio.

"Chicken-man One-Niner, Quan Loi Arty, send it, over."

About two minutes later, Captain Ngnan was having a shit fit as the first rounds impacted on the road intersection. As the second flight of six rounds was adjusted and landed in the middle of the group, Sergeant Davidson was in panic mode. "Mr. Cory, you can't be hitting them with arty. They're supposed to surrender."

"Sergeant Davidson, my first responsibility is to the safety of my crew while accomplishing the mission. They started shooting at us, which told me they had no intention of surrendering. You told me you wanted an altitude of fifteen hundred feet, and that's what I was flying when they fired first. I was just protecting my aircraft and doing what you asked. You may want to tell Captain Ngnan that I bet they're more receptive to his speech now. I'll take us back up to twenty-five hundred and continue to orbit if you like."

Captain Ngnan was in no mood to continue his speech and indicated that he wanted to go back to Quan Loi. When we reached Quan Loi, the psyops captain, US, was waiting for us. Captain Ngnan started jabbering and pointing at me. They were taking the equipment out of the aircraft when the captain came over and climbed on the skids.

"You know Captain Ngnan isn't real happy with you, don't you?" he asked.

"Hey, sir, he doesn't write my efficiency report. Did what was asked and protected my aircraft and crew, yours too," I replied.

"Well, I guess we'll have to write this one up as a mission failure," he said with a smile on his face, and he patted me on the shoulder as he departed my aircraft. He was an infantry officer in a shitty job.

The next psyops mission was almost a payback. We flew to Tay Ninh on the northwestern side of the division operations area. We had worked in this area several months before but hadn't been back in some time. Landing, we were met by the psyops team on the helipad. No loudspeaker this time, just boxes of leaflets—lots of boxes. As they loaded, the team leader, a sergeant first class, broke out a map. I could see he was an infantry grunt as well. He wore a First Cavalry Division patch on both shoulders, which told me this wasn't his first tour in Vietnam.

"Sir, we need to fly to this location, and we're going to drop leaflets," he said as he pointed at his map.

"Okay." I got out my map and started plotting the location. "Holy shit. This puts us right on the Cambodian border, if not over!"

"Yes, sir. And could we fly at, say, eight or nine thousand feet?"

"What? At that altitude, those leaflets will be scattered all over Vietnam and Cambodia as well. We never fly that high."

"Sir, we're just going to kick the boxes out of the aircraft and hopefully they'll open on the way down," he replied, not looking me in the eye.

"Okay, what's going on? Something smells about this mission. What are you not telling me?" I asked.

Reluctantly, he explained. "Sir, intelligence says that this location is the headquarters of the Communist Forces in South Vietnam. Their main headquarters. We're going to drop these and then get out of there. Intelligence believes there may be 23 mm antiaircraft guns, possibly 37 mm antiaircraft guns as well."

"Holy shit! A 37 mm has a range of about twenty-five thousand feet, and the 23 mm is up around ten thousand," I replied, but I was bullshitting. I only knew that these two weapons could reach way up and tag an aircraft.

"Okay, it's cloudy today, so we can pop in and out of clouds while we do the drop. Will that be sufficient?" I asked.

"Yes, sir. Oh, if you hear a beeping noise on the FM radio, followed by two more beeps about twelve to fifteen seconds apart, make a hard turn before a fourth beep sounds, please," he pleaded.

"And why is that?"

"The 37 mm are radar tracking, and the beeps are the radar sweeping the target. On the fourth beep it has a lock," he said.

"You've got to be shitting me now."

"Wish I was, sir. We're ready," he replied.

We headed out and I was climbing for all the altitude I could get. We finally got to ten thousand feet, which was a new experience for me and one that I did not relish. At ten thousand feet, the air is thin and the flight controls of the aircraft are very sloppy, requiring large movements of the cyclic to get the aircraft to respond, unlike at ground level, where you just think of movement to get the aircraft to respond. My copilot was glued to the instruments as his side of the aircraft had the primary instruments for weather flying, which we were doing, popping into one cloud after another. When we reached the intended point, the sergeant began kicking the boxes out of the aircraft and gave me a "Let's get the hell out of here" signal, which I did, losing altitude and changing course several times as we got down to the treetops and entered contour-level flight safely below the altitude that a 23 mm or a 37 mm would fire at a helicopter. To this day, I am convinced that the best use of those Chieu Hoi leaflets was as toilet paper, which I'm sure the NVA appreciated.

Days later, our mission had us fly to the helipad next to the division chemical company. In our mission brief, we were told to have our gas masks with us. I had to look to find mine as I had never used it since arriving in-country six months ago. At the helipad, several large white canisters about the size of fifty-five-gallon drums were lying on the ground. They appeared to be plastic. As I shut down, a lieutenant approached.

"Are you Chicken-man?" he asked.

"Yes, sir, at your service. What you got for us?"

"We have an NVA hospital complex at this location." He pointed at his map. "At thirteen hundred, an air assault is going in to seize it, landing here." Again he pointed at the map. "The division commander wants to take this complex with minimal casualties on either side. He's hoping that if we can get enough CS gas on the complex, they'll come out with minimal fighting. Our job is to start dropping these canisters as soon as the troops are on the ground and before they move into the complex."

"Okay, what kind of air defense are we looking at?"

"They don't expect any," the lieutenant stated.

"How long you been in-country, sir? Because there's always some air-defense guns with this type of complex. Someone didn't give you the whole picture."

"I've been in-country long enough," he responded, some indignation in his tone.

"Well, sir, I've been flying long enough to know that whoever gave you this enemy situation didn't know their ass from a hole in the ground."

The aircraft was loaded by chemical-qualified soldiers from Division. These canisters had a timer attached, so when they were dropped from the helicopter, they would explode at a certain altitude, generally a few hundred feet above the ground, and spread CS gas over a wide area.

"Hey, Lieutenant, please do not arm those things until I tell you it's okay. I do not want them going off in the aircraft," I stated.

"Mister, I am in charge here and I will arm them when I like," he replied.

"No, Lieutenant, you are not in charge here. I am! You are a passenger in my aircraft. I am the aircraft commander, and that makes me in charge. Now, if you can't accept that fact, then your ass can sit here while I take your NCO, who obviously understands this better than you, and we will get the job done without you."

The lieutenant started to say something, but his NCO, who was a sergeant first class, escorted him off to the side and had a conversation. They came back to the aircraft and climbed in without saying anything. The sergeant did give me a wink, however. Once everything was loaded, we headed to the intended drop point. I was monitoring the flight of helicopters from our sister company that was putting in the troops. We had gas masks; they did not. As I observed their intended flight path and LZ, I realized there was a problem.

"Hey, sir. We can't drop where you indicated. If I do, I'm going to be gassing those flight crews," I informed him.

"No! We have to drop at this point. The division commander directed it." He was panicking.

"Beg your pardon, Lieutenant, but the division commander didn't direct the drop point, only the target. We're going to drop but allow the wind to carry the gas over the target and not gas the flight," I told him.

"No! I want this drop—"

"Hey, Lieutenant, I really don't give a rat's ass what you want. I know what the division commander wants, and I will give it to him, but how I do it is my business. Now get ready to drop on my command, and shut up." I was starting to be pissed. No second lieutenant was going to tell me how to carry out my mission.

We approached the drop point I had selected and pushed the canisters out. Each exploded at the desired altitude and covered the area. Once the last one was out, we took the lieutenant back. He never said a word to me or the crew but jumped out and kept on walking. I must have bruised his ego. The sergeant waved goodbye with a big smile.

## 22

## TIMES WITH DAD

I HAD NINETY-NINE DAYS LEFT BEFORE I WOULD GO back to the States. Actually, it was my first day of being a double-digit midget. I hadn't taken an R&R or leave since I'd come to Vietnam. Why should I? I had no one to meet in Hawaii, which I had been to before and hadn't cared for. I had lived in Japan for two years of high school and knew all the tourist sites of Tokyo and Yokohama as well as some places off the tourist route. I had spent six months as a merchant sailor and had been to Singapore. I figured Kuala Lumpur and Bangkok were just the same as Singapore except not as nice, and I had been to the Philippines and saw no need to go back there. The only place I didn't get to before joining the Army was Australia, and every other GI from Vietnam was there, so why would I want to go where everyone else was? No, I decided to save my money for when I got back to the States so I could buy my first car and set up an apartment.

My dad, a naval officer and former Navy master chief, was stationed in Saigon. He had been there for a couple of months, and the major would let me take off a couple of times to go down and stay with him. He had a very nice set of quarters with a living room, bedroom and bathroom. His bathroom even had a flush toilet and a hot shower. The first time there, another pilot, Mike George, was with me, and I found him sitting on the floor of the shower, just letting the hot water run over him. I had known Mike George since flight school although he was three classes behind me. I remembered his room well, as he had a picture of a very attractive brunette wearing a pair of shorts, sitting on a rock at the beach with her legs tucked under her. Her eyes were cast down; her blouse was totally unbuttoned with no bra, tastefully exposing her chest but not her breasts. I loved to inspect Mike's room when I was the cadet battalion commander. He always passed inspection. He was from Sacramento and, like me, a bit older than most of the guys in flight school, having been a Sacramento firefighter before joining the Army. Clean sheets, hot and cold running water and a flush toilet made this trip heaven for Mike and me. Dad had a small grill on his balcony, and we cooked steaks that night that had soaked all day in Jack Daniels. Time to explore Saigon.

Mike and I caught a cab into the city. We weren't used to being in crowds, especially crowds of Vietnamese. It was a bit uncomfortable at first, but we loosened up after a bit. Some rules were pointed out to us by Dad.

"Sit in the back of a bar with your backs to the wall. Know the exits out of any place you go into. Careful what you drink, and watch your drink at all times." Okay, we got it. Walking down one of the main thoroughfares, we had our first encounter, with none other than the US military police.

"Excuse me, sir, but you can't be in Saigon with a weapon," he stopped me and said. Now this young man was just doing his duty in his starched fatigues and spit-shined jungle boots. Hell, we couldn't even get jungle boots, let alone get a spit shine on them.

"And whose rule is that one?" I asked.

"Sir, those are the orders of the Saigon garrison commander," he replied.

"Okay, but I don't work for him. I work for the commanding general of the First Cavalry Division, and he said that we would carry our sidearms at all times," I said with all the authority a warrant officer could muster. This discussion continued until Mike came up with a solution that was satisfactory to all parties. Mike and I were both wearing shoulder holsters. We simply took our shirts off and put them back on over the pistols. That made the MPs happy and us as well. *How incredibly stupid*, I thought. We were in a war zone, and yet we shouldn't carry our weapons.

As the morning wore on, Mike and I stopped for some liquid refreshments at an outside cafe. Sitting there, we were approached by a Vietnamese man who asked if we wanted to sell our single-lens reflex cameras. "GI, you want to sell. I give you four hundred dollars each for your camera."

There was an old saying that Dad had taught me. *If it sounds too good to be true, then it probably is.* Or was it, *If it sounds too good to be true, then it probably isn't?* I couldn't remember. Mike was all over this transaction. I was not. Finally Mike wore me down into submission and the man asked us to come with him around the corner so he could make the exchange. This was just wrong, selling on the black market. I knew it and Mike knew it, but we went along. Still on a public street, the man took our camera and counted out eight hundred dollars, folding the money up and wrapping it with a rubber band. He thanked us and disappeared into the crowd. We went back to the bar and Mike unrolled the money. But there was no money, only a twenty-dollar bill wrapped around newspaper clippings. That was the smoothest con job I had ever experienced, and the sleight of hand was perfect. We were taken big-time. We both felt as stupid as could be but learned a valuable lesson. If it seems too good to be true, then pass it up.

Later that day, we met Dad at an officers' club for lunch. This place had an in-ground freshwater pool and provided bathing suits and towels. It even had American women sitting around in two-piece bathing suits. Oh my God! We entered with Dad and noticed that several weapons were hanging from the walls on the coatracks. Unsecured weapons would never be tolerated in our outfit. We entered and took a seat at a table with tablecloths, cloth napkins and real silverware. The plates weren't paper and food wasn't being served on trays that doubled as plates. And a menu! A waiter came up and took our order for drinks. Beer, but there was a bar with everything you could imagine. This was going to be nice. So we thought.

As the waiter was taking our order, a master sergeant approached the table and addressed my dad, a lieutenant commander in the Navy. "Excuse me, sir, but I must ask you to leave."

Dad looked up. "Are you talking to me?"

"Well, yes, sir. Actually, sir, you may stay, but these gentlemen are not permitted in this club," he said. "See, this club is for field-grade officers only."

"This officer is my son," Dad said, pointing at me.

"I do apologize, sir, but they're not permitted in this club." By now some majors and above were looking our way.

"Dad," I said quietly. "It's okay." I stood up with Mike. As Dad was starting to stand in a rather loud voice, I said, "I have no desire to eat with a bunch of rear-echelon mothers anyway. Screw you all." And with that we walked out. Now I had been wanting to get a better weapon than the .38-caliber pistol I had been issued. When Mike and I got back to Lai Khe that night, we both had .45-caliber M1911 automatic pistols.

Getting back to the unit, I went and talked to the CO.

"Hey, sir, would it be all right for my dad to come up and

spend a couple of days with me? Fly on some of my missions as well."

I thought this idea would be shot down in flames, but the major said, "Sure, bring him up."

I really liked Major Saunders. A couple of days later, I flew to Saigon and picked Dad up. Dad had a private pilot's license but had never flown or been on the controls of a helicopter. My copilot jumped in the back and Dad climbed into the right seat. We took off out of the helipad, and I explained the controls to him as we climbed out. Once we were at altitude, I turned the controls over to him. To my surprise, he was maintaining altitude, airspeed and heading. *Damn, he's good.* Then I started watching him and noticed his eyes were glued to the artificial horizon on the instrument panel. This instrument tells the attitude of the aircraft in relation to the horizon. It indicates a climb or dive, right or left turn. He wasn't flying the aircraft, he was flying the instrument! *Cocky SOB.* The circuit breaker for this particular instrument was on the overhead DC electrical panel between the pilots. *I'll fix his ass.* I reached up as if I was stretching and pulled the circuit breaker. Ever so slowly, the attitude indicator internal gyro began to slow down, resulting in the indicator showing a slow left downturn. Dad compensated for it, but it did nothing for the instrument but put the aircraft in a right climbing turn. It didn't take him long to realize he had been had, and he turned to me with a laugh.

"Okay, smart-ass, you have the aircraft."

"Damn, Commander Cory, I really thought you knew how to fly this thing," Specialist Linam tossed over.

"Don't encourage him," I demanded and gave the controls back to Dad. By the time we reached Lai Khe and the refuel point, he was flying the aircraft quite successfully, but I wasn't about to let him try hovering.

The next morning, with the CO's permission, I left

Specialist Francis behind and Dad filled in for that position. The night before, Francis had given Dad a class on how to operate and maintain the guns. Francis got to sleep in. Our mission for the day was resupply and one air assault. Just a normal day for a slick crew. Having Dad aboard made it anything but normal. Dad was wearing the same uniform as the rest of us, jungle fatigues. The new NOMEX two-piece flight suits hadn't been introduced yet for flight crews, so we wore the same uniform as everyone else, except we wore leather boots instead of jungle boots. Jungle boots would melt in a fire, and fire was the one thing every crew member feared the most. *Shoot me, but don't let me burn.* Since World War I and the birth of Army Aviation, burning was the one fear all pilots had. The one difference in Dad's uniform was that his rank insignia was smaller than the gold oak leaf insignia for an Army major, but that was it. To an untrained eye, he looked like an Army major.

We had been working the morning resupplying companies, and all was going well. Dad was doing a good job of clearing the aircraft down in hover holes. Then we picked up the first load of troops for an insertion. I looked back and saw some discussion going on between the soldiers but didn't think anything of it. Suddenly someone was pulling on my shirt.

"Hey. Hey, what's your rank, sir?" a young soldier asked as he attempted to see my insignia on my collar.

"I'm a warrant," I explained. "Why?"

"Well, sir, you have a major for a door gunner. How bad did he screw up?" he asked with all seriousness.

I passed that on to my crew, and we had a good laugh, to include Dad. As this was his first combat assault, I had briefed him on what to do and when to do it. Although this was Dad's first helicopter combat assault, he wasn't a stranger to combat. In World War II, he had served aboard the USS

*Lexington* in the Battle of the Coral Sea, manning a 20 mm antiaircraft gun until the order to abandon ship was given. He then served aboard submarines for the duration of the war in the Pacific.

We were in the Chalk Five position of a six-ship lift and would be making three turns to the landing zone, with six grunts on each trip. It was a narrow landing zone, so we went into trail formation. At H minus six, the artillery began hitting the LZ; at H minus two, the Cobras rolled in with rockets and miniguns.

At H minus one, I said, "Door gunner, open fire!" Immediately a green tracer reached up and we had a hot LZ, with Chalk Two taking a hit and smoke coming from his engine.

"Mayday, Chalk Two is going down."

"Chalk Three is taking fire."

"Yellow One is going long and taking fire."

We were committed now, with Chalk Two landing on the edge of the LZ, and it was a hot LZ. My crew chief was ripping the tree line with machine-gun fire, but crap, I wasn't hearing anything from my dad's gun.

"Dad, open fire. *Dad!*" Nothing. Thinking he was hit, I looked back over my right shoulder, expecting to see him slumped over his gun. But no, he had his monkey harness on, which I'd insisted upon, and was standing on the skids, hanging out with only the strap holding him, taking pictures of the flight going in and the soldiers in the back of my aircraft shooting their rifles.

"Taking damn pictures," I bellowed. "*Dad!* Get your ass back on that gun."

He got back behind the gun and started shooting the tree line. We took no hits, and the mission was completed. However, when we arrived at the refuel point, Dad and I had a one-sided conversation about the duties and responsibilities of the door gunner in a combat assault. He knew he'd screwed up, and to his credit, he took his ass chewing in a professional manner. He knew he deserved it for leaving us unprotected and for scaring the crap out of me.[1]

The next day, I had arranged for him to fly in an OV-10 Bronco. The Bronco was an Air Force aircraft used for adjusting air strikes. It was a twin-engine split-tail aircraft with tandem seating for the pilot and one other. Dad had spent the evening with the pilot that would fly the mission and was ready the next morning. He spent the day putting in air strikes and totally enjoyed himself, it seemed as he related the day's activities that night in the club over beer. In typical fighter pilot fashion, it was all hand motions demonstrating how the Bronco dove, rolled upside down and fired his rockets to mark the target.

"I noticed one thing different about those Air Force pilots from you guys. Air Force pilots seem to be outgoing and always in positive moods, versus you guys, who seem withdrawn and pensive," he explained.

"Dad, an Air Force pilot is that way because he's flying a machine that wants to fly and if left alone will generally fly quite well on its own. In addition, compared to a helicopter, an airplane has very few moving parts that can cause a serious malfunction. On the other hand, helicopter pilots fly a machine that does not want to fly and only does so by the interactions of the pilot to balance four forces all opposed to each other. Plus, a helicopter has lots of moving parts, any one of which breaking can and does cause a major disaster. Helicopter pilots are moody because we know something is going to break if it hasn't already done so." That gave the old man something to think about.

# 23

## CHERRY BROKEN

FLYING FOR THE PAST TEN MONTHS IN-COUNTRY, I had been fortunate. I had only one broken chin bubble and one tail rotor strike to blemish my record. I had been shot at but never hit. I was a cherry. Most other pilots had already had at least one hole in their aircraft. Dave's was the only aircraft we had lost to enemy action, and that still hurt. I had my own aircraft and crew chief and we clicked pretty good. Specialist Linam was older and more mature than most of the others. My door gunner was a different story.

Actually, Specialist Francis was a good door gunner, but he had rotated back to the States the day before. What I was getting was totally new to me and new to the unit, as he had just transferred in from the infantry. This was to be his first mission. I woke up that morning with a weird feeling. A sense of dread hung over me. I had never had the feeling and couldn't shake it. Something wasn't right. I did an extra-good preflight. We had an early-morning takeoff, and Private Johnson, my new door gunner, was late. Specialist Linam went to find him, and I could hear Linam cussing across the Chicken Pen. Private Johnson was the recipient of the verbal attacks.

Seemed Private Johnson had rolled over and had gone back to sleep after he had been told to get to the flight line.

When Private Johnson got to the aircraft, I asked him if he was going to bring the guns. "I thought they would be on the aircraft already," he said.

"What made you think that? You know they're kept in the arms room at night," I asked.

"I thought you would have gotten them," he said.

I went ballistic and approached him with my face in his. "I don't mind doing someone else's job coordinated ahead of time, but don't just expect me to do yours, Private. Now get those damn guns, and don't forget the ammo." Now besides not feeling right, I was pissed. Could this morning get any better? Careful what you wish for. The only thing that saved Johnson was a jeep coming by. I stopped it and had it take him to get the guns and the six thousand rounds of ammo that we carried. When he got back, he started mounting the weapons along with Specialist Linam.

Then Specialist Linam went ballistic, "Holy shit, this stuff is filthy! Did you clean them last night?"

"No, I thought that other guy would have done that," Private Johnson mumbled.

"Johnson," I exploded after seeing the condition of the guns and ammo, "the first stop we make today, you will strip these guns and get them cleaned. If we take fire today before you get them cleaned, I hope to God you're the one that takes the hit. Now let's go." We cranked the aircraft and got off a few minutes late, which I made up and joined the rest of the flight.

En route, Yellow One gave a briefing. "Flight, this is Flight Lead. We're picking up a company at the airfield in Song Be and inserting them along the river." He gave the coordinates of the landing zone, which I was plotting on my map while my copilot flew. Russel had been in the unit for about three months and all indications were that he was going to be a fine aircraft commander. He was patient and unflappable and had a great sense of humor. "We'll have three turns landing in staggered right formation. Landing will be from south to north."

This would place our aircraft closest to the tree line as we were Chalk Two for this mission. Specialist Linam was on the left side of the aircraft and Johnson was on the right side, facing the tree line. Russel was almost ready to make aircraft commander, so I decided to let him take us in on the initial assault. I would be ready to take the controls but really didn't think it would be necessary.

Things started out as usual, the artillery and Cobra gunships doing their thing at the appropriate times. We reached the H minus one time hack, and Russel gave the command, "Door gunner, open fire."

Specialist Linam depressed the trigger, and nothing! Private Johnson did the same, and nothing! Our damn guns and ammo were so dirty that both weapons malfunctioned. The flight of six aircraft had a serious gap in our coverage because I couldn't lend any firepower to the suppression.

"Yellow One is taking fire!" Chalk One was being impacted by green tracers, and he was still about four feet in the air. Slowly he started a pedal turn to the left, which began to accelerate. Shit, his tail rotor had been shot out and he had no control over it. As the aircraft continued to accelerate in the left turn, grunts were thrown out and were crawling as fast as they could away from the aircraft. Suddenly a sledgehammer began beating on the side of our aircraft as we were about to touch down. To Russel's credit, he concentrated on putting us on the ground for the three seconds, but the grunts were already jumping off and engaging the tree line.

"Chalk Two is taking fire!" I reported. I was watching our instruments, especially engine and transmission oil pressure gauges. No master caution light and no fluctuation in the gauges, so we were good. Must have hit the tail boom. Still no fire from my guns.

"I'm hit!" Private Johnson screamed.

*Damn, I can't believe I wished this on him. Bullshit! He deserved this.*

"Where are you hit?" I asked.

"In the ankle," Johnson replied. Now I was pissed. That was a ticket home. He was going to be in the VA medical system for the rest of his life, and from what I had seen of him, he was going to milk that system for the rest of his life.

As we were coming out of the LZ, Yellow One called me to take the flight and lead position. Only Chalk One was left back in the LZ with one-third of a rifle company. Cobra gunships were working the tree line, and I was taking the remaining ships back to get the next turn. We loaded quickly and it was obvious that the grunts knew it was a hot LZ. Johnson was taken out by a waiting medic and ambulance, and that was the last I saw of him. A quick inspection of the exterior of the aircraft by Specialist Linam indicated we'd acquired some extra air vents in the tail boom, courtesy of the NVA. The only important items in the tail boom were the tail rotor drive shaft, which looked like a four-inch metal pipe that ran along the top of the tail boom, and the two cables that controlled the tail rotor. The rest was just hollow. Linam said we were good to go and Russel led the next lift to the LZ, which was still in contact. One of the grunts had been working on Johnson's gun and had it working, as had Linam, so on this turn, both guns were firing. Chalk One crew were waiting on the ground for us to land, and as soon as the grunts were off, they were on, with their door gunner taking over.

The last turn into the LZ was uneventful, but a couple of prisoners were tossed on my aircraft, with Linam holding a gun on them. I looked back and for the first time saw an enemy that would like nothing better than to shoot me. No remorse in their eyes, just pure hatred. This was the enemy up close and personal. These were NVA soldiers. They were dedicated, disciplined and physically tough. No fat on those bodies. They were as good as our grunts, lacking only the technology that our guys enjoyed. I had seen Chieu Hois with their grins and waves. These were not Chieu Hois. This was the real enemy. An enemy that I would come to respect.

## 24

## SHANGHAI

It was the end of November, and I was looking forward to Thanksgiving dinner the next day. When I came in from flying, the orderly room clerk stopped me.

"Mr. Cory, I have an RFO for you," he said, handing me a piece of onionskin paper. Clerks typed everything on the original paper with carbon copies underneath, five copies. The world seemed to work just fine with a manual typewriter and onionskin paper, five copies. The RFO was a request for orders, which came from higher headquarters, directing the receiving unit to prepare transfer orders in accordance with the instructions on the RFO. This was my ticket home.

"Yes!" I said with a fist pump. "Where am I going?"

"Sir, you are to report to Fort Ord, California," he said with a smile. Fort Ord is located in Monterey, on the coast. It's beautiful there. This was a plum assignment. God had smiled on me.

*I am blessed*, I thought as I walked into our little officers' club. "Bartender, set 'em up. I'm buying. Give the rooster a scotch." About fifteen pilots were sitting there and joined me in the celebration. The rooster was already on the bar, pecking at his glass.

"Hey, Dan. What are we celebrating?" asked Mike. "You find a woman that will sleep with you?"

"Screw you. No, I've found an entire town of women. California surfer girls. My RFO came in, and I'm going to Fort Ord," I said, raising my beer. A cheer went up, and comments about how lucky I was.

"How the hell did you pull those orders? Just about everyone goes to Mother Rucker or Fort Wolters for flight instructor duty," Hess interjected. He had just dropped his request for an extension.

"I know, but these just came in. Anyone know what it's like back there?" I asked. From the back of the room came a voice.

"Yeah, it sucks," Lieutenant Weed spoke up. We had tolerated each other and been professional, but that was the extent of our relationship.

"Why do you say that, sir?" I asked, keeping it professional.

"I lived near there before I joined the Army. My first assignment was as a training officer there." To me, that explained a lot about his leadership ability. "When I got there," he continued, "I come to find that it's the basic training base for the West Coast. They have very few aircraft and very little flying time, since basic training doesn't teach airmobile operations. They only get that when they go to AIT. The surrounding towns are Monterey, Pacific Beach and Carmel, all very expensive. High school kids drive Jags and Mercedes while schoolteachers drive Fords and Chevys. You'll be scraping by on warrant officer pay. Oh, and forget about getting a flying job. Warrant officers there are generally used as mess officers, since they have so few flying positions there. You'll be placed in charge of overseeing about five or six company mess halls and will only fly on weekends or after hours to get your required hours. Good luck with that assignment," he concluded.

Now I didn't know if I should trust Lieutenant Weed's words or not, but it certainly put a damper on the celebration. I was going to have to do some research on this. I'd joined the Army to fly, not work in mess hall management.

For the next couple of days, I asked around about Fort Ord among other pilots, not only in our outfit but also in other units that I came across. It appeared after a week that Lieutenant Weed had spoken the truth. I was headed to a shit sandwich assignment.

I went to see the major to see if I could get my orders changed.

"Excuse me, sir. I'm on orders to Fort Ord and—"

"Yeah, I know, and good luck with that. You're too good of a pilot to be stuck in that place. You're going to waste your time there," he interrupted.

"Well, sir, that's what I wanted to talk to you about. Can you change those orders to send me to Rucker or Savannah?" I asked.

"Shit, Cory, do I have a magic wand? No, I can't change your orders. If I could, I would have as soon as they came in. No way," he said. *I'm screwed.* "Now wait one. There is a way *you* can change your orders, however," he added.

Now I was excited. "There is? How?"

"You can extend for six months and stay in Nam." He was grinning. *Did he have something to do with my RFO?* I wondered.

"Sir, you're kidding. Hell! I've already had my cherry busted, had a door gunner wounded, had a hydraulic failure and a compressor stall. Add to that, I'm over thirteen hundred hours flying here." I didn't mention the aircraft that had gone down with the pitch change horn failure, the one I'd almost ridden in. He knew that was on the score card without me mentioning it.

"Yeah, you've racked up some time, but that's the only choice you have. Think about it." And he headed to the bar.

Seldom did we discuss business with the CO in a formal setting. He and his XO were easy to talk to, as were most of the RLOs now in the unit. My platoon leader came over and dragged up a chair as I sat at the bar.

"I hear you're going to go to Fort Ord," Captain Beauchamp said. He was a new guy, having been with us about two months now. Easy going and very likable. He was an artillery officer from New York City. He wanted to open a haberdashery when he got out. I had to ask him what a haber-dashery was.

"A men's tailor shop" was his response, as if everyone knew what that was. I bought my jeans off the rack.

"Yeah. I guess the only way of getting out of it is to extend my tour by six months."

"Well, why not?" he asked.

"Sir, I've been pressing my luck. Between Night Hunter Killer missions, combat assaults and all the other stuff—"

"Well, extend for some outfit that doesn't do this crazy shit. Extend for a VIP flight out of Saigon. Your dad is there, isn't he?"

"Sir, I never thought of that. Shit, I could live good, but I don't know. I probably wouldn't do well with all the spit and polish that goes with one of those outfits. I also don't care to be around field grades that think they're too good to be with the common grunt," I said, thinking back to when Mike and I had been asked to leave the "O" Club with Dad that time.

"What did you want to fly when you came out of flight school?" he asked.

"Truthfully, sir, I wanted to fly medivac," I told him.

"God, you're nuts. Why?" he asked.

"Well, they don't fly formations, which, before I came here, I didn't like."

"But you do now, and you're one of the best in formation that I've seen."

"I had a good teacher when I first got here. What he taught me, I've been passing on to you."

"Why else were you looking at medevac?"

"I like helping guys. Grunts need someone who's willing to get in and get them, especially when they're in bad shape. I just thought medevac would be a good fit for me. Besides, nurses are with medevac units," I added with a smile.

"Well, extend for the Forty-Fourth Med Brigade, where all the medevac birds are located," he instructed.

"I hadn't thought of that. Sure as shit wouldn't extend for helping the Vietnamese."

"Yeah, why not?" he asked.

"Sir, I'm convinced that these people could give a rat's ass about who the government is. They want to raise their families and grow their rice in peace and quiet. They'd be just as happy to see our asses out of here and the Commies in charge as long as they leave them alone. Look how often we get hit with mortars or rockets and they say nothing to us but *didi* out of here at fifteen hundred or thereabouts. They know it's coming, but will they tell us? No way!" Thinking out loud, I added, "Now I would come back to help our grunts. God knows they need it. I could go home on a thirty-day leave and come back to go there. Thanks, sir. I'll do that right now." I finished off my beer and headed for the orderly room to fill out the paperwork.

What I didn't hear was the conversation between the major and Captain Beauchamp. It was something to the effect of "Okay, we got him to extend. Now we just need to get him to change his mind and extend to stay here." At this point, the US Army was running out of pilots. Flight schools were at capacity, but between normal tours being up and guys getting out, as well as crew losses, the demand was beyond the supply of pilots. We had twenty aircraft in the unit and were supposed to have forty-one pilots, barely enough pilots to put two pilots in the cockpit of each at one time. We had on hand enough pilots to launch only seventeen aircraft. We had never gotten a mission requiring all twenty aircraft, the most being sixteen at one time, which usually accounted for two in sched-uled maintenance at the same time and the others down for unplanned maintenance.

"Okay, how do we get Cory to extend for this unit?" That was the question, and Captain Wehr, our XO, came up with an answer: make Cory the unit instructor pilot. Our unit had one instructor pilot, who was also rotating home and out of the Army at the end of the month. We had a new pilot that had attended the instructor course right out of flight school but was so new he wasn't even being considered for AC. A new instructor pilot hadn't been chosen, and there were limited choices. Had to be an aircraft commander, and prefer-ably someone who'd previously been a flight instructor at one of the flight schools. However, the major put that last require-ment in the toilet, if we had a toilet.

"This isn't flight school. I want an instructor that can teach how we fly in combat and who has done it. Besides, we have no former instructor pilots."

A couple of days later, I noticed I was on the flight schedule with the major. I was down as aircraft commander, which I thought a bit odd since he was also an aircraft commander now. Our takeoff time was 1300 hours, the middle of the day, and that was odd. No mission information, and that was odd. This whole thing was odd. When we got to the aircraft, the crew chief and gunner were there and waiting. There was a marmite can in the back of the aircraft and I asked what it was for. Marmite cans kept food hot or cold, the Army version of an ice chest.

"Don't know, sir. The CO called down and told me to pick it up in the orderly room and bring it to the aircraft," the crew chief said. This was the CO's aircraft.

"What's in it?" I asked.

"Don't know. I didn't open it, but it's heavy."

About this time, Major Saunders walked up and climbed into the aircraft, taking the copilot seat. I had already performed the preflight, so no need to delay.

"Ah, sir, can you tell me where we're going and what we're doing?" I asked.

"Yeah, I can. When we get there," he said with a smile.

He started the aircraft and I got our clearances to depart to the north. The CO was flying the aircraft and took us to the Special Forces camp up Highway 13 with its dirt airstrip at Chon Thanh. He landed us there and turned to the crew.

"Okay, guys, hop out and take the marmite with you. Mr. Cory and I are going to be doing some work." As the crew got out, the marmite chest was opened and two very cold sodas came out. One was handed to me and the other to the major, who opened his with a smile. "Let's go shoot some autorotations. You're first."

I took the controls and set myself up for a schoolhouse by-the-book autorotation, which I might add was flawlessly executed with a perfect touchdown.

"My turn," he said, taking the controls. "Enjoy your soda."

We had taken beer with us on previous flights and drank a cold one during the day on missions, but only when we were on the ground and waiting. Usually one beer per man, and if we had a half case on board, we'd share it with the grunts on the first lift going into an LZ. They loved it, and our unit got a reputation for being the one that took care of the grunts. Beer was cheap and it brightened up their lives just a bit. On resupply missions into hover holes, it was just as important to get the mail and beer in as it was the water and ammo in our book.

Coming around, the major executed his autorotation but had a bit of a slide at the end. He asked me how I had no slide. I explained that when I made the flare at seventy-five feet, I popped just a touch of collective to the flare, which cut my forward momentum just a touch. He said he wanted to go around and do it again. This time he nailed it.

"Damn, Dan, if that didn't work. They didn't teach that in flight school. Okay, take me around for a low-level autorotation." He turned the aircraft over to me. I took us out low-level and came back on final. There was a fifty-five-gallon drum on the side of the runway about halfway down.

"See that drum, sir? I'll put us down next to it," I said while concentrating on my flying. Cutting the throttle, I eased the nose up and glided us to the drum, stopping midship of it.

"My turn." And he took it. Around we went, and he executed the autorotation but was short of the drum. "What the hell? What did I do wrong?"

"Sir, you did nothing wrong, but you didn't milk the collective to extend your glide." And I went into an explanation of how to do it. Around we went again, and he did it better but with a slide, and long this time.

As we were sitting on the strip, bringing the throttle up to full power, he waved to the crew chief, who was lounging under a tree. He held up two fingers, and without a word, the crew chief retrieved two more sodas. It was hot, and we were sweating out any liquid we were taking in.

"Okay, show me loss of tail rotor at a hover. I heard you've shown some of the others this technique," he said.

"Okay, sir, but this isn't a school-approved maneuver. Me and some of the other ACs thought this through after we saw what happened a couple of weeks ago when Chalk One lost his tail rotor in the LZ," I said.

"Let's hear it," he said as he sipped some soda.

"Okay, you're at a hover and the tail rotor fails. The nose is going to start coming around to the left, and if you do nothing, it only accelerates in that direction until you're in an uncontrollable spin, which will result in a rollover when you do hit the ground. You have two choices. The first is to try to maintain the aircraft while pulling power and climbing out as you're spinning until you get some airspeed to help streamline the aircraft and let you fly it as best you can to a runway for a running landing. Not the best of situations. The second is to stay in the LZ. As the aircraft begins to turn left, roll the throttle off, but don't chop it as you would for a hovering autorotation as that would accelerate your rotation. With the power coming off and pulling up on the collective, the aircraft won't have the power to turn the nose or keep itself in the air. You'll land with a turning nose, but the chance of a rollover is greatly reduced. If it does lean into a rollover, move the cyclic to the right to tip the aircraft to that side. The key is recognizing quickly that you have a tail rotor failure and reacting just as quick," I explained.

"Okay, show me," he said, just as calm as could be. Meanwhile I was about to shit in my pants.

"Sir, you know I could screw this one up," I said timidly.

"You won't," he said as he gave me a thumbs-up to get to a hover. As I got to a hover, he jammed the left pedal and the nose started around. *Shit.* I reacted, and we set down with just one bounce.

"Told you you wouldn't fuck it up," he said. "My turn." And we executed it with him on the controls and me pushing the pedal, although I didn't jam it to the stops as he had done to me.

I was feeling a bit cocky now. "Sir, you ever done a zero-airspeed one-eighty autorotation?" I asked.

"What the hell is that?" he asked with surprise on his face.

"It would be easier to demonstrate if you'll allow me," I said without looking at him. How far was I going to be able to push him? I pulled in power and started climbing. "Suppose you're at an altitude of a thousand feet and have an engine failure. The only clearing is behind you. You have two options. The first is to fly a hundred and eighty degrees and hope you make it back to that clearing, but as you're making that turn, you're losing altitude rapidly, and unless you're trading altitude for airspeed, you may not make it back to the clearing in a low-level autorotation. The second is to trade airspeed off for altitude while you make a pedal turn and then execute a normal autorotation."

He looked at me as if I was nuts. I flew the aircraft over the runway and passed it at one thousand feet. When it was behind us, I chopped the throttle and immediately raised the nose of the aircraft, bleeding off the airspeed to zero, but our altitude stayed at one thousand feet. As we passed through ten knots, I kicked in a left pedal turn, bringing the nose of the aircraft around 180 degrees. Our rotor rpms were going down slowly as I then pushed the nose of the aircraft forward and put us into a fifteen-hundred-feet-per-minute dive, pointed right at the runway. Rotor rpm was building rapidly, as was airspeed, and I pulled in some collective to maintain it in the correct operating range. As we were operating the rotor in the green, the landing point was where it should be. I raised the nose and reduced our airspeed, which was at one hundred and ten in the dive, to sixty knots and executed a normal autorotation, setting the bird down as pretty as I pleased. The major was just staring wide-eyed at me.

"Where the hell did you learn that?" he asked. "Surely not in flight school."

"No, sir. I met a guy that was a test pilot at the Hughes aircraft factory once, and he showed me the maneuver, along with a zero-airspeed three-sixty autorotation," I said.

"A what?" he asked with a shocked look.

"A zero-airspeed three-sixty autorotation. You do it the same way but just rotate the aircraft three hundred and sixty degrees. It's best if you have a bit more altitude, but you can do it from a thousand feet as well. This guy did one back in sixty-six up north under fire. He said he was at about twelve hundred feet when two .51-cals opened up on him. He pulled up short right away as he could see he was going to get hit, and he did. He immediately zeroed out the airspeed and chopped the throttle and went into the pedal turn. They stopped shooting 'cause they thought they had hit him mortally. As he got into his dive, he brought the power back and went contour over the trees. Must have pissed the gooks off, but at least they stopped shooting at him," I said. "He told me he read about pilots in World War I doing something similar when shot at by ground crews. Those pilot would abruptly pull into a stall, roll over into a spin, a classic split S maneuver, and then a spin down to a thousand feet before pulling out."

"Have you ever done it, this zero-airspeed three-sixty autorotation?" he asked. *Oh, the moment of truth*, I thought.

"Yes, sir," I answered. No denying it. I wasn't a liar, and I was sure he had flown with a right seat pilot that I'd demonstrated this to and he had been told about it.

"Well, let's not just sit here. Show me," he said, tightening his seat belt. Off we went and climbed to altitude. Everything came off fine just like a ride at Disneyland, and the old man was grinning like a Cheshire Cat when we got to the ground.

"Very nice, Dan. Let's get the crew and head for home," he said, and we did. Kind of a fun couple of hours just being able to hone skills.

Two days later, we were at the club after a long day of

flying. I was told that tomorrow would be a stand-down day for me, so I was working on my third beer when Captain Armstrong and Captain Beauchamp came over and dragged up chairs. Captain Armstrong was just a great guy and one of the few black pilots in the outfit. We had two, the other being First Lieutenant "Hobie" Hicks, also a fine man. As he and Captain Beauchamp sat down, he took my glass of beer.

"Let me touch that up for you a bit." To my beer, he added a large shot of Jack Daniels. Now I was never a whiskey drinker, so this surprised me a bit. But, hey, it was my platoon leader, and I wasn't about to refuse a drink. This was a bit odd. We had another, and another, with the conversation revolving around my flight with the major two days ago. Both were asking questions about the flight.

After about an hour of this, the company clerk came up to me in the Officers' Club and asked me to sign some papers.

"What's this for?" I asked with a slight slur and blurry eyes. I was becoming as drunk as our rooster who frequented the club each night and was fed scotch. Damn rooster would not drink beer. Expensive taste.

"Oh, it's just some paperwork I need your signature on for your extension," he said. And I signed it without another thought. I thought I had submitted everything. As he left, the RLOs excused themselves, slapping each other on the back and laughing their asses off. Two nights later, I found out what was so funny. The major wanted all the pilots in the club for a meeting.

"Okay, gentlemen, I have an announcement to make. First let me introduce two newbies that arrived today. Warrant Officer Rick Dumas joins us along with Warrant Officer John Reynolds, both just out of flight school. Welcome, gentlemen," he said as he pointed at them. "Both of you will have an opportunity to fly with our new instructor pilot very soon. Listen to what he has to teach you, because he's going to take you above flight school training and teach you combat flying. You both will be flying with him for the next month, one each day, and on the other day you'll be flying with another aircraft commander who's going to be teaching you as well, so you can learn from all of them. They've all been flying a minimum of four months and all have over five hundred hours in-country. Learn well and learn fast."

Who the hell was the new instructor pilot? I wondered. The major went on, "Sit down, newbies. In addition, I'm happy to announce that one of our chickens has decided to stay in the Coop. Mr. Cory has graciously modified his extension to remain with us instead of going to a medivac unit. Thank you, Dan."

"Wait one!" I yelled in shock. "Sir, I didn't change my extension. What are you talking about?" I was trying to be respectful and noticed that most of the other pilots were laughing, to include Captain Armstrong and Captain Beauchamp.

"I beg your pardon, Mr. Cory, but you most certainly did," the major said with all the seriousness of a criminal prosecutor. "Two nights ago, you signed the papers to change your extension from a medevac assignment to remain with us. You did it right here with Captain Armstrong and Captain Beauchamp as witnesses. Isn't that right?" he asked, looking right at them with a very straight face.

With equally straight faces, they stood in unison and said, "Yes, sir." And then they broke down laughing.

"Sir, they were getting me drunk with Jack Daniels when your clerk pushed those papers in my face," I stated.

Maintaining his prosecutor's face, he insisted, "Now, Mr. Cory, we all know that you're not a whiskey drinker, and I will not have you trash the honest reputation of these fine officers. Does everyone agree with me that we know Mr. Cory is not a whiskey drinker? Whoever denies that fact, let him stand and speak." No one came to my defense, and the major was now having trouble keeping a straight face. My goose was cooked.

"Hey, sir, one question," one of the pilots sounded off. "Who is the new instructor pilot?" Silence. A long pregnant pause as the CO stared at the floor. Slowly he looked up and studied the room, with his eyes falling finally on me.

"Mr. Cory is our new instructor pilot. Congratulations, Dan," he said. The room went into hysterics. For the rest of the night, I didn't have to buy beer as everyone was feeding it to me and all having a good laugh at my expense. Some even offered to buy me, and the rooster, a shot of Jack Daniels. *Bastards!*

## 25

## ENTER THE WORLD OF THE INSTRUCTOR

THE NEXT MORNING, MY MOUTH FELT LIKE THE entire Russian Army had walked through it in their socks, if they wore socks. Someone was smart enough to tell Flight Ops not to put me in the air as the previous evening's activities were taking a toll on my condition. At about 0900 hours, I was afraid I was going to live, I felt so bad. By 1500 hours, I was beginning to function and the major paid me a visit.

"How you feeling?" he asked.

"Sir, I'm not feeling."

"Well, you best be feeling by tomorrow morning because you're going back in the air. Look, we shanghaied you and I'll admit it, but I need good pilots here and can't afford to ship you off to some other unit. I barely have enough pilots to get all the birds in the air, and with you leaving and a couple of other DROSing, unless I get some pilots in, we won't be able to put two pilots in each aircraft. If you really have your heart set on leaving, I can understand and won't stop you, but I and a lot of others really want you to stay."

Damn, now I felt even worse. "Sir, the Chicken Coop is family. I'm not going anywhere now," I said.

"Good. Now when are you taking your extension leave?" he asked.

"I planned to take it in January when my twelve months was up. Mom is back in the States attending the University of Maryland while Dad's in Saigon, and I was going home to spend it with her."

"No girlfriend?" he asked.

"No, sir. I've gotten some letters from a girl I met two years ago in Morocco, but we never dated and her parents are good friends with mine. Just friends, nothing serious or anything."

"Well, if you're going home in January, I need you to get the orientation flights done on any pilot that comes in, and that's your priority for the next two months. If a newbie walks in, he's in the air the next morning with you. I'll notify Ops that you and your crew are devoted to flying with every new pilot we receive, be it their first day in the unit or just getting them up to speed. Any questions?"

"Just one, sir. How come I got the IP position? I've never been to the flight schools as an instructor."

"Flying with you, especially the other day, told me you have the combat experience and know the techniques that these guys need to survive. Flight school taught them the basics. You're going to take them a step higher along with the other ACs. We're going to start running into more NVA and less VC. The NVA know how to shoot at helicopters, whereas the VC can't hit shit unless it's on the ground right in front of them. Look at how many aircraft we've had take hits in the last two months versus the last eight months. Triple the number, and each time was a lot more hits in each aircraft," he explained.

"Okay, sir, I'll schedule Mr. Reynolds for first thing in the morning and Mr. Dumas for thirteen hundred. For the new guys, I'll get with Ops and work out a schedule. Anything else, sir?"

"No, that about covers it," he said as he held out his hand. We had a real CO, and he was a hard man to turn down. He was leadership that I hadn't seen in the unit for the first eight months I was in the outfit, and his leadership was making great strides in raising the morale and esprit de corps in the unit. Unit pride was becoming more and more evident.

That night after I got some food in my stomach, I tracked down Mr. Reynolds and Mr. Dumas. Both were in the club. I took a chair at their table and introduced myself to them, although after last night I was sure they knew who I was.

"Mr. Reynolds, you and I will launch at zero nine hundred for your orientation flight. Have you made up a map of the AO yet?"

"Yes, sir."

"Don't call me sir. I'm the same rank as you. How about you? Have you put a map together?" I addressed Mr. Dumas.

"Ah, no. Should I?" he responded. Something told me this wasn't good.

"Well, yeah. You need a map. Go to Flight Ops in the morning and they'll give you the sheets and show you how to arrange it so it opens easy in the aircraft. Have you been to supply and drawn your chicken plates?"

Both responded in the affirmative.

"Good. I'll meet you over at Flight Ops tomorrow, then. Thirteen hundred hours for you," I said, looking at Mr. Dumas.

"One question," Mr. Reynolds spoke up. "What are we going to be doing tomorrow?"

"Good question. We'll leave here and go to a dirt strip up north and shoot some autorotations, then fly north and give you an orientation of the area, where the major towns are at, where the key firebases are located and how to get clearances through artillery. We'll stop someplace and refuel and put in about three hours flying time. You might look over the dead man chart in the aircraft operator's manual, the -10, tonight." With that, I left them and headed to bed.

At 0500 hours, the damn rooster was raising hell over by the RLO hooch. Better there than next to my bed. He used to crow next to my bed on the sandbags until I hit him one morning with a broom. After that, I started leaving corn over at the RLO hooch, and he moved over there.

At breakfast, I saw Mr. Reynolds, John, and sat with him. He was full of good questions and spent the time picking my brain. I started to wonder if this was me ten months ago. Was I this inquisitive? Had I badgered Lou with questions, attempting to suck him dry of his flight knowledge? Lou was one of the best pilots I had ever flown with. I wished he was here now. Since John and I were both up, we agreed to meet at 0800 hours at Flight Ops and go over a few things before preflight. Specialist Linam was there, and I gave him a heads-up about the change in plans. He said he had no problem with the change of times.

John was right on time and we got to it. I discussed some of the finer points of the preflight inspection and discussed how to get out of the revetment. In flight school, you never hovered the aircraft in such a confined space as a revetment. The first time, it could be a bit nerve-racking. Taking off, we flew to the SF camp on Highway 13 and shot some autorotations, with me demonstrating and then allowing him to execute. He did all right and showed that with some practice he would be even better. We then flew to the northwest and refueled in Tay Ninh. From there, we went on to Quan Loi and Song Be with a return to Lai Khe at 1200 hours. Walking back to Flight Ops, I signed John off as qualified to fly. He was on the board for the next day with me again, but for missions. After chow, I met Mr.

Dumas at Flight Ops. There was something about him. He did not ask questions.

As with John, I went over a few things in Ops and then we went out to the aircraft and conducted another preflight, which wasn't normal, but it was his first flight of the day. Like me when I'd first arrived, he was looking for a written checklist, not only for the preflight but also for start-up. He started the aircraft, and I talked about exiting the revetments, asking if he had any questions. He said no.

"Okay, back us out."

The crew cleared us, and I said, "Let's go." Before I could do anything, we were ten feet in the air and climbing. I grabbed the controls and stopped the ascent.

"What the hell! What are you doing?" I asked, attempting to hide my shock.

"I wanted to be sure to be above the revetment before I came back," he said with a look of sincerity that really made me wonder.

"Rick—can I call you Rick?"

"Sure."

"Rick, we discussed how to come out of the revetment. We don't jump above the revetment and then back out. You come to a hover, three feet, and slide out of the revetment. Let me show you." I took the aircraft, brought it back to a three-foot hover inside the revetment, and slid it back.

"There isn't much room in here at a three-foot hover," he said, looking around and measuring the distance to the walls with his calibrated eyeballs.

"There's plenty of room. Take it slow and just think about moving the controls. You'll be all right. You have the aircraft."

Rick reached for the controls, almost moving reluctantly. I did not let go, however. "Rick, when I say you have the aircraft, your response is 'I have the aircraft.' Positive control transfer."

"I have the aircraft," he responded.

"Okay, let's try this again."

"Clear left."

"Clear right."

"Clear back."

This time I heard fear in the crew's voices. Rick came in slow with power, and the aircraft was light on the skids. As he continued to increase power, the nose was coming up as it should to five degrees and the aircraft broke ground. Rick was dancing on the pedals, which had the tail starting to swing back and forth. He was shaking and the cyclic was moving, which was causing the aircraft to drift from one side of the revetment to the other. We hadn't touched, but we were getting close. I wanted to grab the controls, but he had to learn, and flight school didn't teach this. Finally we were clear of the revetment.

"Okay, not so hard, was it, Rick? Now while we're here, let's put the aircraft back in the revetment. Just do what you did coming out, but do it in reverse and you'll be fine. Slow, steady movements and just think about the movements. Okay, let's go."

It was called technique, and everyone had the opportunity to develop new techniques in combat, but newbies shouldn't try new techniques until they'd learned the tried and true techniques developed by those that had gone before them. Rick was innovative in his technique. Lowering the collective so that the aircraft was lightly on the ground, he slid the aircraft into the revetment. I was too stunned to say anything. Finally after we stopped and were solid on the ground, I spoke up.

"Rick, if the maintenance officer sees you entering a revetment that way, he's going to be all over you. That technique is rough on the skids. You have to hover the aircraft into the revetment, not slide it along the ground. We'll work on that when we come back, but we need to get going. I got the aircraft."

After clearances, I took the aircraft and flew north. I just wanted to relax for a couple of minutes, and flying the aircraft myself was relaxing at this point. Rick was looking around, and I was pointing out landmarks that he needed to know. Reaching the Chon Thanh, I landed the aircraft and told Linam and Private Diedrich, my gunner that replaced Private Johnson, to get out. Specialist Linam seemed to demonstrate some relief as he left the aircraft.

"Okay, Rick, we're going to be shooting some autorotations. The first one will be textbook flight school. You haven't flown in a couple of weeks, so I'll do the first and you the next. Ready?"

"Yeah."

"Any questions?"

"No," he said matter-of-factly. Now, if I hadn't flown in a couple of weeks and hadn't done an autorotation in probably two months, I would have had more enthusiasm or apprehension in my response. We took off and climbed to one thousand feet and turned on final. Over the end of the runway, I cut the throttle, lowered the collective and set the airspeed for sixty knots. At seventy-five feet, I flared the aircraft, cutting our forward speed and rate of descent. At five feet, I popped the collective and lowered the nose and proceeded to pull in the remaining collective, setting the aircraft down gently. Rick was looking straight ahead.

"Just like in flight school. Any questions?" I asked.

"No."

"Okay, you have the aircraft. Let's go."

"I have the aircraft." And Rick pulled in power and brought us up to a five-foot hover before pushing the nose over and climbing out. Coming around on final at one thousand feet, he closed the throttle and lowered the collective while slowing the aircraft to sixty knots. So far so good. Now in helicopters, any landing you walk away from is a good landing. At seventy-five feet, he hadn't changed the flight attitude of the aircraft. My hand slid down to the throttle and collective. At fifty feet, he flared the aircraft, standing the aircraft on its tail, and popped the collective. I knew what was going to happen and was ready for it. On the end of the tail of the UH-1H, there was a metal rod protruding back and down under the tail rotor, and it was there to protect the tail rotor from hitting the ground. Flaring as low as we did, the stinger, as it was called, hit the ground, thus forcing the nose of the aircraft to pitch forward.

"I got it," I growled as I snatched the controls, rolled on the throttle and pulled in the collective, increasing the power and bringing us to a hover. To continue the autorotation would have resulted in a hard landing at best, possibly spreading the skids or a rollover at worst. Rick just looked at me.

"A bit rusty, are we, Rick? When's the last time you shot autorotations?" *Stupid question to have asked*, I thought.

"Back in flight school." No emotion, almost detachment.

"Okay. Let's do a hovering autorotation. I'll go first. Bring the aircraft to a three-foot hover," I said as I demonstrated. "Once stable, cut the throttle and pop the collective. Hold and pull in as we settle. Any questions?"

"No."

"You have the aircraft."

"I have it." Rick brought the throttle to full power. Nothing was smooth or gentle with him. He jerked in an armful of collective, causing the aircraft to leap into the air to a six-foot hover. It took full control for me not to grab the controls.

"Okay, Rick, get us at a three-foot hover."

He brought us down but was sliding left and right. The

aircraft wasn't stable. Before I could say anything, like "Get it stable," he cut the throttle but didn't pop the collective until we were about a foot off the ground. We landed hard and had used little of the available power. Mentally, I was making some notes. Rick lacked confidence; he didn't have a touch for hovering, and possibly his depth perception was off. At this point, my nerves were in serious need of relaxing, so I motioned the crew to join us. They appeared reluctant. The rest of the day was spent touring the area of operations and trying to get Rick oriented on his map. I let him fly and I held the map and pointed out landmarks. Maybe he was just rusty from flight school.

Arriving back at Lai Khe with Rick flying the aircraft, we entered the Chicken Coop and turned to our revetment. At about a five-foot hover, Rick worked us into the revetment almost like a pinball would in a pinball game. We didn't touch, but it was an experience. Getting back to Flight Ops, I told the assistant ops officer I would get back to him on crew assignments for the next day. I wanted to talk to the CO first and headed for his office.

"Excuse me, sir, can I talk to you?"

"Sure, Dan. How did it go today? Want some coffee, or a cold beer?"

"Sir, I need the beer," I said, reaching for it as he pulled it from his mini refrigerator that we all had acquired since moving to hooches. He had known what my answer would be before he'd asked the question.

"Mr. Reynolds did good, and I have him with me tomorrow on the board. Mr. Dumas is another story. Sir, the guy can't fly. Oh, he can move the aircraft at altitude okay, but he has trouble hovering, and his autorotation was simply a controlled crash if I hadn't taken it. If I sign him off, he needs to be with our most seasoned ACs for a time."

"What do you mean he can't hover?" the major asked. I

explained the drill entering and exiting the revetments as well as the hover autorotation. Giving Rick the benefit of the doubt, I told the CO that Rick might have a depth perception problem and maybe the flight surgeon should check his eyes. The old man thought this over for a minute.

"I'll talk to Doc about this and see when his last flight physical was. It should have been just before he left flight school. Might be something in there. Okay, are you going to sign him off for copilot duty?" Oh boy, the major was laying it all on me. My responsibility.

"Well, sir, he screwed up the autorotations, but we would have walked away. He did okay flying at altitude. Yeah, I guess I'll sign him off. I'll see who Flight Ops is putting him up with and talk to the AC for that mission." With that, I excused myself and went back to Flight Ops to sign him off and see who his AC for the next day would be. Ops put him up with Mike George.

Mike George's room was across the hall from mine, and Mike was a good pilot that I had a lot of respect for.

"Hey, Mike," I said as I entered his room. "You're flying with Mr. Dumas tomorrow, the newbie. Watch yourself."

"Why? You signed him off, didn't you?"

"Yeah, but he isn't the most stable guy when it comes to flying. His autorotations are controlled crashes and his hovering is horrible. I'll warn you right now, there's something about the guy. He isn't there."

"Thanks for the heads-up." And Mike went back to writing his letter. Big Rick would not prove me wrong.

## 26

## SELF-INFLICTED WOUNDS

Working around and flying helicopters is dangerous work even when people are careful. Accidents do happen when there are mental lapses, which occur when people are tired or in a hurry. Accidents also occur when people aren't properly trained or are inexperienced. Each day when returning to Lai Khe from a mission, if we didn't have an opportunity to fire our guns, I would contact the controlling artillery center and request a free-fire box. Free-fire boxes were designated areas that no friendly forces were operating in. With clearance, helicopters were free to shoot up anything they saw in that box. Having obtained a clearance, I told the crew to get ready.

My copilot was a newbie, an RLO on his orientation flight. He was a first lieutenant and a rather easygoing, jovial fellow. His flying for the day was satisfactory, and we had a good day flying not only his orientation but also a resupply mission for a unit.

"Okay, crew, I'm dropping down to treetop and you can open fire when you want. Linam, there's a water hole coming up at ten o'clock. Let's see you nail it. Diedrich, same for you on the one at two o'clock," I said.

Linam and Diedrich both opened fire and both were right on target. I was concentrating on Linam's shooting when over the intercom, my copilot asked, "Hey, Dan, can I shoot my pistol out the window?"

"Sure, just be careful," I responded. I heard the copilot's .38 popping off. *Bang, bang, BAM. Damn, that sounded loud.* The intercom system allowed the pilots to speak and the entire crew could hear the conversation, or it could be switched so only selected members of the crew could hear. Suddenly mine switched to private conversation.

"Ah, Dan," this voice called to me.

"Yeah?" I was still watching Specialist Linam's shooting.

"I just shot the aircraft," the voice told me. My eyes shot to the instrument panel. All appeared well.

"What the hell! How the hell did you do that?" I asked, almost laughing and looking at my newbie copilot.

"I had my arm out the window and was shooting at a water hole, and the water hole passed under us and I shot the nose."

"Are you hit?" I looked at him, searching for blood.

"No, I'm okay and the instruments are fine."

"Okay, we'll look at it when we get in," I said as we continued to the Chicken Coop. I let the newbie take the aircraft into parking while I called Flight Ops.

"Chicken-man Three, this is Chicken-man One-Niner."

"Go ahead, One-Niner."

"Yeah, One-Niner here. I'm coming in with battle damage. Can you have maintenance meet me?"

"Roger, maintenance is on the way." Battle damage! Those words always got maintenance excited.

As we were shutting the aircraft down, Captain Kempf, the maintenance officer, came over and I pointed to the nose of the aircraft on the right side. Captain Kempf walked over and studied it for a minute. From looking at the metal, it was obvious that the round had come from above the aircraft. He climbed up on the skid next to my copilot, who had opened his door, so the two of them were about two feet apart.

Speaking to me, the maintenance office said, "Sniper?"

"No," I responded with a snicker. He looked at the hole again, which was about three inches long entering the aircraft and the size of a dime exiting the plexiglass chin bubble.

"Cobra fired too close," he guessed, now looking at the rotor blades for damage.

"No." My snickering hadn't changed.

He looked back at me with a deadpan face, then at my copilot. "Your damn copilot shot the aircraft!"

"Yeeees." And with that, I couldn't stop my laughing. We hadn't had one of our own shot by one of our own since I'd been in the unit. Newbie would be buying the crew a case of beer and spending the night learning how to replace a chin bubble and do sheet metal work to cover the hole. To say the least, he was the brunt of the jokes as well. Until another newbie managed to outdo him, which would not take long.

Bill Hess burst into my room, madder than a wet hen. "Do you know what that damn newbie Eckerd just did?" he asked.

"No telling, Bill. He is a newbie. What?" I asked.

Ralph and Bob Eckerd, both recent arrivals, were sitting across from each other with a desk between them. Bob was Bill's new roommate.

"I'll tell you what dip-shit just did. Bob was about to clean his .45-caliber automatic pistol. When he pulled the slide back, it slipped and slammed forward with his finger on the trigger. The gun went off. The bullet just missed Ralph's head, put a hole in the screen right above my bed, traveled into the mess hall and hit a sugar bowl that was sitting next to a colonel as he was eating lunch. To say the least, the colonel was not happy when he reached my hooch and wanted to know who fired the shot. My room smells of gunpowder and he's checking my weapon with the CO to see if it's been fired or cleaned recently."

"Well, has it?" I asked.

"No, and the major's biting me in the ass because it's dirty." Bob stayed out of sight for the day, and Ralph was absent as well. But not all casualties were to aircraft, buildings or sugar bowls; some were creatures.

A newbie had been in the village and purchased a monkey. We had a rooster and a snake, but a monkey we did not have. The major wasn't keen on this new addition but didn't say no, so the monkey stayed, temporarily. The copilot showed up one morning for the mission with the monkey. The monkey sat on the back of his chair and ran from one first aid kit mounted on the bulkheads behind the pilots to the other. Cute. The first mission of the day was a combat assault.

With the troops loaded, the flight took off and the typical sequence of events began. At H minus one, the door gunners opened up with machine-gun fire, and so did the monkey. His bowels opened up all over the copilot and the aircraft commander. That monkey was going nuts with the machine-gun fire! Jumping between the seats, he was shitting his brains out and pissing on everything. That was when the aircraft commander reached up, grabbed the monkey by the neck and threw him out the window. I didn't know if that monkey could fly, but at about two hundred feet and ninety knots airspeed, I was sure he made a rapid descent into the jungle. For the rest of the day, no one would go near that aircraft or those pilots. Even their own crew chief wanted nothing to do with them, as he was the one stuck with cleaning the mess up in the aircraft. But as funny as some of these incidents were, others were tragic.

A very popular crew chief from our sisters, the El Lobos,

was pulling maintenance on an aircraft that was at full rpm. The crew chief was running walnut shells through the intake to clean the compressor blades on the engine. He must have had something on his mind, as he walked right into the tail rotor blade and was killed instantly. Crew chiefs were just as important to the unit as pilots. They maintained the aircraft that kept us in the air. A good crew chief was worth his weight in gold, and ACs fought over the better ones. Much to the first sergeant's displeasure, we protected our crew chiefs, and more than once, the CO or XO had to get involved.

To clean the engines, especially in dusty conditions, water would be poured into the intake while the engine was running. Really dirty engines would receive a gallon pail of crushed walnut shells that would get the dirt off the turbine blades in the engine. One of our crew chiefs found out the hard way not to run JP-4 through the engine intake. He was up top and asked the gunner to get some water. Somewhere the transmission got garbled and instead of water the gunner passed up a pail of JP-4 jet fuel. As soon as the crew chief poured it into the intake, the engine blew up, removing the crew chief's mustache, eyebrows, eyelashes and most of his hair. The engine had to be replaced, and the gunner was transferred out of the unit.

Another crew chief from our unit was jumping off the stinger when his wedding ring caught on a bolt and stripped all the flesh and meat off his ring finger. He lost the finger and was sent back to the States.

Talking on the company phone system could be equally dangerous in a thunderstorm. The company phone system was TA-1 field phones connected by steel wire covered in plastic. It was strung throughout the company area from hooch roof to hooch roof. One evening one of the pilots was talking on the phone to Flight Ops during a thunderstorm when a bolt of lightning struck. The electric shock ran down the wire to the phone. In an instant, the pilot was picked up and tossed across the four-foot-wide hall. He recovered, but phone calls during thunderstorms were curtailed.

Flying one rotor blade apart was normally comfortable, but mishaps did occur, and some could be deadly. On May 4, 1969, two aircraft from our sister company, Company B, joined a formation with the second aircraft in a right echelon to the first. The second aircraft attempted to pass the first aircraft on his right side. There was a miscommunication between the two aircraft, resulting in a midair collision. All crew members on both aircraft were killed.

Again, in August 1969, a Chicken-man aircraft and a Cobra gunship from Delta Company had a midair collision, but fortunately no one was killed, with only one of the Cobra pilots being hurt. Accidents happened, and only through diligent observation by all crew members, clear communications between aircraft, and adherence to standard operating procedures could they be avoided.

## 27

### ALMOST HOME

I GOT THROUGH THE FIRST WEEK AFTER Thanksgiving flying Night Hunter Killer again and checking some of the newer copilots out on the mission. Bob Hope was going to be in Lai Khe for a show, but I was too tired to walk over and see it. I needed some sleep before going back out for the next mission that night. We were working in the Song Be region almost exclusively now, supporting the Third Brigade. The first week of December, I got pulled off Night Hunter Killer and was back to flying days. I drew a sniffer mission.

The flight ops clerk woke me at 0500 hours for a 0600 hours launch. Something didn't feel right. I had a weight on my shoulders, it felt like. I felt like I had the day Johnson had been hit.

"Hey, Linam, the aircraft in good shape?"

"Yes, sir."

"How do the guns look?" I asked Diedrich.

"They're good, sir. I replaced feed trays last night and trigger housings as well. Ammo is clean as I just opened the cans. You feel all right, Mr. Cory?" he asked.

"No, I don't. I just got a feeling. It's nothing. Let's crank and get going."

Bruce Sinkey was my copilot and we were flying in an area that had low vegetation and rice paddies along the river basin. Rice paddies weren't common up here as the jungle was thick hardwood trees for the most part. The Song Be River meandered through the area. About twenty minutes' flying time northeast of Song Be proper was an old Special Forces camp known as Bu Gia Map. This camp had been attacked and abandoned back in early 1966, along with a Special Forces camp at Bu Dop, and no one had been back. Both had abandoned dirt runways, and Bu Dop even had the remains of a couple of C-130 transport aircraft that had been hit with mortar rounds during the siege. While flying Night Hawk missions, we had noticed some lights up at Bu Gia Map but didn't have authority to go there on those missions as both camps were right on the Cambodian border. The camp was located at the maximum range of eight-inch artillery and outside the range of the 105 mm howitzer or the 175 mm howitzer, both of which had a faster rate of fire than the eight-inch howitzer. The first run of the day turned up nothing. No people, no monkeys, nothing. Since the Song Be River came down from the camp, I sat down with the sniffer team when we came back to refuel and eat.

"Hey, guys. Since we didn't get any hits in this area, what say we fly the road going to Bu Gia Map and see if we can find something up there?" I asked as we opened a case of C-rations for a morning snack.

"I don't know, Mr. Cory. We've never been up there, and it's really outside our box," the team leader mumbled.

"Yeah, but we're not getting anything down here. If we go up there and get some hits, then we will have accomplished something. And if we don't get any hits, then we just don't say anything to anyone."

"Where is Bu Gia Map?" he asked.

I pulled out the map and showed him where a dirt road had once existed that went from Song Be northeast to Bu Gia Map.

"Well, the bottom part of the road is in our area. We could run that again, I suppose," mumbled the team leader.

"We sure could," I agreed, thinking that once we were heading that way, well, who knows?

"Okay, let's run this area around the road." He pointed at the top portion in our box.

"You got it. Let's load up."

We started working the road moving northeast. The road was in the chin bubble, and Linam and Diedrich were on the guns as we were only low-level and sixty knots airspeed. At first we got nothing, and I continued to fly us north.

As we approached the end of the box, the team leader cried, "Max Mark," and the crew opened fire. Nothing came back at us. I told Lobo to hold off shooting.

"Chicken-man One-Niner, Lobo Three-Eight, over."

"Go ahead, Lobo."

"Where you going, Chicken-man? Are we out of the box?"

"Ah, Lobo Three-Eight, as we got nothing in the portion of the box but something right here at the top, I thought we'd move up a bit and see if we can pick something up."

"Roger, Chicken-man. Lobo is climbing to fifteen hundred feet. Got you covered. Out."

Lobo wanted to stay out of .51-cal range but still be able to cover us. I could see that coming, but he didn't object, and so we pressed forward. We hit a couple of more "Max Mark" indicators but took no fire, so Lobo didn't roll hot. Following on the map while Bruce flew, I could see we were approaching the old camp, which was on the south end of the runway at Bu Gia Map. To the west was a narrow valley about five hundred feet below the old Special Forces camp and runway. I told

Bruce to drop into the valley and run it to the north, thinking we might catch someone harvesting rice. The valley was empty. As we reached the end, I said, "I have the aircraft. Take a break."

"You have the aircraft." And Bruce pulled out a cigarette.

"Okay, we're heading back. We'll go over the camp and follow the road back south."

Coming around the end of the valley, I climbed up the ridge and popped up looking south right down the runway. On the left, Specialist Linam started shooting. The sniffer team leader let loose with a 40 mm round. Under the bamboo canopy on the edge of the runway was a regular village of NVA soldiers lying around. Some were in uniform, some lying in hammocks, some cooking chow. Tables were made out of bamboo, as were chairs. They were totally surprised, as were we.

"Lobo, on my left in the bamboo. Fire!" I screamed as I increased power and airspeed rapidly, staying low to the ground. I had never seen so many enemy soldiers before. As soon as I spoke, 2.75-inch rockets were slamming into the bamboo as NVA troops ran and dove for cover. Lobo was firing ripple effect, automatically launching twenty-eight rockets with just one pull of the trigger and punching the target. Then his minigun opened on the tree line on my left as we were hauling ass out down the runway. As we cleared the abandoned SF camp and runway, we stayed low-level until we were confident that we could climb to altitude and not get hit by a .51-cal machine gun. But something wasn't right in the feel of the aircraft. The cyclic felt stiff and was getting stiffer.

"Lobo, Chicken-man One-Niner, over."

"Chicken-man, Lobo, that was awesome." The excitement in his voice was noticeable.

"Lobo Three-Eight, we have a problem," I said, the

concern in my voice equally obvious. "My cyclic is stiffening up. I may have to put it down."

"Roger. Let me know what I can do."

"Linam, the cyclic is getting stiff. What causes this?" Linam was climbing from behind his gun and grabbing tools. We were at one thousand feet, flying straight and level. The master caution light and caution panel didn't indicate anything wrong, such as a hydraulics leak.

"Don't change course or move anything, Mr. Cory, until I can check it out." And he started opening up the floor panels. All the flight controls were push-pull tubes in the UH-1H, and they were all located under the floor panels of the aircraft, going back to the transmission well, where they turned upward to the rotor head. Only the tail rotor was operated by a cable attached at some point to the push-pull tubes. Linam had the panels up and was looking below.

"Mr. Cory, we have a problem. The housing for the push-pull tube is shot away, and each time you move the cyclic control, it's binding the rods."

"Can you fix it?" I was surprised at how calm I sounded when I was shitting bricks here.

"No, sir. I could hold the tubes up, but then I would be flying the aircraft from here," he said.

"Well, what do you suggest?"

"Slowly descend and find a clear area that we can do a running landing into. You might be able to raise the nose, but it will be a one-time move, not to be countered by attempting to lower the nose."

*Okay, I can do this*. Running landings were practiced, and the further south I flew, the better the terrain for this. A runway would be nice, but the closest was Song Be, and it was laid out east to west whereas I was flying north to south. *That ain't going to work.*

"Guys, start looking for an open area."

"What about the road?" Bruce said. He was now on his third cigarette since I had taken the controls. *Damn, he better save a couple of me*, I thought. In the distance, we could see a straight stretch, but the trees were close and the sides were lined with bamboo.

"It's going to have to do. I want everyone up forward and seat belts on. Linam, make sure everyone is strapped in tight." I explained to Lobo what we were going to do. He started making a mayday call for me, and right away I heard other aircraft responding to the call. He was giving my location and condition. We were approaching the north end of the box, and the road was in front of me as I slowly lowered the collective. Our descent began, but the airspeed remained the same, ninety knots. As we got lower, John pointed out, "We're going to be taking some tree limbs out."

"Nothing we can do about it now."

"Chicken-man One-Niner, Lobo Three-Eight, over."

"Go, Lobo."

"Chicken-man, I'm expended, but Blue Max has two aircraft about five minutes out to cover you. I'll remain on station until they contact you."

"Roger."

"Chicken-man One-Niner, Chicken-man One-Six, over." It was Mike George.

"Talk to him," I told Bruce.

"Chicken-man One-Six, Chicken-man One-Niner, go."

"Hey, got yourself in a fine mess this time. I have you in sight and will stand by. You get that thing stopped and get your ass over to my ship. I'm going to land right behind you. You got that?"

"Affirmative, Chicken-man One-Six," John came back.

As I got to treetop level with the road under the chin bubble, I started easing the nose up. Slowly the airspeed began to bleed off. Eighty knots; seventy knots; sixty knots;

and our speed continued to drop. We were slapping the tops of bamboo stalks now—twenty knots. Bamboo stalks were breaking and I could feel the main rotor buffeting as we hit thicker vegetation. I just didn't want to know what kind of vegetation at this point. *Just don't let us hit a hardwood tree trunk and rip the rotor head off.* At twenty knots, the skids touched the ground and we were sliding along, steering with the pedals to maintain a straight line. Broken bamboo was whirling about as if it was in a tornado. As the aircraft came to a stop, I was shutting the engine down while Linam and Diedrich had the guns in hand, with belts of ammo in their arms, and we were un-assing the aircraft as Mike landed right behind me. He didn't worry about tree limbs. One look at my rotor blades told him that I'd cleared out everything for him as if a giant lawn mower had passed over the bamboo field.

As Mike flew us back to Song Be, Diedrich asked the question that I knew was coming. "Hey, Mr. Sinkey, was that your first time shot down?"

Bruce walked into it. "Yeah, I've only been country a couple of months."

"Thank you, sir, you're buying the beer tonight." I considered if I should speak up as it was my first as well. Then Mike spoke up. "Hey, Cory, that's your first too, isn't it? There will be lots of free beer tonight, guys." I started to protest, but to no avail.

Blue Max had taken up a station over us and informed us that they would remain there until a recovery team was inserted from First Battalion, Ninth Cavalry. My aircraft was flown out a couple of hours later under a CH-47. One lone AK-47 round had hit the bottom of the aircraft. Oh, UH-1Hs could be such fragile things.

Back at the brigade TOC, I had to explain what had happened. When I was done, there was a long pause from the brigade commander. "What made you go up there, Mr. Cory?"

"Sir, I was seeing stuff up there on Night Hunter and thought it would be worth a look."

"And was it?" he asked.

"I think so, sir. You've got a major concentration up there just relaxing."

"I do too. Three," he said, meaning the S-3 operations officer, "let's get an air strike up there and see if we can't get a LRRS team in that area. Thanks, Mr. Cory. You have a ride home?"

"Yes, sir."

With that, my crew and I climbed into Mike's aircraft and went home. Feelings would not leave me.

# 28

## PSYCHIC

WHEN ONE EXTENDED FOR AN ADDITIONAL SIX months in-country, a free thirty-day leave was granted, to include a plane ticket to wherever in the world you wanted to go. Most guys that extended chose to go back to the States, but some went to Europe. Mom was a student at the University of Maryland in College Park. I thought I would just go home and hang with her for the duration of my leave. I would be leaving on my birthday in January, and the CO asked me to get one more pilot signed off as aircraft commander. I had three days before I was to leave. The night before, I had spoken with Roy about the upcoming mission.

"Roy, you good for tomorrow? I asked that we get a log mission and possibly an air assault as well."

"Yeah, I'm good." Roy was a man of few words, or maybe just a typical helicopter pilot, always brooding because you knew something was going to happen.

"We'll be taking my aircraft, and Specialist Linam is the crew chief if you want to go over anything with him tonight."

"Did maintenance get it back up today?"

"Yeah, they replaced the push-pull housing, two bolts,

patched the hole, replaced the blades. That was all they had to do. Pretty amazing that one bullet could have done so much damage. I'm going to turn in." And I headed for my hooch.

As usual, at 0500 hours, the ops clerk came and woke me up. Something wasn't right. I had that feeling of a weight on my shoulders. I shrugged it off as just being tired. I met Roy in Flight Ops, where we got the mission brief and headed for the aircraft. Specialist Linam was already there waiting for us along with Specialist Underwood. Seemed Private Diedrich was on sick call that morning, so Specialist Underwood was filling in for him. Underwood was a good kid who I had flown with on a couple of occasions over the past six months.

"Hey, guys, Mr. Blevins is the aircraft commander on this one today. It's his AC check ride. I'll be flying right seat. What he says goes today." I was pretty confident in Roy, so I was looking forward to a day of not being in charge for a change.

Mounting the guns, Specialist Underwood asked, "How you feeling today, Mr. Cory?"

"I feel good," I lied. "Why?"

"Well, sir, no disrespect meant, but word is that you're psychic—that you get these feelings and then your aircraft takes hits, like the other day and the day Johnson was hit."

"Well, to be truthful, I do have some feelings about today, but hey..." And I left it at that.

Linam and Underwood exchanged looks and started brushing off their guns again as Roy conducted and supervised the preflight. Once all was ready, we strapped in and headed north to Song Be. On the flight up, I quizzed Roy on flight procedures and what-if situations. He was nailing the answers, as I had known he would. I would have really been surprised if I'd tripped him up on anything and really wasn't trying to do that. He was a solid pilot.

When we reached Song Be, we refueled the aircraft and Roy went into the TOC and got with the S-3 air for a mission brief, as we were scheduled to work for the brigade, which meant we would be resupplying a couple of units. One was a Vietnamese airborne brigade that had recently been attached to the division and was operating in the area.

The S-3 air saw me walk in and asked, "Mr. Cory, they have you back in the air already?" He had been in the TOC when my ship was downed.

"Morning, sir. Yeah, and my aircraft is back up flying. Had to replace the blades, but that was about it. Mr. Blevins is aircraft commander today. I'm just along for the ride."

"I thought you were going home soon."

"I am. Three days and a wakeup, but I'll be back. I extended for another six months," I added.

"You're nuts!" And the S-3 air turned to Roy and commenced the brief.

Back at the aircraft, Roy laid the mission out to the crew.

"We're going to this firebase on the Song Be River to pick up an American advisor and a Vietnamese officer and fly east to this location, where the Vietnamese airborne unit is setting up a firebase. From there, we'll be doing some resupply missions. Any questions?"

There were none, and we cranked the aircraft and headed to the first stop. LZ Liz was set up on a small hill overlooking open areas and a view of the Song Be River, as well as the LZ where Johnson had been shot. Across the river was flat open ground for the most part for a quarter of a mile, then the hills started again. The sky was clear. Roy made contact with the TOC and I landed the aircraft. My concentration was momently broken when the 105 mm howitzer battery opened fire. Five guns going off at once tends to get one's attention. They were shooting towards the east, the direction we were going to go when we left. The TOC asked us to shut down the aircraft as someone wasn't ready to go. "Hurry up and wait" is a standing order for helicopter pilots and crews.

Sitting there, I also noticed that across the river on the edge of the LZ where Johnson had been shot, there was a small fire putting off white smoke. *Must be a unit over there*, I thought. Coming off the Razorbacks out of Tay Ninh one day, I had seen a small campfire putting up white smoke on the edge of a clearing. As I thought I knew the location of each unit in that area, I came in low and had the door gunners open fire. As soon as they did, green smoke grenades came flying out of the tree line. Shit! A US unit was there. I'd screwed up. Gaining altitude, we started to get out of there but decided to go back and see if we'd hurt anyone. Returning to the clearing and dropping in altitude, I made a slow pass. Out of the tree line came a soldier who gave us a thumbs-up. Everyone was okay. Lesson learned: don't shoot at campfires.

Finally a US captain with a MACV shoulder patch came out of the TOC and gave the *start it up* signal. MACV stood for Military Advisor Corps, Vietnam. He was wearing a soft cap, starched fatigues and spit-shined boots. Trailing behind him was a Vietnamese captain about half the US captain's size, wearing Ray-Ban sunglasses and starched fatigues as well. I was thinking these guys were Saigon warriors, and that was not a term of endearment or respect.

"Hey, guys, check out the perfume princess." I indicated with a flick of my head as I started the aircraft. Linam looked over his shoulder at them.

"Which one you talking about?" asked Underwood.

"Both, come to think of it," I responded.

Roy took the controls once everyone was strapped in. The artillery was still shooting in the direction we were going, so a decision had to be made. Would we take a flight that put us on the gun target line, or change our course and stay off the gun target line?

"We're going to go contour out of here, down to the river, and cross at treetop level. That'll keep us below the gun target line. Once across the river, we'll turn slightly south and get off the gun target line and climb out," he said. I said nothing. He was in charge and it sounded reasonable to me. You didn't want to be flying an artillery gun target line.

He pulled in power and we came up. Once we were airborne and heading for the river, the small fire was right along our flight path. We were eighty knots and right down on the deck. As we passed over the fire, I looked through the chin bubble and stopped breathing. Five guys in khaki uniforms were standing up in slow motion. Time had just stopped in my mind. They were raising five AK-47s. I thought they were going to shoot at me and only me as I was the only thing they saw. They didn't see the aircraft, but me passing over them. That was when the center console and all our radios exploded into pieces, just as Roy jerked the aircraft to the right. The sound of gunfire was deafening.

"I'm hit!" yelled Underwood. Roy was banking the aircraft towards Song Be.

"How bad?" asked Roy.

"Through my leg. The captain's looking at it." Suddenly my shoulder straps were being pulled and Linam was standing over me.

"Are you hit, Mr. C?" he screamed while patting my chest and shoulders. He had a first aid kit in his hand.

"What makes you think I'm hit?" Now I started checking myself out, thinking I might be in shock. Roy was attempting to make a radio call, but the radios were shot to pieces. The master caution light was on and the master caution warning was sounding, indicating some electrical problems. Engine and transmission oil pressure and temperatures were good, so no fear of the aircraft falling out of the sky.

"Sir, the way you were bouncing around in your seat, I thought for sure you were hit by several rounds," Linam said, backing up a bit.

"Shit, I was trying to swat those rounds away from me." I really felt stupid. I was attempting out of reflex to bat the incoming rounds away as if they were attacking bees. That had been close.

"Linam, are we trailing smoke?" asked Roy. He was about as cool as I had ever seen anyone under fire.

Hanging out of the aircraft, Linam said, "Sir, we have about four holes in the engine cowling that I can see, but there's no smoke. How long before we get to Song Be?"

"We're five out."

"In that case, we should be okay. Do we still have oil pressure? How's the temperature?"

"Pressure and temp are good."

"Roy, just keep your airspeed up in case the engine suddenly dies. If you can get some altitude, so much the better," I said. Roy knew what the hell he was doing, but I had to do something. As we approached the airfield at Song Be, an ambulance was waiting on the runway for us. Not really an ambulance, but a jeep with a stretcher in the back and two medics. Someone at brigade must have been notified from the battalion that we had taken fire and broken for Song Be rather than continue the mission.

"Guys, I'm coming in hot to make sure we can make the runway. Hang on." And with that, Roy dropped the nose and set himself up for a low-level autorotation. However, the aircraft didn't fail us but continued to fly just fine.

Once the aircraft was on the ground, I turned my attention to Underwood. I hadn't had much time with him, but he was a good kid from the Mississippi bayou. His wound would be a million-dollar wound with the round passing clean through the meat of his leg. No major arteries were hit, and no broken bones. Some skin grafting would be necessary, and that was his ticket home. As they loaded him into an ambulance to go over to the aid station, he waved me over.

"Hey, Mr. Cory."

"Yeah, you're going to be fine," I said as I grabbed his hand.

"I know. You be careful, sir, and trust in your feelings. You got something going with the spirit world. Someone is watching over you." With that, the ambulance rolled away.

Roy came over to me, and we walked to the TOC.

"You got a cigarette?"

"Yeah, I thought you didn't smoke." He pulled out a pack and offered one to me with a lighter.

"I don't," I said as I inhaled, "but I might just start."

Inside the TOC, the S-3 air met us, and Roy briefed him on the location of the shooters. The infantry battalion we'd initially stopped at had heard the shooting and watched us limp off to Song Be. They'd called and told the TOC what had happened, and already a scout team from First Battalion, Ninth Cavalry was on station and looking for them. In hindsight, it was a well-planned trap, putting up the small campfire as they had known it would attract someone to investigate, be it us or a scout team. We'd just happened to get there first.

Back at Lai Khe, the maintenance officer was not a happy camper. He now had another aircraft in for some unscheduled maintenance. The first sergeant wasn't happy as he had to get another door gunner. The only one happy was the CO, as I told him that Roy was more than ready to be an aircraft commander. Three days later, I left to come home.

Roy went on to be a fine aircraft commander and a bit of an icon in the company. A man of few words, he did make his presence known on one memorable mission. The mission was a combat assault that had turned to crap with both a hot LZ and a hot PZ. Aircraft were down in both, with the grunts pinned down in both. Our battalion commander, Lightning Bolt Six, was flying Chuck Chuck aircraft at twenty-five hundred feet, calling for more aircraft to support the lift. The infantry battalion commander was also up there with Lightning Bolt Six calling for more infantry and artillery support. Both were calling Yellow One with instructions that contradicted each other. To say the least, a lot of confusion was crossing the airwaves. Then the aviation brigade commander, Pouvoir Six, Colonel Merrill, suddenly came up on the radio and started giving instructions to Yellow One, in a panicked, almost screaming tone. Pouvoir Six seldom flew, had never flown in a combat assault, and did not know the first thing about being a flight leader. At his level, he managed assets and did not fight the battles. Yellow One was catching hell from everyone when the situation called for everyone to leave him alone and let him do his job. Suddenly everyone stopped talking for just a moment, except for this lone voice. "That's it, Merrill, blow your cool." You could have heard a pin drop. The world became silent. We never heard another word from the brigade commander, ever again, and calm returned to the mission. Roy had said it all.

## 29

## HOME

Landing at McCord Air Force Base outside of Seattle in January was a major change from the ninety-degree days in Vietnam. It was forty degrees when I stepped out of the plane to the awaiting bus. An overcast sky and light drizzle were present, as always in Seattle. I was in jungle fatigues that had the red clay dirt of Vietnam clinging to them, and I didn't care. I was back in the States.

The bus ride to a reception station was short. Most of the guys on the flight with me would remain at Fort Lewis, which was adjacent to McCord Air Force Base, and out-process from the Army as their enlistments were completed. Some would go on to assignments in Germany or the States, but most were being discharged. I figured I was going to be stuck waiting around for hours to get released. Was I in for a surprise.

As I walked into the reception station, a staff sergeant approached me and tapped me on the shoulder.

"Mr. Cory, welcome home." It was none other than a former classmate from primary flight school, almost two years ago. He had fallen down a flight of stairs one morning and dislocated his knee. They had taken him to the hospital, and we had never seen him again.

"What the—how the hell are you, Brad?"

"Fine, sir. I'm the NCOIC of this facility now."

"What happened to you? We lost track of you once they took you away."

As we walked to his office for a pot of fresh coffee, he explained.

"I got to the hospital and it was bad. They had to do surgery on my knee and put some pins in it. Told me it would be six months before I could get back in the flight program. We were already E-5s, and now I was a holdover. In the hospital, I got tired of sitting around and asked if I could do something. They had me help out in administration, and after waiting the six months, they said I wouldn't get back into flying because of the knee. I have limited range of motion. I couldn't go into the infantry, so they put me in administration, and since I already had the experience, they let me keep my E-5 rank. I made E-6 a few months ago and only have two more years to go before I can get out. I'll stay right here."

"That's great." And we swapped stories about who had and hadn't made it through flight school and who he had seen pass through his reception station. I mentioned a few that I had seen in the back of my helicopter. It was really good seeing him.

"But, sir, I'm sure you want to get going," he finally said. "Where's your next assignment?"

"Hell, my next assignment is right back to my old unit. I extended and am home on thirty days' leave."

"In that case, sir, you don't want to waste it sitting here talking to me. Where do you need to go?"

"I need to get to the Greyhound bus station in Seattle, where a friend's father is going to pick me up. I'm going to spend a couple of days with them in Monroe, Washington."

"Not a problem. I have a bus going there in about thirty minutes. You have a reserved seat on it. Let's get your stuff loaded."

Sitting in the front seat of a Greyhound bus moving down the interstate to Seattle was relaxing. Brought back memories of when I'd spent five days and nights on one going from Key West, Florida, to Coos Bay, Oregon, before starting my freshman year of high school. It was almost surreal watching cars going past us with civilians stressing out over traffic, or schoolwork, or fixing dinner. These people thought they had stressful, busy lives. The phrase that was engraved on my Zippo lighter came to mind: "Life has a flavor the protected will never know." They don't and won't.

Arriving at the Greyhound bus depot, I called Bill Michel's parents, and his dad said he would be there in an hour to get me. Mom and Pop Michel became like second parents to me. Bill's younger brother, Norm, was a senior in high school and one sharp young man. He was also a character. When we'd left to go to Vietnam, I had stayed with the Michels and had left my dress blue uniform and my class A greens with them. I needed to get my class A cleaned and the patches sewn on. I also needed to purchase some civilian clothes, since I had none. Norm took me clothes shopping. The clothing styles had changed dramatically in the two years that had passed since the last time I had gone shopping, from straight-leg pants and button-down collars to bell bottoms, wide collars and baggy sleeves. I wasn't impressed with the new fashions, nor was Norm. I settled on a few conservative items to get me going, as well as a warm jacket. I was freezing! After two days, Pop drove me over to SeaTac and I boarded a flight to Baltimore.

When I arrived at BWI, it was after 9:00 p.m. Mom was there, all excited with a gentleman. *Hmm.* After hugs and kisses, she introduced him. "Dan, this is Father Bob. He's a friend of mine." *Holy shit, she's hanging with a priest.* Mom was an attractive woman, along the lines of Sophia Loren: Italian, dark hair, slim figure. She also wrote letters to the Pope telling him how to run the Catholic church. When I was a kid, we lived in Naples for a time and Mom used to go to the horse racing track with Lucky Luciano, the mobster.

"How do you do, Father?" I extended my hand. He seemed nice enough, but what was going on? We went back to her three-bedroom apartment, and he excused himself and went home.

"So, Mom, what's up with the priest?"

"Oh, we're just good friends. He's considering leaving the priesthood and becoming a psychologist. He's studying at the university for his doctorate in psychology."

"Really! And am I his first patient?" I asked.

"Well, if you need to talk to someone, he'd be a good listener. Your dad needed to talk to someone when he came home from the Pacific but never did. How is he doing now?"

"Dad is fine and safe. He has a desk job at a very well-protected compound and a really nice set of quarters in Saigon." I didn't have the heart to tell her he was probably getting laid once a week by his hooch maid.

"How long are you going to be here with me?" she asked. *Boy, got off the Dad subject real quick, we did.*

"My leave is for thirty days. I really don't have any plans. Anything you want to do?"

"How about we take off after my last exam and run up to New York to see family? Your Aunt Joanie and Uncle Bill would love to see you, and so would your cousin Kathy. My last exam is the day after tomorrow."

"Yeah, sounds good. I do want to get over to Warrant Officer Personnel Branch and sit down with an assignments officer, but that's only one day."

"Oh, do you remember the Simmons? You met them in

Morocco. Their daughter is Mary. I was talking to Margie, and they would like to see you in Virginia Beach as well."

"Yeah, that might be nice to get back to Virginia Beach, see if it's changed any since we lived there in the fifties. Mary wrote to me a couple of times. I think she's in New York City still." I had met the Simmons when I'd visited my parents in Morocco, before I'd joined the Army and before I'd graduated from flight school. They had a daughter who was a senior in high school. I'd met her in church on my first trip to Morocco. We'd talked a bit, and I'd taken her for a ride in my parents' MG sports car. That was it. When I came back from Morocco the second time, I had a layover in New York and she came out to the airport to see me. She had graduated and was working in New York City at an accounting firm. She wrote to me a couple of times in Nam, I guess at the urging of her mother, who talked frequently to my mother, both being of Italian descent and both from Queens, New York. *See a connection here? Hmmm.*

Grabbing my third beer since I'd walked into the apartment twenty minutes ago, I said, "Mom, there have to be a couple of ground rules with me staying here."

"Okay, what are they?"

"First, I know how you are about waking me up. No coming up to me while I'm sleeping and kissing me. Stand at the foot of the bed and shake my foot, but otherwise no touching. Please."

"Okay, what else?"

"Make sure we have beer. That's it. Now I'm going to bed and sleeping for about twelve hours. Which room is mine?" And off to bed I went. Clean sheets, a flush toilet and hot showers. What more could a guy ask for from his mom? No, my mom wasn't a great cook, so I didn't ask for hot meals from her. She tried, but... Mom also couldn't follow simple instructions.

The air was cool and I was snuggled in warmth. There was no sound. The night was still. The blackness was all around me. I felt a presence penetrating my world. I reached for my sidearm ever so slowly, but it wasn't there under my pillow. God, they were coming closer. I could feel them. *Strike—strike now before it's too late!* And I came out of the bed with a roundhouse punch, smashing my attacker to the floor. Except it wasn't a VC sneaking up on me but my mother. She'd tried to kiss me good morning. She was lying on the floor and her cheek was starting to swell. Oh, someone was going to have a black eye.

"Damn, Mom, are you all right!" I asked as I finished getting out of bed and picking her up. "What the hell are you doing? I told you not to do that."

"Oh God, I'm sorry. I thought—"

"Mom, I'm a light sleeper and always on guard for an intruder. Don't sneak up on me. Damn, I could have really hurt you. Are you all right?"

"I'll be fine. Let me put some ice on it. Do you want some breakfast?"

"Just coffee." *She can't screw that up*, I thought, and she didn't. She got ready for school and left me in the apartment. Pretty nice setup. I turned on the TV, which was a two-year first. After coffee and watching *The Dating Game*, I decided to get out and walk some. Little did I realize that for the first couple of days, that would be my routine. Walking about in a college town was an experience in 1970.

Antiwar protesters were evident but not really antagonistic. I didn't reveal I was a GI and kept to myself. I was uncomfortable in crowds and avoided large gatherings. Quite coffee shops were my speed in the morning, and a local bar in the afternoon. Again, I got my beer and found a quiet place to watch a game or whatever mindless thing was on TV at that time of day. It would be nice if there was a channel devoted to sports twenty-four hours a day.

Mom was telling me about different students that she knew and thought I should meet. They were all girls, which was fine by me, but I never took the initiative to call any of them. She even attempted to hook me up with a young lady standing in the grocery store checkout line.

"Excuse me," she said to the girl's mother, "but you have a very attractive daughter." They both turned and looked at Mom. I grabbed the *National Enquirer* and kept my head down in embarrassment.

"Why, thank you," the mother responded. "Is that your son?" I looked up. *Way to go, Mom.* The daughter was now grabbing the *Reader's Digest.*

"Why, yes. He's an Army helicopter pilot, home from Vietnam and going back in three weeks. He doesn't have a girl-friend." *Crap, Mom, get your boyfriend over here and he can do the wedding right now here in the grocery store.*

The young lady was as embarrassed at this point as I was and grabbed her mother by the arm, but she did look back at me with a smile. Wonder what she was thinking. When we got outside, she was pulling out of the parking lot and flashed another smile. Probably thinking, *And with that for a mother, he isn't going to get a girlfriend either.*

Girls in the past had been trouble for me, and I really wasn't interested at this point. Truth be told, I had been dating a girl in college who had trashed my heart, and I had sworn afterwards that I would never again let myself be that vulnerable. Someday, maybe, I thought I'd like to get married, but right now, no thanks, not interested. Drink my beer and fly my helicopter—that was all I needed at this point.

Finally, we drove up to New York and stayed with my aunt and uncle. My cousin Kathy was a senior in high school and as pretty as could be. We hung out together a lot and had some good laughs. Some might think it weird, since I wasn't from the backwoods of Kentucky, where much older cousins could date much younger cousins, but I really liked Kathy. I would have liked to have dated her even, except for the fact that her dad scared the crap out of me. I didn't know why, because he was a great guy. I'd had a crush on Kathy since we were little kids, but that couldn't be, because they were from New York City and not someplace where cousins were allowed to date. Cousins weren't allowed to date in New York City unless you were in the Corleone family, and then you had to have the Godfather's blessing. Godfather Uncle Bill wouldn't give it, I was sure. So I drank my beer instead, and he drank my beer too.

Back home, Mom brought up the subject of Virginia Beach. "Why don't you get out of here and go down to Virginia Beach? The Simmons would love to see you," she nagged.

"Yeah, I might do that." Mom was starting to get on my nerves. I needed to get out. I was becoming very restless. It was only ten days into my thirty-day leave and I felt out of place, a boat without a rudder.

"I'll call Margie and tell her you'll fly down tomorrow. I can drive you to the airport." And she was immediately on the phone. Something felt odd about this. I hardly knew these people, although the last time I had seen them, at a party at the officers' club in Morocco, I was draped over the truck of my dad's MG, drunk out of my mind, asking them how their daughter was. They thought that was funny, I was told. I was too drunk to remember. I didn't have that much to drink that night, but the hundred-degree temperature had adversely affected me with what little alcohol I'd had. That was my story and I was sticking to it.

The next day, Mom dropped me off at the airport and I went up to the ticket counter to get a ticket. Quantico must

have graduated a bunch of new second lieutenant Marine officers, as they were in the airport with their Sam Brown belts.
Full of bravado, they were letting the entire airport know that
they were going to Vietnam and win the war. *Good luck, guys.* I
was now a chief warrant officer, having been promoted in
December. I had shaved off my immature mustache and still
had a reasonable haircut. I didn't stand out in a crowd, and I
was in civilian clothes. They ignored me. Good.

The flight to Norfolk, Virginia, from Baltimore was a
short hop. I got off the plane and walked into the terminal.
The Simmons' daughter was standing there with shoulder-
length blond hair, wearing a blue pantsuit. Damn, I thought
she was in New York.

"Hi, Mary!" No hug, no kissy.

"Hi, Dan, got any bags checked? How you been? You look
good." Small talk it was going to be.

"You do too." And she did. We headed to her car, a
Corvair Monza. The drive to her folks' house was more small
talk. She was no longer working in New York but at a local
radio station in Virginia Beach and going to school. But I
couldn't figure out what kind of school it was. When we got
to her house, her folks and one younger brother and sister
were there. They were in high school. This was a big family.
The oldest son lived in New York, having done four years in
the Army and a long tour in Vietnam, Infantry. An older sister
was in college at Shippensburg State. Her dad was a civil
servant with the Navy but had served in the Army in World
War II and seen plenty of action as a forward observer at
North Africa, Sicily, Anzio and finally at Normandy, where he
had been severely wounded, resulting in one leg being shorter
than the other. He was a quiet man; it was his Italian wife who
carried the conversations. He introduced me to whiskey sour
cocktails, and I have never had a better one than the ones he
made.

I spent a week there. Mary and I ran all over Virginia Beach, which had changed considerably since I was a kid when Dad was stationed aboard a submarine at the base. Back in the mid-1950s, the only hotel was the Cavalier Hotel, which sat about a half mile back from the beach. We would go to the beach in the winter and shoot .30-06 rifles at targets as the place was deserted. Now I was finding that from Fort Story along the entire beach was hotels and homes. At the very end was a restaurant called the Lighthouse, where all the tables were picnic tables, and for five dollars, you got all the boiled shrimp you could eat, poured out on butcher paper. Pitchers of beer were two dollars.

Grabbing a table and placing an order, Mary asked, "So why fly helicopters? Why not airplanes?"

"Since I saw my first helicopter, I've wanted to fly them. I was in the fourth grade, I think, or third, and thought it was so cool that they could hover and land about anywhere. I used to draw pictures of an OH-13 helicopter—you know, the one with the big glass bubble that the pilot sits in—landing on a lake next to a log cabin. That was my dream. I'd forgotten it until the chance to go to flight school came along," I explained.

"But you were in college," she stated with a puzzled look.

"Yeah, that was a worthless two years. I hated where I was going to school and really didn't know what I wanted to study anyway. I had been accepted to the University of Kansas School of Architecture and was excited about going, but that fell through."

"How come?" she asked.

"Seems that as I was getting ready to go, the principal of my high school told my parents that I would be lost at a big school like that and probably flunk out. So they stopped me and told me to go to Eastern Oregon. I hated it there."

"Why?"

"First, it was a teacher's college. I didn't think I wanted to be a teacher, at least not as much as I wanted to be an architect. Second, it was up in the mountains of eastern Oregon, and once the snows came, you didn't leave there, especially as I didn't have a car. Third, the town is a one-horse town. It's a wide spot in the road. The town really didn't welcome the college students, but sure liked our money," I explained.

"So why are you going back to Vietnam?" she asked.

"I can tell you I'm not going back to save the people of Vietnam. Those people could care less about us being there. They would be just as happy to see us get out. We, the South Koreans, and the Aussies are all there to help them, and what do we get in return? Rocketed, mortared and shot at. The Vietnamese will lie to your face and think nothing of it. It's their culture to save face, even if it means lying to you. Americans are so damn eager to have everyone like us, we'll believe anything and do anything for people. It's gotten us in trouble in the past and it will get us in trouble in the future. As far as I'm concerned, trust no one and do only those things that are in our national interest. I'm going back because we're running out of pilots, and the guy on the ground needs pilots willing to go the extra mile for him. He needs someone who will make sure to get the beer and mail in as well as the ammo. He needs someone that will put him first for a change and be there for him. Grunts have a shitty life, and doing anything I can do to ease it a bit for them is my intention."

"Don't you get scared? I mean, being shot at and possibly crashing or worse?" she asked.

"There are worse things than being shot. Fire is worse. The fear of all crew members. We're supposed to be getting fire-retardant two-piece flight suits, but they're only starting to arrive. That will help, but not prevent getting burned. Besides, you don't think about it. If you did, you wouldn't get in the bird. You think if something happens, it will happen to the other guy. You don't wish it on them, but that's the way you look at it. When the shit hits the fan, you're too busy to be scared, you just do your job. When you get back to the Chicken Coop, you drown your fear in beer. And the next day you do it over again."

Mary reached across the table and laid her hand on mine. "Just be careful," she said in a soft, almost pleading voice. Her eyes were speaking as well.

Mary was a good listener. She never judged but would listen and ask simple questions that got me to open up like no one else ever could. After a week, I headed back to D.C. We said we would stay in touch and she would write to me if I wrote to her.

Once I got home, Mom started in about how I should speak to Father Bob. "He's studying to be a psychologist," she told me yet again, "and he might be able to help you."

"Help me? What's this about? I don't need any help."

"Your father said you should talk to someone. You know, about Dave and your crew." Okay, the cat was out of the bag. Evidently I must have said something to Dad about the loss of Dave and the crew of my aircraft when the rotor head went to pieces. I hadn't told him about the two recent incidents. He in turn must have written Mom and told her something.

"Mom, I'm fine. I don't need to talk to anyone. I'm okay." Joking, I added, "Ah, Mom, we're out of beer."

"You're not fine! You're drinking too much. And why are you going back there? You've done your time."

"I'm going back because they need good pilots. We're short pilots with experience that can teach the new guys. And the grunts need good pilots. Now drop it!" Holy shit, it was time to get back to Nam. This discussion went on for another hour. Finally she agreed to drop it or I was going out the door.

The next morning, I decided to head over and see the warrant officers' personnel manager, located at Fort McNair.

Before I got dressed in my Class A uniform, I grabbed a cup of coffee and started to read the newspaper. One particular headline caught my eye. "Helicopter shot down 100 miles northeast of Saigon." Why would this be newsworthy when it happened every day in Vietnam? The article didn't indicate who was on the aircraft or what unit it belonged to. I had a feeling that it might have been one of ours, as that was the area around Song Be.

At the entrance to the Warrant Officer Personnel Office, a receptionist greeted me.

"Good morning, sir, how can I help you?"

"I'd like to talk to an assignments officer, please. I don't have an appointment." I gave her my name.

"Have a seat and I'll get someone. Appointments aren't necessary." And she headed off. Phones were ringing and old mechanical typewriters were clicking away. Around the corner she came with an officer in tow. I stood.

"Mr. Cory, this is Chief Warrant Officer Cummings," she stated.

"Hi, Mr. Cory. I'm David Cummings, but call me Dave." He extended his hand. He wasn't wearing his jacket, so I didn't know if he outranked me as a warrant officer, since all warrant officers were referred to as Chief after making W2.

"Morning, it's Dan," I responded. Little did I know at that moment that within the next hour, Dave Cummings would change my life forever. "Let's go back to my office. Want some coffee?"

"Yes, sir—ah, Dave, that would be great. Black, please."

"Black it is. Have a seat. Be right back." I settled in his office. "So what can I do for you?" he asked a minute later, handing me a mug of coffee.

"Well, I'm back from Nam on my extension leave—"

"Wait, you're still assigned to Nam and home on leave?"

"Yeah, and I was wonder—"

"Wait one and let me get your file." He stood and walked out of the room, returning a few minutes later with a file folder. He leafed through the pages.

"Give me a minute to look over your file." I kept my mouth shut and drank my coffee. I didn't know I had a file here. I thought all my records were in Nam, back at First Cav Division Rear in An Khe. He kept reading, finally looking up. "You have a pretty damn good file here, Dan."

"What?"

"You have a letter of recommendation for a commission from flight school as you were the WOC battalion student commander. Your officer efficiency reports are some of the best I've ever seen. Your awards are impressive."

"Dave, I've never seen that stuff. Officer efficiency reports —what do they say?"

"You signed them. You must have seen them."

"When I got to my unit, the CO had me sign a bunch of blank forms, but I never saw them once they were filled in. Can I look at them?"

"Yeah, look them over. Want some more coffee?" He rose to get another cup, and I started reading. Damn, I guess my platoon leader and COs were happy with me after all. They'd said some nice stuff in there about me. This letter of recommendation from the school brigade commander from my time as the student battalion commander was pretty nice as well. Maybe the ass chewings were worth something after all. My awards were just the standard stuff every pilot got, except I did have that Air Medal with "V" for pulling the Cobra pilots out, and a second Air Medal with "V" for covering some grunts with artillery fire.

Coming back, he handed me my coffee. "So what can we do for you?"

"I don't know. I was wondering what my options are."

"Let me ask you, what are your plans for when you come back?"

"I don't know. I'll probably go back to college. I'm thinking about applying to Georgetown and getting a law degree."

"Good option. How you going to pay for it?" he asked.

"I've saved, and I have the GI Bill."

"Why not stay in, and we'll send you to college? We'll pay you your normal pay and allowances as well as flight pay and housing allowance, and you can use your GI Bill to pay the tuition," he explained.

"Excuse me, you'll do that?" A bit surprised, I was.

"Yeah, we assign you to the US Army Student Detachment, you choose a university you want to attend and you go to school. Going to school is your job. You don't put on a uniform. And you still get all your pay and allowances. How does that sound?"

"I had no idea you would do that."

"Look, Dan. You have a great file. You could have a great future staying in the Army. We can send you to college. I can get you a fixed-wing transition. I could send you to the Aviation Safety Program, or the flight instructor program. You could even get a commission with this file if you wanted to become an RLO."

We talked for another thirty minutes. In closing, Dave said, "Look, when you have one hundred days left in-country, send me a letter and tell me what you intend to do. If you decide that you're staying in, I'll work with you to get to college or whatever you want to do, wherever you want to get stationed. Fair enough?"

I thanked him and told him he had certainly given me something to think about. As I walked out, I was pretty sure I had decided that I was going to be making the Army a career.

Doing what, I didn't know, but getting them to send me to college was the first goal and then we would see from there.

After another day of sitting around the house with nothing to do, I thought I would see the sights in D.C. *Wonder if Mary Simmons would want to come up for the weekend and tour D.C. with me?* Couldn't hurt to ask. So I called her. It was Wednesday morning, and I figured she could come up on Friday night. I would get her a plane ticket.

"Hey, Mary, it's Dan. How would you like to come up and tour D.C. with me?"

"Yeah, I could come up on Friday for the weekend," she indicated.

"Great, I'll have a plane ticket at the counter waiting for you."

"It would be easier and cheaper for me to catch a bus. I'll call you before I leave and tell you our arrival time. This will be fun. Thanks."

She arrived on Friday, and a weekend turned into five days in the city taking in the sights. Mary stayed at my mother's apartment. Mom was suffering with a horrible cold that kept her up all night coughing and sneezing with frequent trips to the one bathroom down the hall. I loved my mother, but she could be the most conniving, interfering, snooping Italian mother you had ever met. When Mary left, her departure at the airport was more than a kiss on the cheek. She promised to write, and she did, almost every day for the next six months. After a couple of more days, it was time to head back to Seattle for the flight.

## 30

## BACK IN THE SADDLE AGAIN, FEBRUARY 1970

THE FLIGHT BACK TO NAM WAS A REPEAT OF MY first trip, almost. I stopped at Mom and Pop Michel's house and spent a day dropping off uniforms and getting my jungle fatigues and boots out. Pop drove me down to Fort Lewis as he had done a year ago to send Bill and me off the first time. They were excited because Bill had extended as well and was coming home in a few days. Checking in at the terminal, I was placed on a flight that was leaving in a couple of hours, so I got comfortable. Two brand-new pilots came up and started picking my brain. They ended up picking my brain for the next fourteen hours, all the way to Nam. Upon landing, the first thing we did was brush our teeth. Some things don't change. The next morning I was back at the airport and started hitching rides that eventually got me back to Lai Khe. Walking into the club in the early afternoon, I got a beer and joined some of the pilots that were there, some old guys and a couple of newbies that had arrived while I was gone.

"Hey, I read in a paper back in D.C. that an aircraft went down. Was it one of ours?" No one said anything, but everyone looked uncomfortable. Finally one spoke up.

"Yeah, it was one of us." That was all he would say.

"Well, who was it? Did the crew get out? Everyone okay?"

"It was your aircraft, One-Nine. No one got out."

"What the...! What happened?" I asked, in total shock.

"They were on a resupply over a hover hole. The gooks opened fire on them on their third pass, and they crashed into the trees. Grunts said they made each of their three approaches over the same ground. They had five new replacements on board. The grunts got to the aircraft and were shooting gooks in the cabin and cockpit."

"Who was the crew?"

"It was Ash as AC, and a newbie, Taylor. Your crew chief, Linam, and Dietrich were on board too. Sorry," they told me. I didn't know the copilot, who had arrived the day after I'd left to go home. The AC, like all our guys, was a good man. He had just received a Dear John letter from his wife, telling him she was getting a divorce. I guessed she didn't need to now. I raised my glass, and they joined me. "To absent comrades."

"Hey, while you were gone, word came down that we're being awarded the Valorous Unit Award," Mike stated.

"No shit. What for?" I asked, pulling on my beer.

"Well, it was for that lift back in March that got all shot up. Evidently the Lobo Company commander put us in for it."

"Great, something else to hang on a uniform," I said.

The next day, I was back on the board for missions with a new aircraft—well, new to me—and a new crew. My crew chief was Specialist Lovelace from Louisville, Kentucky. He had curly blond hair and an accent that said "speak Southern," leaving no doubt about where this boy was from. He was a quiet kid with a dry sense of humor. *Kid*—he was nineteen and I was twenty-three, an old man. My new door gunner was Specialist Peters. Peters had a temper that I had to get in check more than once as he would flare up at the maintenance people if something wasn't right on the aircraft. It cost him a summary court-martial once, when I couldn't intervene quick enough as he went after the maintenance officer, CWO Dee. I was able to get his sentence for the reduction in rank suspended. The three of us quickly gelled, but the first month back was a bit rough.

Quickly, I began to realize that my touch wasn't what it used to be. The very first day, flying contour over a bamboo field, I hit the lone sprout that was standing ten feet above everyone else. Bam, and the chin bubble was busted out on my side. I was buying beer again. Not a couple of days later, setting down in an LZ, one skid was on a log and I bent the skid. Another case of beer. A week later it was a tail rotor strike. I started to realize that being gone over a month took the fine edge off one's ability to fly in these conditions. I had a talk with the CO.

"Sir, I've been back less than a month and I have to admit I don't have my touch back. I lost it."

"Hey, you'll get it back soon enough. I've seen this before. Hell, I was gone for a year and didn't have the touch I had when I left the first time."

"Well, sir, can I recommend that when an AC comes back from an extended leave, we put them up with another couple of hours before we put them back to full duty?"

"You can recommend it, but I'll have to think about it. Right now I need all the ACs we have."

The unit was continuing to support the brigade operating in the Song Be region and moving slowly towards the abandoned SF camps at Bu Gia Map and Bu Dop. The NVA were getting more active in the area and sliding eastward, resulting in longer flights just to get to the firebases to begin resupply missions. No new pilots had joined the unit, so everyone was flying every day, racking up a hundred and thirty to a hundred and fifty hours a month. And pilots were leaving as their tours came to an end after twelve months. Bill Hess, Mike George and Ralph put in for extensions but were on their extension leaves in February and March. If the unit had to move all its aircraft, some would have to be flown with just one pilot. Some ACs began training crew chiefs how to fly, at least well enough to make a running landing if necessary. Everyone was tired.

"*Incoming!*" screamed someone in the hooch. It was night, and I was asleep and dead to the world.

"Dan, wake up. We got incoming!" Someone was shaking me. We had no bunkers as we had when we'd lived in tents. Our hooches were lined on the outside with a sandbag wall about four feet high, so there was really no place to run to. You could lie on the floor, but that was about it, and what good would that do? If a hooch took a direct hit, then your time had come. A hit on the outside next to the hooch would be stopped by the sandbags outside, as the beds were only about two feet off the ground.

"Leave me alone. I'm staying here and sleeping," I said and rolled over.

As we rolled into early March, the shortage of pilots was taking its toll. The assistant maintenance officer found himself on the board to fly a mission. It was a log mission and he gladly jumped on it. Maintenance officers seldom got a chance to fly combat missions, stuck most of the time working on aircraft, supervising the maintenance or conducting test flights. He was flying with an inexperienced copilot, and they went into the Song Be to fly resupply for an infantry battalion.

"Mayday, mayday! Chicken-man Two-Seven is taking fire," came over the radio on our company air-to-air frequency. It was the copilot speaking.

"Chicken-man Two-Seven, Chicken-man One-Niner, what is your location?" I asked as I, along with most of our crews, was working the Song Be area.

"One-Niner, I'm ten klicks north of Song Be and heading for the airfield. I need medics standing by," he responded.

"Two-Seven, so you're not going down? What's your damage?" I asked.

"One-Niner, Dee was hit coming out of a PZ and is bleeding bad from his wrist and leg. The crew chief pulled him out of his seat and is stuffing the leg with bandages."

"Roger. What's the condition of your aircraft?" I asked again.

"One-Niner, all the gauges are normal. Over."

"Roger, contact Tower at Song Be and request medics meet you. The medic pad is in front of the tower."

"Chicken-man Two-Seven, Chicken-man Six, over." The CO was monitoring the net.

"Chicken-man Six, Two-Seven, over."

"Two-Seven, I'll meet you at the pad. How's he doing?"

"Chicken-man Six, he's sitting up. Looks pale, but he's breathing okay and talking."

"Roger, then let's clear the net. See you on the pad. Chicken-man Six out."

The bullet hole in Dee's wrist was small. The hole in his leg was large due to the fact that his watch was in his leg, carried there by the bullet. Dee came back to the unit after a month in the hospital in Japan. His wounds were sufficient to have him rotated back to the States, but it seemed that while on a pass one night from the hospital at Kishine Barracks, Dee got into a bar fight. He was arrested by the MPs and taken back to the hospital, and it was decided that if he could hold his own in a bar fight, he could go back to Vietnam. I had first met Dee on our first day in Preflight. He was a staff sergeant and had applied for flight school. A very quiet man, but someone always willing to help a fellow cadet. He wasn't married. Off duty, he stayed to himself.

Our maintenance operation was pretty good, but mistakes

should be expected. After all, these were helicopters that really didn't want to fly and only did so by man's manipulation of controls. Things would break once the aircraft left the flight line, and that was why a good preflight was necessary before the first flight of the day and any other time the aircraft was shut down. With Dee missing now, we noticed a slowdown in maintenance operations as the remaining maintenance officer, Captain Kempf, and one remaining assistant maintenance officer, WO Bob Young, could only do so much. In addition to aircraft breaking down, pilots were as well.

We needed pilots. The long hours were starting to take their toll on us. For days we were flying twelve to fifteen hours. Leaving the aircraft, our butts were actually sore, and we would wake up in the morning with them still sore and know we had another twelve-hour day ahead of us. The rule of a three-day rest after a hundred and forty hours in the past thirty days was being extended to a hundred and fifty hours, and then a hundred and sixty hours in the last thirty days. Doc was getting involved as pilots reported to sick call and it was apparent that sleep was the remedy. It got to the point that pilots were going to sleep in shifts while flying. Crew chiefs and gunners could sleep while we were flying, waking up just when needed prior to landings, but normally the pilots remained awake. If we were on a long flight, one pilot would catch a few minutes' sleep while the other flew.

It was a beautiful moonlit night with a full moon. We were flying back from Tay Ninh to Lai Khe, and I told my copilot I was going to catch a few minutes of sleep. This was the same lieutenant who'd shot the aircraft.

"Okay, I have the aircraft," he said.

"You have the aircraft." I locked my shoulder harness back so I wouldn't fall forward into the cyclic and closed my eyes. I was asleep in less than a minute. A feeling was invading my sleep. Something wasn't right. I opened my eyes but didn't move. All appeared normal. Slowly I turned my head and looked over at my copilot. His hands were on the controls but his head was tilted forward. Was he looking down at something? Oh shit, his eyes were closed! He was asleep. The crew was asleep in the back. This aircraft was flying with a sleeping crew. I didn't move but watched him to see what would happen. At first, nothing did. I slowly moved my right hand close to the cyclic in case he might jerk it in his sleep or over-react when he did wake up. We continued to fly straight and level for another fifteen or thirty seconds, and then a slight nose-low attitude began. He must have released some pressure on the cyclic to cause that. As the low nose attitude continued, we began to lose altitude and increase our airspeed. The sounds began to change with each increase in airspeed and decrease in altitude. And with each second, things picked up. Finally he woke with a startled look and began recovering the aircraft, looking over to see if I had noticed.

"Have a good nap there?" I asked.

"Oh shit, I'm sorry, Dan. I don't know what happened," he said nervously.

"I got the aircraft," I said.

"No, I can take it in. I'm really sorry."

"Hey, I got it. And don't beat yourself up. We've all been flying too much," I said as I took control of the aircraft.

Tuning the radio to our Flight Operations, I called, "Chicken-man Six, Chicken-man One-Niner, over."

"One-Niner, Chicken-man Six India, go ahead."

"Chicken-man Six, could you have Band-Aid Six meet us when we arrive in about thirty mikes? Over."

With some excitement in his voice, he asked, "One-Niner, do you need an ambulance on standby? Over."

"Chicken-man Six, that is a negative. Just Band-Aid Six. Over."

"One-Niner, roger, understood. Wilco."

"Chicken-man One-Niner out."

Addressing the crew, who were awake now, I said, "Guys, when we land, we're all going to see Doc. We're over a hundred and sixty hours for the month. Don't bullshit him, but we all need some sleep."

When we landed, not only was Doc—Band-Aid Six—standing there, but so were Major Saunders and the ops officer with the maintenance officer and my flight logs, the copilot's flight logs and the aircraft log. Major Saunders started the conversation as the aircraft engine and main rotor wound down.

"What's up, Mr. Cory?" This might not be good. He'd called me Mr. Cory.

"Sir, me and my crew are over a hundred and sixty hours for the past thirty days. We just flew back with all of us, me and the copilot, falling asleep at the same time. Sir, we need some sleep. I'm asking for a couple of days' downtime."

He looked away at the ground. I could see his mind spinning. Turning to the Doc, he said, "Doc, look at them and get back to me."

"Sir, I don't have to look at them. I can see from just watching them that they're in sleep deprivation, just like the other crews today." *What? What other crews today?*

The ops officer spoke up without being asked.

"Sir, Mr. Cory is over the one hundred and sixty hours for the past thirty days. Only one other pilot has him beat, and he's now down for a three-day rest. The other two are just behind Mr. Cory. We're running out of pilots, sir." I couldn't tell if he was pleading my case or trying to get me more hours. Then the maintenance officer jumped in, and honestly he looked more tired than us as the assistant maintenance officer hadn't returned from the hospital.

"Sir, this aircraft has been going hard for the past thirty days. We have an overdue hundred-hour inspection. We really need to ground it for a day or two." I thought he was supporting me. We were all still standing around the aircraft with the major thinking.

"How much time do you need for the hundred-hour inspection?" he asked the maintenance officer.

"I can get it in tomorrow afternoon and have it back up the day after, sometime in the morning," the maintenance officer responded.

"Dan, if I give you two days, would that be sufficient?" the CO asked me.

"Sir, if I can have one day just to sleep all day and night, I'll be good."

The major asked, "Doc, would that be sufficient?"

"If he gets to bed and stays there undisturbed and gets at least fourteen hours of sleep—no drinking, no reading, no writing letters, but fourteen hours of sleep—then I will clear him," Doc said, but I could tell he wasn't happy.

"Dan, get to bed. You and your crew are grounded for the next twenty-four hours. No drinking, no letter writing, no reading. Your crew chief won't pull the hundred-hour inspection, but maintenance will have someone take care of it." Addressing the maintenance officer and the ops officer, he added, "I want to see you two in my office with everyone's flight times and with aircraft status. Thirty minutes." And he walked off.

"Hey, Doc, what's going on?" I asked as we gathered our stuff and started to leave the Chicken Pen.

"You're not the first today to come in and report falling asleep. Three other crews came in earlier and the old man had to ground them. He put each of them down for three days. You just broke the camel's back. Tomorrow we'll have some more, I'm sure, coming in and reporting the same thing. We need some downtime for both the crews and the aircraft.

Taking only one day, you helped him out, but you need to get to bed." He walked off, shaking his head.

I climbed into bed and slept for twelve hours. When I woke, everything was strangely quiet. During the night, the CO had gotten with the battalion commander and explained the situation. Battalion ordered us to stand down for forty-eight hours, which would start the clock over on the thirty-day rule. Once the CO got that, he and the XO went around and informed the leadership that everything was to remain quiet in the company area for the next twenty-four hours. The club was closed and no one complained. There were to be no volleyball games, no card playing, and no drinking. Maintenance was working, but it was located at the Chicken Pen, so where the flight crews slept, we couldn't hear that noise. Maintenance was happy because now they could work on aircraft and get things done without being rushed. This down period made a world of difference in our morale.

# 31

## STAND DOWN

As I lay on my stomach in bed, half-asleep, the only sound was my fan quietly moving the air around my mosquito net. There were no other sounds, not even our rooster crowing, but the sun was already up. *Damn, I must have slept through the night. Surprised I didn't hear other crews waking up. Must have been more tired than I thought.* Groping on the floor for my watch, I managed to find it. *Crap, it's 0930.* I'd slept twelve hours and still felt like I'd been dragged through a knothole backwards. Crawling out from under the mosquito net, I heard snoring coming from elsewhere in the hooch. In my flippy-flops and boxer shorts, I headed for the company piss tubes. *Hooch maids won't be here yet, so can't embarrass them.* Going outside, I noticed that there wasn't a lot of activity in the company area. As I was relieving myself, the company clerk walked by.

"Morning, Mr. Cory," he said. "Nice day for a stand-down."

"What? Oh crap, we have a stand-down!" I replied with some surprise.

"Yes, sir. Battalion ordered us to stand down twenty-four

hours because of the number of hours flown. It looks like Bravo Company will have one tomorrow, with us picking up the slack, but today it's still us."

"No wonder none of us got a wakeup call," I said.

"The CO has a company formation scheduled for twelve hundred hours, and then the mess hall is cooking hamburgers, dogs and chicken on the grills for the afternoon. Sounds like party time," he announced over his shoulder as he walked off.

Back in the hooch, a couple of other pilots were just getting up and I spread the word for the company formation and afternoon cookout. No one complained about a stand-down day. Knowing the maintenance folks, however, they were already on the flight line and would be working for the morning to make sure birds were ready the next day as we would be picking up the load for Bravo Company, but they would knock off in time for the CO's 1200 formation.

At 1145 hours, my platoon leader was wandering through the hooch rounding us up. The CO didn't ask for much as far as formations went, so we really didn't mind attending. At 1200 hours, everyone was in formation when the first sergeant stepped to the front next to our company guidon.

"Company, attention!" he bellowed out, and we came to attention. Doing a smart about-face, he saluted the company commander. "Sir, all present and accounted for."

Returning the first sergeant's salute, he didn't tell us to stand at ease as was normally done but instead stated, "Attention to Orders. General Orders Number 203, Valorous Unit Award. The following award is announced. By the direction of the Secretary of the Army, under the provisions of Paragraph 202.1g(2), AR 672-5-1, the Valorous Unit Award is awarded to the following named unit of the United States Army for extraordinary heroism while engaged in military operations during the period indicated. The 227th Aviation Assault Helicopter Battalion distinguished itself by extraordinary heroism while engaged in military operations on March sixth, 1969, in Bien Hoa Province, Republic of Vietnam..." And he continued to read the entire citation.

When he was done reading, the first sergeant announced, "The following personnel, front and center." He called forward a couple of soldiers. The CO stepped up in front of the first soldier with the company clerk right next to him. The first sergeant continued, "Attention to Orders, Award of the Distinguished Flying Cross is awarded to Specialist Fourth Class Joseph W. Leonard for heroism while participating in aerial flight evidenced by voluntary action above and beyond the call of duty in the Republic of Vietnam on March sixth, 1969, while serving as a door gunner of a UH-1H helicopter with Company A, 227th Aviation Battalion (Assault Helicopter) during combat operations in Bien Hoa, Republic of Vietnam. After inserting a small combat party, the landing zone came under intense enemy fire. Realizing the need for reinforcements, Specialist Four Leonard's aircraft returned to the base camp and picked up the needed infantrymen. Returning to the contact, his aircraft came under heavy enemy fire while landing. Specialist Four Leonard provided accurate suppressive fire although wounded in the initial barrage of enemy fire. His actions helped immeasurably in the successful completion of the mission. His outstanding ability and devotion to duty are in keeping with the highest traditions of the military service, and reflects great credit upon himself, his unit and the United States Army. Signed Robert M. Shoemaker, Chief of Staff." The CO stepped up and, taking the Distinguished Flying Cross Medal from the company clerk, he pinned it on Leonard's chest. He then moved down the line and, with each reading by the first sergeant, pinned a medal on each soldier.

When done, the CO said, "At ease. You have every right to be proud of this accomplishment, even if you were not on the lift that day. The extraordinary action of these soldiers was accomplished by the support of every man in this company. Maintenance, they could not have been there without your efforts before the mission was even started. Company support, they could not have done the mission if you were not here to get them fed, get them up, and see that they had the right equipment. And flight crews, you demonstrated what it takes to take care of the grunts. My compliments, gentlemen. My only regret is that I was not your commander at that time. Battalion recognizes the effort you all put forth every day and has given us a stand-down today. We will be back in the air tomorrow, but for today, let's have a cookout. Company, attention!"

As we all executed the command, it was followed immediately by a second command. "Dismissed." And we scattered towards the smell of hot dogs, hamburgers and chicken on the grills.

# 32

## BAD DAYS AHEAD, MARCH 1970

COMMANDING OFFICERS IN VIETNAM ONLY SERVED
for six months and then were replaced. If you had a good
commander, this was unfortunate. We had a great commander
in my opinion, but he only had about another month left in
the unit. He set high standards and exercised sound judgment
and common sense. He never asked us to do what he wouldn't
do. We were flying our asses off, and he was right there with us.
You could tell by looking at him, as he was tired too.

The major was a flight leader and flew many missions as
Yellow One. Prior to his arrival, only commissioned officers,
RLOs, had served as flight leader. Unfortunately we were
getting so low on qualified commissioned officers that he had
to fly most of the combat assault missions. The unit was down
to the CO and the XO, the flight ops officer, and two platoon
leaders, of which only one was experienced and flight leader
qualified. We still had Lieutenant Dick Weed, who had been
promoted to captain but hadn't made flight leader as of yet
and was due to rotate back to the States within a month.
Something had to be done. And the CO did it one night at the
club.

"Mr. Cory, the CO wants to see all the pilots in the club. Now, sir," the flight ops clerk said, sticking his head in my room before moving down the hall to tell the other warrants the same thing. I was writing a letter, which I would finish up later. Along with the four or five others, I drifted to the club.

Once everyone was assembled, the major stepped to the front of the room.

"Sorry to get you all up, but we need to discuss something. Battalion says that we're going to keep flying the six-two flights. We can expect to be putting up at least twelve aircraft a day to meet the needs, with at least an additional five for log missions and ash and trash."

I could hear the maintenance officer moan and say under his breath, "Shit, that's seventeen aircraft a day. I'm not sure we can do that."

"Want to add something to the conversation?" the major asked, looking straight at the maintenance officer.

"No, sir," the maintenance officer replied, a bit dejected.

"I know this is going to be tough on the maintenance crews, but Division is stepping up the game with more mini-caves to be conducted. You guys have got to help maintenance out and not break anything as well as stay on top of your own aircraft. Preventive maintenance practices will go a long ways."

"Doc, how are the guys looking?"

"Well, sir, the stand-down did a pretty good job. Almost everyone got a good day's sleep, and if they only got fourteen to sixteen hours, then that's sufficient to revive them for a while. Looking at most of them, I believe a lot of them got around twenty-four hours in those two days' time. Even the crew chiefs look a lot better," Doc replied.

"Okay, then. The last issue we need to address, then, is flight leaders."

A small murmur was heard from the warrant officers, and a few chairs shuffled. We all suspected he was going to announce a new flight leader from the RLO pool. In the opinion of the warrant officers and mostly the aircraft commanders, none of the commissioned officers were a good choice for flight leader. A lot of potential, but they were new for the most part, either in their experience level or their time as AC. A couple just did not have the common sense to be a good flight leader.

"Brigade instituted the policy of only the commissioned officers being flight leaders. They are the tactical officers, while you warrants are the technical officers. The commissioned officers should shoulder the responsibility of tactical decisions. However, we're running out of commissioned officers and there are none inbound for a time. So I'm going to add two new flight leaders tonight. They'll fly with me for a couple of missions until I can sign them off. Any questions, Mr. Cory, Mr. Roberts?"

We both responded, "No, sir, no questions." *Why would I have any questions?*

"Good, then. Mr. Cory, you and I will have three lifts tomorrow and that should about do it. Mr. Roberts, you and I will fly together the day after tomorrow."

"Sir?" Mr. Roberts responded, looking at me and I at him.

"You two are going to be the next flight leaders. The policy about warrant officers not being flight leaders has changed. You will be our first if you guys want the assignment." All the warrants in the room were smiling and talking softly. My platoon leader was smiling, and while Captain Weed wasn't, he didn't protest, nor did any of the commissioned officers. I never knew if the major had spoken with them before the meeting or not.

"Yes, sir, I'll take it," I said.

And the next morning, I was back in the copilot seat, learning to be a flight leader. The major and I went to the brigade TOC, launching an hour ahead of everyone else to talk with the S-3 about the day's missions. Three combat assault and three extractions were planned. I took the briefing and all the pertinent information we needed. We then took off and flew out to each PZ and LZ, passing by and over at two thousand feet. He talked me through how to judge the size from that altitude so we put maximum number of aircraft into each on the first lift as well as determining the type of formation. He further showed me how to pick checkpoints to be at on the H minus six and H minus two mark. Arriving too early in the LZ wasn't conducive to morale as the artillery would still be shooting at the H minus two time hack. You didn't want to cross the H minus two checkpoint until you saw the white smoke, and you didn't want to be hovering over the H minus two checkpoint waiting for the white smoke. Arrive at the H minus two checkpoint too late and you gave the enemy time to come out of their bunkers and set up to shoot at us. Timing was critical.

The day's missions mostly went off with success. Some fire was taken on the second insertion, but nothing serious. A bullet hole here, a bullet hole there. Nothing that maintenance couldn't patch overnight. At the end of the day, we headed back to the Chicken Coop feeling pretty good.

"Okay, you're ready. You take a mission tomorrow, and I'll take the other with Mr. Roberts. I'll see you at the club, and you're buying," he said as we shut the aircraft down.

"Yes, sir, and I'll be happy to buy," I added. I dropped my gear off in my room and headed over to the club. Mike George was coming out of his room and asked if I'd heard that we had a new pilot come in.

"No, I hadn't," I replied.

"Yeah, I guess he's going to bunk in my room with me. His stuff was on the empty bed," he added as we walked through the door of the Officers' Club and bellied up to the bar. I ordered three beers, expecting the CO to come in shortly. As

Mike and I were talking, a hand reached around me to the third beer.

"Thanks, you're finally learning, New Guy," this guy said. Mike and I both turned to see who this asshole was, talking to two old ACs in such a disrespectful tone. The look on my face told Mike I knew the guy.

"Lou, what the hell are you doing here?" I said as I wrapped both arms around him in a hug.

"Hey, people will talk!" He backed away.

"What are you doing here? Oh, Mike, this is Lou Price, the guy that taught me to fly."

Shaking Mike's hand, Lou said, "I got tired of the stateside bullshit at Mother Rucker, so I volunteered for coming back here. Did you miss me?"

"Shit, we missed you. It's great to see you." And we started to play "what happened to so and so?" Soon the major came in looking for his beer. He hadn't met Lou yet.

"Sir, here's your beer"—I pointed to the beer in Lou's hand—"and this is Mr. Price, the guy that taught me to fly."

"Well, Mr. Price, welcome back to the roost, and thanks for nursing my beer in my absence. You're buying," the major said while shaking Lou's hand and smiling. "Good to have experience in new pilots. What have you been doing since you left us?"

"Sir, I was a flight instructor at Mother Rucker. Decided it was safer flying back here, so I dropped my paperwork to come back. I guess they wanted to get rid of me, because it was approved in less than thirty days."

"Good. You're familiar with the AO, then, as you've only been gone, what, eight or nine months?"

"Actually, it's been ten, but who's counting?"

"Okay. What say you take a couple of missions as a copilot to learn the Song Be, Bu Dop, Bu Gia Map area, and then we'll put you in as an AC? Sound okay to you?"

"That will be fine, sir," Lou responded, taking a long pull on his beer and ordering another for all of us. Some of the older ACs that were getting ready to rotate home came over and expressed their condolences to Lou for coming back, but all in good humor. He told them what they could expect going to be flight instructors at Mother Rucker or one of the other two locations. He advised them to reconsider extending, but they were married and had other commitments, if they wanted to stay married.

# 33

## THE IDES OF MARCH

Ops woke me at 0430 hours in the morning so I could launch early. Something wasn't feeling right about the missions, and I asked Lovelace and Peters if everything was in order.

"You feeling okay, Mr. Cory?" Lovelace asked.

"Yeah," I lied. "Why?"

"We've heard about you and your feelings. Every time you've had one, your aircraft has taken hits. You sure you're okay?"

"Okay, I'll be honest. I got a feeling about today. It's nothing. Superstition," I said.

After a thorough preflight and crew brief, we were off and got up to Song Be for the morning briefing. When I walked in, the brigade commander was there and asked where the flight leader was at.

"Sir, I'm flight leader today," I told him.

"Well, are congratulations or condolences in order, Mr. Cory?"

"Depends on how I do today, sir."

"I'm not worried about it. You've been flying long enough

and worked this area enough to know what's what. Three, get on with it." The S-3 took over the morning brief and I was taking notes. After the brief, the S-2 intelligence officer came over.

"Hey, Mr. Cory, let me go over a couple of other things. We have indications that some antiaircraft .51-cals may be in this area, which you may want to consider in your flight planning." *Ya think so?* He pointed at the map. "In addition, we have some indications that the gooks are moving down from the north in this area and towards the last LZ you'll be inserting into. I hope to have more concrete intel later today on that." He had been pointing these locations out on the map, and I jotted them down as well.

Getting into the air, we did a high recon of the three LZs and PZs, and I made my decisions on formations, direction of landings and checkpoints. The flight joined up with me as I was refueling at Song Be, and we departed for the first mission. All went well and it was routine. The second mission went off equally well.

"Rattler Six, Chicken-man One-Niner, over."

"Chicken-man One-Niner, Rattler Six India, go ahead."

"Rattler Six, Chicken-man inbound for pickup. Six pax per aircraft, and I have six aircraft. Staggered right formation."

The ground commander already knew this information, but I thought it was best just to confirm it. No need for confusion on the PZ in case someone didn't get the word. Rattler Six was talking not only to me but also his battalion commander, who was in a command-and-control aircraft at twenty-five hundred feet with the artillery fire coordinator on board as well. As we were coming out of the PZ, I received an H minus six time hack and the artillery began impacting on the LZ. At ninety knots airspeed, we would hit the H minus two checkpoint right on time, and we did. At H minus two, a white phosphorous round impacted on the LZ, indicating the artillery was done shooting and the Cobras were cleared to roll hot. At H minus one, the door gunners opened fire, concentrating on the tree line. As we touched down, the grunts started off the aircraft. That was when a sledgehammer hit the side of the aircraft, one, two times, and then I lost count. The engine started winding down. The rotor rpm immediately started dropping as the engine rpm went to zero.

"We're taking fire!" screamed Peters. It was on his side of the aircraft, and it was concentrated on our engine. His gun was ripping through ammunition.

"Get out!" I yelled. And we began un-assing the aircraft. Chalk Two was leading the rest of the flight out. We were now on the ground with the grunts. Peters was on his M60 machine gun until I told him to get down. No need for him to sit in the gunner's position and be a target. To his credit, he did and took his gun with him, dragging ammo as well. Specialist Lovelace was doing the same. The Cobras were coming around for a second pass and using the remaining rockets and 40 mm ammo that they had. Rattler Six was on the ground next to me and began calling for artillery support. As the second flight came into view, the artillery silenced the antiaircraft gun that had worked us over as well as the small-arms fire that was coming from the trees. We remained in the LZ until the third lift and jumped on an aircraft to get out. Already the battalion commander had notified brigade that an aircraft was down in the LZ. A recovery team was getting ready to come get the aircraft and fly it back to Lai Khe under a CH-47. A new engine would be installed that night, and that aircraft would be flying in the morning, hopefully.

Flying back, Lovelace turned to me. "Damn, Mr. Cory, you're psychic with your feelings."

I said nothing as it was starting to bother me that each time I woke with the feeling, the day ended badly.

Two days later, the Ides of March were upon us. It started

out as a stand-down day for me, until the ops clerk came into my room.

"Mr. Cory, they need to crank and get up to Song Be. Your crew is already getting the aircraft ready."

"Okay, what happened?"

"Not sure, sir. The old man called and said to get you up there ASAP."

"Okay." I picked my gear up and headed to the flight line. The crew had everything ready to go, so off we went, not knowing what was in store for us. As we proceeded, I called Chicken-man Six for instructions.

"Chicken-man Six, Chicken-man One-Niner, over."

"One-Niner, Six, go ahead."

"Six, One-Niner is off Lai Khe for Song Be. Over."

"Roger, meet me at the tower. Shut down after you refuel and I'll brief you. Six out."

Sort of surprised me that he didn't give me a mission brief en route to Song Be, but he was the CO and could do as he liked.

After we arrived and refueled the aircraft, I hovered over and shut the aircraft down. He was already there waiting for me. Even before the rotor blade stopped, he motioned for me to get out. Letting my copilot finish the shutdown, I got out and approached him. He didn't look happy.

"You got something for me, sir?" I asked. He motioned for me to follow him.

"Yeah, I have a job for you to do. No one else needs to do this." We continued to walk across the firebase and entered the first aid/medical tent. The CO asked a medic, "Where is he?"

"Out back, sir."

We stepped out the back of the tent, where there was another GP Large tent with the sides rolled up. Inside, four empty cots were set up. Mr. Fender sat on one of them, a bandage on his knee. Lying on the ground in front of him was a black vinyl bag, commonly referred to as a body bag. Bob Young was occupying the bag.

"Are you okay, Ron?" the CO asked, placing his hand on Ron's shoulder.

"I will be, sir," Ron responded. I just stood there.

"What happened?" the major asked.

Still staring at the black bag, Ron started to explain. "We got a call that Sinkey's bird was down with a transmission chip light. Bob was called to take a look at it. When he heard Sinkey was needed for a lift, Bob volunteered us to take Sinkey's place. We called Flight Lead, and he told us to take Chalk Three position and said that Flight Lead would meet us at LZ Ann.

Once all six aircraft were assembled at LZ Ann, Yellow One started his mission brief. We had ten sorties, so we would do two turns. These are ARVNs, so we were taking eight grunts in each lift. Formation was staggered left. The bad news was that it was only a three-ship LZ, so we went in with a two-minute separation between Three and Four." Ron paused and took a deep breath.

"Lobo's two Cobras were on our flanks. As artillery and door gunner suppression was used, the only aircraft to take fire on the insertion was Yellow One. The operation was moving smoothly for the first lift and the second, Chalk Four and Five. The grunts were fanning out on the LZ. As the first three aircraft on the second turn began to take off, out of the tree line—*boom!* An RPG rocket streaked toward us, striking the left front side through plexiglass and exploding on the front of transmission wall, blowing the crew chief and door gunner out of the aircraft. Because of our armored seats, Bob and I weren't seriously hit, although his leg was messed up and some bone fragments hit me."

Ron raised his arm with a bandage wrapped around his forearm. He went on to explain, "The aircraft dropped five feet as hydraulic fluid and transmission oil sprayed everyone.

Bob immediately reached over and cut off the fuel flow switch. I flipped off the battery switch and we started to get out of the aircraft." Taking another deep breath, Ron continued.

"Lobo had been in position above the flight to see the round as it was fired and rolled in with rockets, impacting the point of origin. I used the door jettison handle and the door flew open. I literally dove out the door to the ground and low-crawled as fast as I could away from the aircraft and into a bomb crater. Bob jumped out as well. I lost sight of him as I was in the bomb crater. After some time, I found out Bob hadn't made it but was killed sometime after he left the aircraft. After about thirty minutes, Lieutenant Hicks returned to the LZ and picked us up. That's about it, sir."

"Okay, well, you fly back with Cory." Turning to me, he said, "Dan, take Bob to Phuoc Vinh. You know where the graves registration pad is, don't you?"

"Yes, sir. I've been there a few times over the last six months."

"When you've dropped off Bob, take Ron back to the Chicken Coop." Taking me aside, away from Ron, he added, "There's a bottle of scotch in my hooch cabinet. Give him some and stay with him."

"Yes, sir. Will do." We all took that one hard, considering that from January of '69 until the loss of Hanna and YA, we hadn't lost a crew in combat, and now in the last five months we had lost three crews and had several wounded. Sinkey took it very hard as Bob Young had been his roommate. The NVA were stepping up their game.

# 34

## BOMBING RUNS

SELDOM AS A SLICK PILOT DID YOU GET TO REALLY hit back at the enemy unless you were flying Night Hunter Killer. When an opportunity presented itself to do so, you took it. My flight school stickmate, Chief Warrant Officer 2 Bill Michel, had been flying VIPs since joining the division. He hadn't flown in a combat assault or a log mission or Night Hunter Killer. He'd been flying for the division commander and the assistant division commanders, which didn't get into the thick of things. Bill wanted to get down with us and fly some combat missions. I went to our CO and asked if it would be okay to take him for a day, and he agreed. With Lovelace in the copilot seat, we flew over to Camp Gorvad and picked Bill up. Lovelace was like a little kid with a new bike. He did not want to get out of the copilot seat when we landed.

"Morning, Bill," I said and introduced him to the crew. "This morning, we're going to Song Be and LZ Judy. We'll be working for First of the Eighth Infantry, doing log resupply and a combat assault in the afternoon as well as anything else they want us to do. You have the aircraft."

"I have the aircraft," Bill said and applied the power, heading for Song Be. As we arrived over LZ Judy, I called the TOC.

"Wrangler Six, Chicken-man One-Niner, over."

"Chicken-man One-Niner, Wrangler Six India, go ahead."

"Roger, Wrangler Six, we're en route to your location. Over."

"Roger, Chicken-man One-Niner. Someone will meet you on our log pad. Shut it down and come up to the TOC. Over."

"Roger, Wrangler Six, Chicken-man One-Niner standing by."

To my crew, I said, "Okay, guys, when we get there I'm shutting down and heading up to the TOC. Any questions?" There were none, and we did as instructed.

Bill and I walked up to the TOC and were met by the battalion operations officer. "Mr. Cory, how ya doing?" I had worked for this unit before and found the battalion commander and ops officer to be very outgoing and energetic. The battalion commander had a red bow tied on the back of his helmet. Guess it reminded him of home. Never asked. I introduced Bill to them.

"How do you feel about dropping bombs?" the battalion commander asked.

"Sir?" I asked, not sure if I'd heard him right.

"How do you feel about dropping bombs?" he repeated.

"Sir, we really don't have the capability to drop bombs."

"Well, if you did, how would you feel?" He had this smile creeping across his face.

"Yeah, I guess I'm all for it," I answered, looking at Bill and he at me.

"Good, we're going to have some fun," he said, and he turned to the S-3 and told him to have the aircraft loaded.

Walking me and Bill over to a map, he pointed out a known river crossing over the Song Be River.

"I don't have any troops near here, but I want Charlie to think we do. So, we're going to drop a couple of bombs here, here and here. We'll drop four bombs at each location. I need you to fly at two thousand feet and ninety knots. When you can see the target through the chin bubble, you say 'drop.' When the target's at the top of your pedals, give me another 'drop,' and when it's at the bottom of the pedals, you give me the last 'drop' and we release. Drop, drop, drop. Just about that fast. Any questions?"

"Sir, my aircraft can't carry that many bombs. Our lift capability is only about two thousand pounds, and we aren't big enough to put that many in the aircraft." The old man had gone crazy, I thought.

"Trust me, Mr. Cory, your aircraft will handle this load easily." He was still smiling. "Let's go out to the aircraft."

As we approached, I saw Lovelace and Peters standing off to the side, watching four grunts loading and strapping a wooden box into the aircraft door. The box had two legs on the inside of the aircraft, which was tilting the box at a forty-five-degree angle with the lower end hanging slightly out the side cargo door. The box was only about six inches deep, two feet wide and four feet in length. On the side hanging out the door was a trapdoor that allowed the entire side to open.

"This, Mr. Cory, is your bomb bay, and these are the bombs."

He held up an 81 mm mortar round. The round had a piece of narrow cloth about six feet long wrapped around the tail fins and an aerial bomb fuse in the nose. The aerial bomb fuse had a small propeller that spun as the bomb was falling and, after so many revolutions, armed the bomb.

"We will stack the bombs in the box. On the third drop,

we open this door and they start falling out. As they fall, the tape comes off and points the bomb downward so the nose is the first to impact the ground. The aerial bomb fuse activates the bomb after one thousand feet. Any questions?"

I was standing there looking at this jury rig, assessing it to make sure it was safe and secured. I didn't want it falling out of the aircraft, and I didn't want those aerial fuses spinning while in the aircraft and arming the bombs. After a minute, I had only two questions. "Sir, who's going to operate this, and when are we going?"

"Good. Let me get my stuff and me and the S3 will be on board." And with that, he and the S-3 turned and headed to the TOC.

Bill looked at me. "You do this shit often?"

"Bill, this is a first for me. Lovelace, Peters, how do you guys feel about this?" I asked.

"Hey, sir, we're good," Lovelace answered for both. Peters just nodded.

"Okay, then, let's get loaded and ready."

As we were loading ourselves into the aircraft, the battalion commander and S-3 joined us and we cranked the aircraft. When all was ready, the crew gave me an up, and we departed the LZ and headed for the first target.

"I'll take the first target and you have the next two. Okay, Bill?"

"Yeah, fine by me. You screw it up, then I'll redeem us," he answered with a smile.

"Lovelace, I want you to tell me how this thing works on the first pass and check out where they're impacting. Bill, we don't have much wind if any, so I doubt if we need to worry about compensation for that in the drop."

Approaching the location, I informed the battalion commander that we were at two thousand feet and ninety knots. He had been following our ground path on his map and was leaning forward, looking out the door at the target area coming up. His hand was on the release. I was concentrating on lining up so I could see the target through the chin bubble.

"Drop," I said as it appeared in the chin bubble. At ninety knots, it was actually three quick "drops."

"Drop. Drop." And with that, the door opened and four 81 mm mortars rolled out.

"Sir, the tape is coming off the tail fins and they're all nose down," Lovelace said. Ten seconds later, the sound of four impacting explosions was heard.

"Bull's-eye," said the battalion commander. "Let's get the next one."

"Bill, you have the aircraft."

"I have the aircraft."

"Turn to a heading of one-three-five and maintain two thousand feet and ninety knots."

"Roger." Bill lined us up and we repeated the bomb run, as we did on the third target as well. I was sure the grin on his face couldn't be removed for the next couple of days. And the day was just beginning.

Getting back to the LZ, we dropped the battalion commander and S-3 off and unloaded the aircraft. Once unloaded, we headed for Song Be to take on fuel and then returned to the LZ for the day's missions. Bill wasn't disappointed. He hadn't flown in formation since flight school nor a combat assault since arriving in Vietnam, so he had difficulty holding position. We were given the Chalk Two position. Naturally the other crews, not knowing my situation and thinking that I had a newbie as a copilot that day, were unmerciful in their comments about his flying ability. I was in instructor mode the whole time. He also got to work in a couple of really good hover holes, which, flying the brass around, he didn't get an opportunity to do either. When we reached Camp Gorvad that night after a ten-hour flight day, Bill thanked the crew. It was the last time I ever saw or spoke to my friend.

# 35

## THE HELLHOLE

WHEN YOU WERE CONDUCTING A RESUPPLY MISSION, a good load that was efficient for the trip but left you enough power to maneuver at a hover was thirty of the five-gallon water cans. These would go in on the first trip so that you could adequately judge the conditions affecting the hover hole and so the grunts could fill canteens while you delivered the rest of the supplies and on the last trip, take the empty water cans back out. Generally for a rifle company, it would take three trips to get all their nightly resupply in to them. Water, food, ammo, mail, beer and soda. The last two items were just as important to the grunts as the first two. These guys had few pleasures in their lives, and a letter from home and a cold beer after a long day of humping a rucksack did wonders for morale.

We had been working the Song Be area for one infantry battalion, but around noon we got a call to break off from our resupply mission and join up with two other aircraft from our company at Song Be along with a flight from our sister company. The sister company commander was flight lead, Green One. The company commander had a reputation and was making a name for himself, one that our unit didn't think too highly of. On the few occasions that I had been around him, it appeared that he had his nose so far up the senior officers' asses that he was being oxygen deprived. But, hey, I was just a warrant officer pilot. What did I know? When we joined up with him, he informed us that we were going to be part of a twelve-ship lift and the Chickenman birds would be the last three chalks. As it was twelve ships, there would be two turns and then we would be released to resume our previous missions. Okay by us. The less time spent with this guy, the more we liked it. Formation would be staggered right.

The initial insertion was uneventful, as was the subsequent insertion. As we were following the flight back to Song Be to refuel before we were released, we were flying low-level, still in a staggered right formation. Looking out ahead, I noticed that we were approaching a known river-crossing site and there was brownish smoke drifting up from the trees. The same appearance as if artillery had recently impacted the location.

"Green One, Chicken-man One-Niner, over."

"Go ahead, Chicken-man."

"Roger, there appears to be some artillery impact recently up at those rapids on the river up ahead. Have we been cleared by Arty?" At ninety knots, we were approaching the spot quickly.

"Chicken-man, Chalk Two handled the clearance. We're good." His tone told me he wasn't happy with me questioning him about this. It was standard procedure in the division that Chalk Two got clearances from Arty.

"Roger, Green One," I said. His aircraft was over the smoke now and the flight pressed on. We were coming up on the spot rapidly as well.

*Kaboom. Kaboom. Kaboom. Kaboom. Kaboom. Kaboom.* Six artillery rounds impacted directly under our aircraft, and I was over it with my two teammates. Six 105 mm rounds impacting all around and under us! Shit!

"Green One, Chalk One-One, we've been hit. Master caution looks like a fucking Christmas tree. You took us through a damn artillery strike, you son of a bitch." It was Lou.

"Chalk One-One, maintain radio silence."

"Radio silence my ass, you son of a bitch. Shit."

No comment from Green One.

"Chicken-man One-Two, Chicken-man One-Niner."

"Go ahead."

"You okay?"

"Yeah, but we're going to have a hydraulic problem, and some of the electrical is messed up. The bird's flying, but I'm leaking fuel as well. I'm going to kick his ass when we get down. You asked that son of a bitch if we were cleared. Damn his ass."

"Chicken-man Two-Three, are you okay?" I asked.

"I'm good but have a busted chin bubble," Chicken-man Two-Three came back.

"Chicken-man aircraft, stay off the net. You are released, Green One out."

"Screw you, Green One. I'll see you on the ground." Lou was pissed and had every right to be. We all had a right. If one of those rounds had hit a rotor blade, there wouldn't be any pieces of the aircraft left. All three aircraft could very easily have been blown out of the sky in an instant. We were all pissed, but Lou especially. We followed the flight into the refuel point, and as soon as we touched down, Lou was out of his aircraft and heading for Flight Leader's aircraft.

"Mr. Price, stop right there," a voice bellowed. It was our company commander, who, although not in the flight, had heard the whole thing on the radio and was also refueling his aircraft. Lou turned and stared at him.

"Sir, that pompous son of a bitch took us—"

"I know, I heard, as did the rest of the division. Let me handle this." And the major walked past Lou and towards Green One's aircraft. Lou started to follow. Turning on his heels, the major told Lou to go back and look after his aircraft, which was leaking fuel. We didn't know what was said as the two commanders walked away from everyone, but our CO was jabbing his finger in Green One's chest and close to his face. Green One was attempting to make it a two-sided conversation, but Chicken-man Six wasn't having any of it. For the next two months, that commander kept a low profile, and no one from any other unit would fly with him.

Released from the flight and refueled, we headed back to our resupply mission. We were already behind schedule, as it was now later in the afternoon. We had one more unit to get supplies to before nightfall. No problem, three turns and we would be easily done before dark. When we got to the log pad, thirty water cans were ready to be loaded along with everything else, to include twenty cases of C-ratios, five boxes of ammo, one mailbag and two mailbags with soda and beer. Piece of cake.

"I'll take us in the first time and you get the second. Any questions?" My copilot was really new. WO1 Fairweather had only arrived a couple of weeks before and had one resupply under his belt. He was older than most of us, having been a sergeant first class when he'd applied for flight school. We called him Grandpa because of his age. Hell, he had gray streaks in his hair as well as his mustache, and a mighty nice mustache it was.

"Naw, I'm good," he said, and I took off with thirty water cans. We had a slight breeze blowing that day, but not much. Trees in the area were about two hundred feet high. Flying out to the company, I contacted them on the radio.

"Dog-meat Six, Chicken-man One-Niner, over."

"Chicken-man One-Niner, Dog-meat Six India. Over."

"Dog-meat Six, Chicken-man One-Niner is inbound to your location. Pop smoke."

"Roger, Chicken-man, smoke out." We started looking for smoke that would give me their exact location. Grandpa saw it first, but we didn't see a place to land. As we made a pass over the smoke, Grandpa said, "I have someone on the ground."

"Dog-meat Six, I have green smoke."

"Affirmative, Chicken-man."

"Roger, coming around," I answered back.

"Grandpa, you saw someone on the ground?" I asked him.

"Yeah, next to the smoke grenade. The grenade is in the bottom of a bomb crater."

"Okay, I'll come around again and look for it." *Crap, we're going down a bomb crater for this trip.* On the second pass, I saw it out my side of the aircraft. *Oh shit, it is a bomb crater, and not a daisy cutter either.* The daisy cutter bomb was designed to clear out everything for a helicopter to land. It was a fifteen-thousand-pound bomb with chain welded to the outside, dropped by a C-130 cargo plane. Once dropped, a parachute deployed, allowing for a slow descent of the bomb. At about fifteen feet from the ground it would detonate, cleaning out a very nice landing zone of one helicopter and no crater. The trees all appeared to be about the same height around this bomb crater, and the wind was blowing north to south, but lightly. Still, in an airplane or a helicopter, you want to land into the wind as it allows for slower speed and increase lift, which means less power used. Power is critical at times like this. Several factors come into play. Using pedals can increase or decrease power, as pressing the pedal in one direction reduces the amount of power needed while pressing the pedals in the other direction increases the amount of power needed. Left pedal takes less and right pedal takes more as it brings the tail against the rotation of the rotor head. Unchecked, the natural tendency of the tail is to swing to the right.

As I made our approach and slowed the aircraft to a hover into what wind there was, I checked my power and all was good. Looking down through the chin bubble, I thought someone had to be kidding me, and I eased the aircraft forward at a hover. I was at almost max power.

"Okay, guys, talk me down."

"You have to bring the tail around to the left about ninety degrees," Lovelace said.

Peters responded, "Tail clear left."

I slowly started the pedal turn, applying more power. I was at max power now and continuing to turn. The tail was fighting me in the wind and the engine was creeping above max power limits.

"You're at forty percent N1," Grandpa said. We weren't even halfway through the turn. *Shit.* I brought the nose back around to the wind and flew out of the hole.

"We need to relook this one. Lovelace, Peters, did you see lower trees back there around the hole that we can come in over?"

"The trees look a bit lower on the north side, sir, but you're going to have a tailwind up the ass," Lovelace told me.

"Okay, let's try that. Might be better than getting in and having to turn it." I set the approach up again, coming in from the opposite direction. As I came in over the hole, the tail boom was dancing with the wind trying to turn us. Before I came to a complete stop, I had the cyclic back hard, attempting to arrest our forward motion, and I was at full power. This was not working, and I flew us out.

"Dog-meat Six, Chicken-man One-Niner, over."

"Chicken-man One-Niner, Dog-meat Six India."

"Dog-meat Six, we got to lighten the load. The wind is just playing hell with a hover. Going to base and will drop some load and be back."

"Roger, Chicken-man. Dog-meat Six India out."

"Guys, when we get back to the log pad, drop fifteen cans off and we'll try with just that. That should lighten us up by about five hundred pounds. Plus with the fuel burn, we should be okay." After unloading, we headed back out.

"Dog-meat Six, Chicken-man One-Niner en route."

"Roger, Chicken-man, do you want smoke?"

"Affirmative, I want to see what the wind is doing."

"Roger, smoke out."

"Roger, I have red smoke."

"Affirmative." The smoke was drifting up but dissipating quickly when it reached the top of the trees. Indications were that it was coming from the north and blowing south.

"Okay, crew, let's try a north approach again." And I turned in, slowing the aircraft and passing over the opening at about five feet above the trees.

"Okay, talk me down."

"You need to bring the tail left, sir." *Damn, same as last time.*

"How much?"

"About ninety degrees." Nothing had changed.

"Clear left," Peters said, and I began to make the turn. With every degree of pedal, a bit more power was required. Grandpa was reading off the power settings to me, and I was glancing at the torque gauge to confirm his information.

"Stop turn," Peters said.

"Clear down left."

"Clear down right."

"Clear down front."

And I began to descend.

"Stop descent. You need to slide right," Lovelace said.

"Clear right," Peters responded. I thought about moving to the right, and the aircraft responded.

"Stop," Peters said. "Clear down right."

Lovelace came back with "Clear down left."

Grandpa said, "Clear down front." I started down another couple of feet.

"Stop," said Lovelace. "You're going to have to move forward."

"Clear to come forward," said Grandpa. I was so focused on keeping the aircraft stable that I didn't dare look up at the tip of the main rotor. "Stop," Grandpa said.

"Clear to come down right and rear."

"Clear left."

"Clear forward."

This continued for a full five minutes. The aircraft was literally sliding under and around tree limbs. Finally I could see a soldier standing on the top of the crater, giving me a stop signal. We were at a hover and not able to put the aircraft down.

"Stop, sir." I did.

"Sir, we can't go any lower. We're at ground level but sitting over a crater that must be fifteen feet deep," Lovelace informed me.

"Okay, gently kick the water cans out. Try not to rock the boat, please," I added. They moved into the cabin from their positions and began tossing the water cans out.

"Dog-meat Six, Chicken-man One-Niner."

"Go ahead, Chicken-man."

"Okay, I can't set down, so I won't be able to backhaul from this location. We'll kick out each turn. Do not, I repeat, do not have anyone standing on the crater or in the crater. If we lose the engine, I'll be coming down right on top of them. I got no place to go. Over."

"Roger, Chicken-man. I have one pack that I need to get out tonight if I can. Over."

"In this hole, there's nothing I can do about that. Over."

"Chicken-man, what can I do to make this better?" Dog-meat Six asked. Using my peripheral vision, I started looking around.

"Dog-meat Six, do you see this large tree off to my right? The one with no limbs except up at the very top?"

"Roger, Chicken-man."

"If you could blow that tree, that would be a major help. Over."

"Chicken-man, I'll have a load of det cord[1] on the next load and blow it."

"Roger, that will help. Chicken-man is coming out." And we reversed the process of sliding out from under tree limbs, turning the tail boom and slowly climbing up. As we finally cleared the treetops and nosed over for speed, I turned to Grandpa.

"You got the aircraft."

"I have the aircraft," he said. My uniform was soaked with perspiration. My right hand was shaking. Grandpa's cigarettes and lighter were on the console.

"Can I have one of your cigarettes?" I asked. I knew he was going to say yes, so I was reaching for the pack.

"I thought you didn't smoke," he said.

"I don't." And I lighted up, inhaling a long drag as I looked upward. Three cigarettes in fifteen months shouldn't hurt me too much. I wished I had something stronger than a beer right now. Grandpa put us on the log pad, and another fifteen cans of water were loaded, along with a case of det cord.

"Ready to come up," Grandpa said.

"Clear right."

"Clear left."

"Clear up," we all responded, and he pulled on power. Checking his power, he was satisfied we had enough with this load and we headed back.

"Dog-meat Six, Chicken-man One-Nine. Over."

"Chicken-man One-Nine, popping smoke. Over." Dog-meat had anticipated our request. Good, we were thinking alike.

"Dog-meat Six, I have Goofy Grape."

"Roger, Chicken-man One-Nine."

Grandpa brought the aircraft around and lined us up. We had no choice but to repeat my approach. I was as nervous as a cat in the middle of a dog pound.

"Clear right."

"Clear left."

"Clear front."

I was looking to the front as Lovelace and Peters cleared us on the sides and behind. Grandpa started working us down.

"Stop. Need to come forward," Lovelace said.

I was watching the main rotor. I honestly couldn't tell how much room we had to go forward.

"Clear to come forward," I said. I was watching the tips of leaves on the closest branches. I started to see movement in the leaves, and still we moved forward.

"Stop," I said as I saw a leaf disappear from touching the main rotor.

"Clear to come down on right."

"Clear left."

"Clear forward."

And we continued working our way down. Instead of taking two to three minutes, it was another five-to-seven-minute ordeal. Again we were at a hover as the aircraft was carefully unloaded.

"Clear up right."

"Clear up left."

"Clear up forward."

And Grandpa started our upward climb ever so slow and careful. When we cleared the trees, I took the aircraft. Grandpa sat back and started breathing again. We landed at the pad, the aircraft was quickly loaded and I headed back.

"Dog-meat Six, Chicken-man One-Nine, over."

"Chicken-man One-Niner, Dog-meat Six India, popping smoke." We knew where the LZ was but still wanted a reference on the wind. As I slid over the top of the hole, the large tree that was causing some of our problems was lying across the bomb crater.

"Dog-meat Six, thanks much, that's going to help."

"Roger, Chicken-man."

"Okay, crew, here we go."

And the process started all over again. It was a bit easier this time with the large tree down and some fuel burned off, but we still took about five minutes to work our way down. This trip was C-rations and ammo.

Finally Lovelace said, "Another two feet and we'll be on the tree across the Carter. Clear down, down, down." And I felt the skid touch. I still had to keep the aircraft light as putting the full weight of the aircraft would bend the skids and cause an accident, but being light at least stabilized us from sliding side to side. Grunts were able to walk on the log and established a human chain, passing empty water cans along to the aircraft. The cargo was tossed out the other side into the crater. At last a grunt climbed in with his gear, smiling and giving me a thumbs-up. He must be going home.

"Chicken-man One-Nine, you are good to go. Thank you much for today."

"Dog-meat Six, I still have one more run with beer and mail."

"Chicken-man, you can forget that for tonight. This is not the best PZ."

"Dog-meat Six, I said I have one more run. You call, Chicken-man hauls. We'll be back in fifteen mikes."

Mr. Fairweather made the last run, and it was a repeat of the previous runs. I wanted this last run for the fact that the grunts deserved their mail and beer, and it would give

Grandpa more experience at balancing the aircraft on a log in a tight hover hole. As the last mailbag was unloaded along with the last bag of beer and soda, I said to no one and everyone, "Dog meat Six, Chicken man One-Niner is out of here. Coming up."

Grandpa laboriously worked our way back up, turning the tail around branches, sliding the main rotor over limbs, and working upward. Power was more than plentiful now as we were low on fuel and had no cargo, except some empty ammo cans and some trash. As I cleared the treetops, I took the controls.

Lovelace was generally quiet, but this time he came over the intercom. "Mr. Cory, sir, that had to be the worst hover hole I've ever been in. We didn't tell you, but there was a time on the first and second trip in that I couldn't see sky because of the overhang."

"Oh, stop bullshitting, Lovelace. It wasn't that bad," I said.

"He's not bullshitting," Peters added. "Please never take us into another one like that."

"Guys, you could have just told me we couldn't do it and I wouldn't have. You don't like it, then it's your fault," I responded and looked over at Grandpa.

"This shit is going to make me old before my time," Grandpa joined in.

"Grandpa, you're already old," I told him.

"Up yours. Get your own cigarettes." He glared at me with a grin.

We returned to the log pad and were released for the day, as it was after sunset by the time the aircraft was unloaded. We were tired, and I felt emotionally drained. I didn't sleep well that night as I was flying this hellhole again.

## 36

## THINGS CHANGE

OUR COMMANDING OFFICER HAD BEEN A GREAT commander, but his time was up. A new CO took command of the company without fanfare, at least not for the flight crews, as we were all flying when he arrived and our old CO left. We said goodbye to the CO in an appropriate fashion. He knew he would be missed. Most of us met the new CO when we came into the club that night for a beer and a meeting. Initial impression was good.

Major Sundstrum said all company policies would remain in effect and, keeping his word, he took his orientation ride with me the next day. He had been on the division staff, so he knew the landscape well and had some insight into what the overall picture and tactical situation was. I sensed in a few comments he made that there was something more that he wasn't sharing, but we all had our secrets, so I let it drop.

A few nights later, Captain Kempf stopped by my room while I was writing a letter.

"Hey, Dan, you got a minute?"

"Sure, sir, want a beer?" I offered as I reached for one in

my mini refrigerator. *Wonder what this is all about. He's never visited me before.*

"Yeah, I could use one," he said as he dragged over my one spare broken down lawn chair and sat. Something told me this was not going to be a short conversation.

Handing him a cold one, I took my seat and said, "So, sir, what's up?"

Leaning in close, he asked in a low voice, "Did the major say anything to you the other day when you flew with him about aircraft availability?" The expression on his face told me he was worried about something.

"No, sir, he talked about flying stuff but nothing about availability. He asked about blade strikes and tail rotor strikes but that was it. Why?"

Taking a sip of his beer, he hesitated for a moment. "He told me to have one hundred percent availability by the end of the month. I was wondering if he said anything to you about it."

"One hundred percent availability? Really? Have we ever had one hundred percent? I mean, you always have at least one or two aircraft in for periodic maintenance, don't you?"

"Yeah, but he wants me to manage our maintenance flow and aircraft availability for missions so at the end of the month we can report one hundred percent availability."

"Did you ask him about it? Why is it so important?"

"I did, and he told me, 'All in good time, all in good time.' What the hell does that mean?" He took a long pull on his beer.

"Sir, I don't know what to tell you. He said nothing to me about availability. We just talked flying stuff and sort of reviewed everyone's flying ability since I've flown with about everyone in the company on check rides. Have you asked some of the other RLOs?

"No, the major said to keep it close, and if I ask one of

them, I'm sure they'll be asking the XO or Ops or even going straight to him and asking why. You warrant officers generally keep to yourselves and don't run to the major with questions," he added with a smile and drained his beer. Tossing the can in the trash, he asked, "If you hear anything, will you let me know? And keep this between us, please."

"Sure, sir."

"Best get back to the shop. You have a good night, Dan."

"You too, sir." And he was gone. *Wonder what this is all about.*

## 37

## THE PACE PICKS UP

APRIL PROVED TO BE A TYPICAL MONTH. HARDLY A day went by without some aircraft returning with battle damage from enemy fire. Most of it was minor and could be patched fairly quickly with some sheet metal work. Each damaged aircraft added to Warren's anguish as he was attempting to get to one hundred percent availability. A couple of pilots returned with battle damage as well. Hot LZs were becoming a frequent event. The NVA were stepping up their game. So did the division. More and more hours were being flown, and crews were getting tired. We were still short of pilots, with little room if a pilot was lost to rotation home or leave. As much as we hated to see a guy go on leave or R&R, we were glad to see him get out of the area for those ten days. The good news was we had a couple of pilots extend. Bill Hess and Mike George decided to stay for another six months. They were on leave, but we knew they would be back. And our unit got the Night Hunter Killer mission back, with a few changes.

"Mr. Cory, you're on Night Hunter tonight, so you might want to sleep in today," the ops clerk told me as he was waking pilots up at 0500 hours. I rolled over and went back to dreamland. When I finally rolled out of bed and got some coffee, I went out to check the aircraft. Specialist Lovelace was there with some maintenance personnel.

"What's up, Lovelace?" I asked as I approached and noticed that the aircraft was being modified.

"Sir, they're replacing the .50-cal with a minigun," he said. Previously, the aircraft had been equipped with an M2, .50-cal machine gun in the crew chief's position and the searchlight with starlight scope mounted on top in the cargo door. This time, instead of a .50-cal, a 7.62 mm minigun was mounted in the crew chief's position. The only problem with this arrangement was that the minigun expended three thousand rounds in a minute at a slow rate of fire! If a crew chief got carried away, he would use all the ammo up very quickly. Short bursts were needed, not sustained suppressive fire. Our guns were there to get us out of trouble. Let the Cobra do the suppressing.

"Just don't burn through all the ammo on the first pass," I instructed. Lovelace loaded three more cans of ammo, a total of nine thousand rounds, just for the minigun. Arriving at the brigade TOC for our mission brief that evening, I was met by not only the operations officer, S-3, but by the brigade S-2 intelligence officer and a lieutenant colonel from division intelligence. I knew the brigade officers; I had never met the lieutenant colonel from division.

"Mr. Cory, how are we tonight?" asked the S-3.

"I'm good, sir, but I can't speak for you," I replied. We had joked and bantered before over the months, so I didn't feel that I was being disrespectful, nor did he.

"If you're good and the aircraft's good, then I'm good too. This is Lieutenant Colonel Mills from division G-2." The lieutenant colonel nodded in acknowledgment. He was across the room and made no effort to move to me, so I made none towards him.

"How do you do, sir?" I addressed him.

"Glad to meet you, Mr. Cory. Mind if I ride along with you tonight? I have my own helmet and chicken plate."

*Wow.* A lieutenant colonel from division intelligence riding along and bringing his own gear. That had never happened before.

"No, sir, glad to have you."

Interrupting, the brigade S-2 piped up, "Do you mind if I come too?"

"Okay, what's going on?" I asked.

The lieutenant colonel walked over to the map and motioned me as well as the Cobra pilot and the flare ship AC to follow.

"We need you to fly this route tonight, and keep the shooting to a minimum. We need to start here"—he pointed at a point on the river—"and work our way up to here."

"Sir, that's over the Cambodian border. We've never even been close to it before. No telling what we're going to get into. And we're going to be stretching our fuel going there."

"Yeah, I know, but when you give us bingo on the fuel, you bring us home and we'll go from there. We need to recon as much as we can tonight," he admitted. Translation: *You are going to fly your ass off tonight.* "Oh, and one other thing. I'd like one of my people to operate the searchlight tonight. Give your crew member a night off. Just don't bring him tomorrow."

"Excuse me, sir, but what is he supposed to do tonight if not fly?" I asked, a bit confused.

The S-3 jumped in. "I have a cot for him to sleep on tonight." I was sensing a setup in the making. This was no last-minute party.

"Okay, sir. Are there any other changes you want to make?" I asked.

All three looked at each other. This was not going to be good. The lieutenant colonel pointed at a spot about five klicks south of the Cambodian border. "When we reach this point, the Cobra and flare ship can't follow us any further on the route, unless we get in serious trouble."

"You mean you want me to fly across that border with no air cover and no illumination if I need it." My voice was slightly strained. Now the truth had come out.

"You're equipped with a minigun tonight, aren't you?" asked the lieutenant colonel.

"Yes, sir, but—"

"Well, there you have it. Suppressive fire if you need it. No need to have them tagging along up there. Besides, there may be things that can reach up one thousand feet easily up there," he concluded. I looked over at the AC for Lobo, and he wasn't objecting, nor was the AC on the flare ship.

"Okay, sir, what's the intel on the gooks up this way?" I asked.

He went into a detailed description of enemy forces, to include some suspected radar 23 mm and 37 mm antiaircraft positions, concluding, "We'll be flying low, below their ability to track us." Now I understood why no high birds.

The Cobra AC spoke. "Dan, we can't go up there in that."

"Yeah, I know, but I sure don't like going up there without you. Okay, sir, let me brief my crew, and when you're ready, we'll take off."

"I'll be out shortly."

As the other ACs and I walked back to the aircraft, we were talking about this crazy mission. We concluded that this wasn't the ordinary, and something must be up. The division must be getting ready for a major push towards the border. Reaching my aircraft, I sent the searchlight operator up to the

TOC after explaining to the crew what was in store for the night. He didn't feel bad about not going with us. Lovelace and Peters, on the other hand, expressed their opinions about this mission, with comments such as "Oh shit," "I'm too short for this shit," and "We're screwed," just to name a few. When the lieutenant colonel arrived, they quieted down and became professional again. We cranked and got into the air. My copilot, Grandpa, was on his first Night Hunter mission, so this was also a training mission for him.

"Flying with you, Dan, is making my hair turn gray," he mumbled.

"Hell, it was already gray when you were born, Grandpa."

"Hope you brought your own cigarettes this time." He was not grinning.

We proceeded to the start point. The lieutenant colonel was seated in the center of the cargo area, following our position closely on his map. I was navigating and Grandpa was doing the flying. We normally flew at sixty knots on this mission, but Grandpa was attempting to increase our speed as we moved further north. I had to slow him down. He gave me this look each time as if to say, *Are you stinking nuts?* Some guys were just not cut out to do this mission. They were usually married men, like Grandpa, with two kids. You had to be a little nuts just to be flying a helicopter in Vietnam. You had to be really nuts to volunteer to fly this kind of mission. You had to be flat-ass insane to fly this particular mission.

As we were moving north on the route the lieutenant colonel had mapped out for us, he was talking with the searchlight operator, but they were keyed to private conversation, so I had no idea what they were saying. The operator would be looking, then turn and say something, and the lieutenant colonel would write on his map. A couple of times he asked us to make a 360-degree turn. I asked if they had something, and the answer would be "No, we just want to have a relook." The searchlight never came on. In fact, the searchlight never got turned on at all that night on this mission. As we approached the Cambodian border, he was having us fly almost exclusively in 360 degree circles, which didn't hurt my feelings as it made it much more difficult for a ground shooter to track us. Finally I called "bingo" because of fuel and we headed back. I took the controls as Grandpa had been doing most of the flying for the past hour and a half.

"Hey, Mr. Cory." The lieutenant colonel had my attention over the intercom.

"Yes, sir."

"We have all we need for tonight, so we'll be getting off when we get back in. The brigade S-2 here will have a few more missions for you tonight. Do not refly this route that we just flew or go anywhere in that area. Understood?"

"Yes, sir."

"Oh, and one more item. Don't discuss this mission with anyone," he added.

"Yes, sir."

I said no more but wondered what the hell was going on. Once we landed, my searchlight operator rejoined us as we were refueling. The lieutenant colonel left, and the brigade S-2 followed him like a puppy dog after he told me where he wanted us to go—Bu Dop. Shutting down, I pulled the other ACs and crews together as everyone had questions.

"Dan, what'd the colonel tell you?" asked the Cobra commander.

"Nothing, except he doesn't want us flying anywhere up there. He didn't say if they saw anything or indicate what he was looking for. The brigade intelligence officer didn't say jack shit either. And we're not to discuss this mission with anyone." We had lots of questions and no answers.

"How far did you get across the border?" the Cobra AC asked.

"Just south of Snuol," I told him.

His only response was, "Holy shit. You were lucky!"

The rest of the night was uneventful. We thought we would have some good hunting, but the night was a bust. For the next week, we flew the same mission, being directed on different routes each night with the same lieutenant colonel and the same results. We didn't turn on the searchlight or engage any targets. Boring! Finally I got off Night Hunter assignment and was glad to get back to daytime missions.

But things changed. Captain Kempf, the maintenance officer, had been pretty good about letting pilots get an aircraft and take soldiers to Bien Hoa or even Saigon for the day as the PX at Lai Khe was reducing its contents since the First Infantry Division had left and there were only a handful of units left at Lai Khe. As April progressed, he was becoming more hard-nosed about releasing an aircraft. The division was getting into more contact, and aircraft were returning with damage. The pilots just assumed that he was husbanding the aircraft.

"Mr. Cory, the CO wants to see you in his hooch," the company clerk stated as I sat writing a letter. It was about 1900 hours on April 31, 1970. *Wonder what this is about?*

Knocking on his door, I was told to come in. There sat Major Sundstrum along with Captain Wehr, the XO, Captain Beauchamp, the ops officer, and Captain Kempf, the maintenance officer, as well as another flight leader, Mr. Roberts.

Once we were all settled, the major broke out seven cups and poured a shot of scotch in each, passing one to each of us. As he did so, Roberts and I looked at each other with *What the hell?* looks.

"Gentlemen, I have been in a meeting this afternoon at Quan Loi with all the aviation company commanders from 227th, 228th, 229th and Second of the Twentieth Aerial Rocket Artillery. General Shoemaker headed up the meeting and gave a mission brief on tomorrow's missions." Caged eyeballs were moving around the room. *What the hell is going to happen?*

"Warren, how many aircraft do we have up for tomorrow?" the major asked, holding his drink in his hand. He hadn't taken a sip yet, nor had anyone else.

"Sir, we have twenty-one aircraft for tomorrow, but two only have ten hours each before they're due for their one-hundred-hour periodic inspections."

"Those aircraft fly tomorrow. I told Battalion twenty-one aircraft, and that's what they expect.

Okay, here's the deal. We have a major mission tomorrow. We have twenty-one aircraft to put up." I looked at Mr. Roberts and he at me. "Mr. Cory, you will be flying Chalk Two in a heavy right formation. I'll be flying flight lead. If I go down, you take the flight in. Mr. Roberts, you are Chalk Three. If Cory goes down, you take the flight in. Understood?"

Mr. Roberts and I looked at each other with our mouths open and our eyes the size of saucers. *What in the world is this about?*

"Yes, sir. Where we going?" Mr. Roberts asked.

"You'll get that info in the morning. We launch at zero seven thirty and will join up with Bravo and Charlie companies at the runway at Chon Thanh, the SF camp."

Again I looked at the other AC. We'd never had a mission with so many aircraft since I'd been in the unit. Those big lifts had been common back in the mid-sixties, when they'd had larger LZs to operate in, but not since the division had moved to Three Corps.

"I want you two to get the other aircraft commanders and preflight all the aircraft now. Any problems should be reported to maintenance immediately. Any questions?"

"No, sir," we both responded.

"Good, gentlemen. To tomorrow." And he raised his glass. We all chugged our drinks and left

at a fast pace to roust other pilots. Within fifteen minutes, the flight line was a beehive of activity as someone had told the crew chiefs to get out and look their aircraft over and the door gunners to double-check the machine guns. It was a busy night.

# 38

## CAMBODIA

Normally, coordinating an operation the size and complexity of the Cambodian Incursion takes time and resources. Time is required to plan the operation; position the attack force; pre-position the logistics to support and sustain the operation; and execute the coordination, especially between foreign allies. In this case, however, attack forces and logistics were already in close proximity to the objectives, so the planning process was greatly reduced. The events that put this operation in motion had begun in March of '70. In the mid- to late 1960s, Prince Sihanouk, the leader of Cambodia, had turned a blind eye to the North Vietnamese use of the border region between Cambodia and South Vietnam. Publicly declaring neutrality, he gave tacit support to North Vietnam, which humiliated many Cambodians. A major port was established on the southwestern coast, where ships with supplies destined for the North Vietnamese forces would offload. The goods were then loaded into trucks and moved north, to the vicinity of the Parrot's Beak and Fishhook regions along the border. This region was northwest of the

South Vietnam city of Tay Ninh, expanding northeast to An Loc and Song Be.

Prior to 1968, no cross-border operations into Cambodia had been authorized by the US government. In 1968, covert cross-border operations had been authorized for the purpose of gathering intelligence. Prince Sihanouk let it be known that he would not object to US bombing in the border region if no Cambodian forces were targeted. Publicly, he condemned the bombing. He was playing both sides. In addition to North Vietnamese forces operating along the border, Khmer Rouge rebels were working inside Cambodia towards the overthrow of the Sihanouk government, but their goal was not better relations with the US but with China, as the Khmer Rouge were sponsored by China. As a result of Tet 1969, President Nixon authorized the bombing of military targets beginning on March 18, 1969 along and over the border.

In January 1970, while on a trip to France, Prince Sihanouk was overthrown by his defense minister, Lon Nol, who quickly sought support from and friendly relations with the US. President Nixon saw this as an opportunity to accelerate the departure of US forces from South Vietnam. Now Cambodian forces not only fought the Khmer Rouge but began to target North Vietnamese forces as well. Unfortunately, the Cambodian military was not a large or strong force.

In early March, ARVN forces had been contemplating and planning an incursion into the border region. As forces and logistical support were already in the Parrot's Beak and Fishhook regions, little preparation was required for such a move. In addition, in March 1970, the Military Assistance Command Vietnam, MACV, had conducted preliminary planning for an incursion into the Parrot's Beak and Fishhook regions of the border. On March 12, Lon Nol, the new leader of Cambodia, told the NVA they had seventy-two hours to get out of Cambodia. This did not sit well with Hanoi, and at the urging of the Khmer Rouge rebels, the NVA launched a major offensive campaign west across Cambodia on March 29. With this new development came new opportunities for the US.

NVA forces and Khmer Rouge rebels worked together to push Cambodian forces to within thirty miles of the capital of Phnom Penh, at which time Lon Nol requested assistance from the US for aviation and armored cavalry units. On April 27, ARVN rangers advanced across the border and destroyed an NVA supply base in the Fishhook region.

US planning for an incursion into the Cambodian border region was held in very tight security. Senior subordinate commanders were not officially notified until a week prior to execution, with battalion commanders not being notified until seventy-two hours in advance and aviation unit commanders notified only twenty-four hours prior to execution. However, in early April, they were notified to increase aircraft availability. No logistical buildup was to be undertaken so as not to tip the hand that an incursion was coming.

The NVA had already considered the possibility of Cambodian and South Vietnamese forces attacking in concert at some point, one from the west and one from the east. Contingency plans had already been prepared, and with the directive from Lon Nol to get out of Cambodia in seventy-two hours, Communist Office South Vietnam, COSVN, began evacuating on March 18. NVA ground combat forces began leaving the area, attacking west towards Phnom Penh on March 29. Thus when ARVN forces launched their attacks on April 30, few combat units were home to meet them.

On April 30, ARVN forces along with some US forces crossed Parrot's Beak into Cambodia. The ARVN force consisted of twelve infantry battalions and three Ranger battalions. The US elements consisted of a brigade from the

Twenty-Fifth Infantry Division and two squadrons of armed cavalry. Operation Rock Crusher was on.

On the May 1, 1970, at 0710 hours, Company C, 227th AHB, inserted an ARVN airborne rifle company to secure a landing zone just across the border inside Cambodia.[1] Once the landing zone was secured, six 105 mm howitzers and three 155 mm howitzers, which would support additional insertions throughout the area of operations, were brought in by CH-47 helicopters. Later that day, the Second Battalion, Seventh Cavalry was inserted into Landing Zone X-Ray, marking the first American ground troops from the First Cavalry Division to enter Cambodia. Throughout the day, First Battalion, Ninth Cavalry flew reconnaissance missions while elements of the 227th and 229th Assault Helicopter Battalions provided lift support to the ARVN grunts and 228th Assault Support Helicopter Battalion provided CH-47 heavy lift capability for the movement of artillery and other heavy equipment.

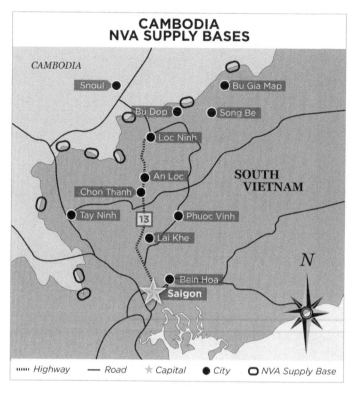

*Map created by Infidium LLC for Matt Jackson Books*

2

## 39

## TAKING THE FIGHT TO THEM

At 0530 hours, the flight ops clerk came around and woke everyone. We straggled into the mess hall. *What the...? Steak and eggs!* By 0645 hours, almost every aircraft was cranked and we were getting clearances. Fourteen aircraft were in the flight, and the other five were picking up normal missions. One aircraft was being loaded for laying down a smokescreen and would be with the formation initially but not carrying troops.

Over in the Snake Pit, most of Lobo's aircraft were cranking up as well. As we departed, they were flying trail behind us and on our flanks. Fifteen Hueys and eight Cobras makes for an impressive formation. The Robin Hoods normally flew for the Twenty-Fifth Infantry Division, and they were cranking up in Sherwood Forest and departing also, but heading in a different direction. The runway at the SF camp at Chon Thanh came into view and Flight Leader set up the approach. Off to the side of the runway was a single aircraft, a speaker's stand and a large covered display board. The aircraft was the battalion commander's aircraft.

"Chicken-man Flight, this is Yellow One. Shut down and

everyone assemble on Lightning Bolt Six." This was getting stranger by the minute. As we climbed out of the aircraft, two more flights were landing behind us, Bravo Company and Charlie Company. This was going to be a battalion lift—a first for me. Then we saw CH-47s coming to land as well and more Cobras from Blue Max. There were forty-two UH-1H aircraft, ten CH-47 Chinooks and twenty-five Cobras. All were shutting down and converging on Lightning Bolt Six's location. Once we were all assembled, the battalion commander stepped onto the speaker's platform, which was a stand used for physical fitness training.

"Gentlemen, we are launching a battalion lift, a first for most of you. We will be picking up elements of the Third ARVN Airborne Brigade at these three locations throughout the day"—the cover was pulled up—"and inserting them in these three LZs in the Parrot's Beak region. These forces are blocking forces for the elements of the Eleventh Armored Cavalry Regiment that's moving north out of Loc Ninh to Snuol, Cambodia." *Holy shit! We were invading Cambodia!*

Almost on cue, most crew chiefs and door gunners got up, returned to their respective aircraft and began cleaning, inspecting weapons and preparing ammo.

"I will be controlling the operation from above and will provide all artillery clearances as well as providing navigation information to Flight Leader. My call sign will be Anger Two-Nine. Alpha flight lead will be Owner Two-Nine; Bravo flight lead will be Desire Two-Nine; Charlie lead will be Hang Two-Nine. Blue Max is Sword Six-Two and Lobo flight lead is Welder Two-Nine. Tenor Two-Nine is the brigade commander. Flight altitude will be low-level. Flight formation will be heavy left. The S-2 will now give you the enemy situation."

The S-2 took the stand and placed a clear plastic cover over the map. Except it wasn't really clear, as it was covered in red symbols that depicted known and suspected enemy positions.

Some of those positions were along the routes I had flown with the Division G-2 a week or so ago.

"The enemy situation is as follows. At this location is the headquarters for the entire North Vietnamese Army in this region of Vietnam." He pointed at the map. *Damn, that's where I was flying at eight thousand, tossing leaflets out on that psyops mission.* "In this area is the Seventh NVA division with the Fifty-Sixth Anti-Aircraft Battalion. The Seventh has three regiments: the 209th south of Snuol; the 165th here"—he pointed at a position on the map—"and the 141st Regiment in this area." Great, that was where we were going. "The anti-aircraft situation is that the Seventh is organized with twelve 12.7 mm antiaircraft guns, fifteen multibarrel 23 mm guns that we know about, and six radar-controlled 37 mm guns. The Fiftieth Rear Service Group is the largest unit in the region, with multiple cache sites and several hospitals of five hundred beds each. Weather for today is clear blue and twenty-two. Any questions?" A long pause. "If there are no questions, that's all I have, sir." And he turned the briefing back over to the battalion commander.

"Gentlemen, this operation is code name Operation Toan Thang 43.[1] The sequence of events is as follows: At zero six thirty, Charlie Company picked up a rifle company of the ARVN Airborne Brigade at Quan Loi and inserted them in this area to secure artillery that was inserted to support the insertions. The first assault will depart here and fly to this PZ. Load at zero nine fifty-five hours. Depart PZ1 at ten hundred hours for a twelve-minute flight to LZ Center, located here," he said, pointing at the map. "We will then break into three company flights to refuel, with Alpha refueling at LZ Jake; Bravo refueling at Loc Ninh; and Charlie refueling at Quan Loi. Upon refueling, Alpha and Bravo will join Charlie at Quan Loi and pick up troops for the second lift, inserting into LZ Right, located here." Again he pointed at the map.

"Everyone will return to Quan Loi to refuel, and we will pick up the third lift and insert them at this location. After the third lift, Bravo will be in direct support for Task Force Shoemaker here at Quan Loi. Charlie and Alpha will resume normal daily commitments. Alpha will lead the first insertion, Bravo the second insertion and Charlie the last insertion. Are there any questions?" There were no questions. "There are obviously going to be changes throughout the day that we're going to have to respond to, so be flexible. Owner Two-Nine is flight lead and Yellow One for this first operation. Are there any questions?" There were none. "Okay, let's do this."

We all returned to our aircraft and got ready. To say the least, we were very proud that our company commander was going to be flight leader for this first operation. Mr. Fairweather again drew the lucky straw to be my copilot for the day. I was glad I had him, as he had proven to be a very stable copilot and he always had cigarettes, a fresh pack even. This was going to be something. Just the sound of this many aircraft was awesome. The liftoff with so many aircraft took longer than any I had done before.

En route to the PZ, I asked, "Hey, Lovelace, what's it look like back there?"

"Sir, it's unbelievable. Wish I had a camera to get a picture of so many aircraft in formation. This just might be the largest airmobile operation ever," he said.

The sky was clear and cloudless. There was no haze from forest fires. It was going to be a beautiful day with low temperatures, at least for Vietnam. We were proceeding northwest by the compass when the pickup zone came into view. I hadn't seen so many troops lined up in one location before. Ground guides were out for each aircraft.

As we touched down, the Vietnamese airborne soldiers were almost immediately on board and they were all smiles. They knew where they were going and what they were about to do, and for the first time since I had come to this place, I saw genuine enthusiasm on their faces. They were ready.

"Owner Yellow One is on the go," the flight leader called out. As we climbed to altitude for low-level, flight leader kept the airspeed back to sixty knots initially but, with a call from the last aircraft, increased our speed to ninety knots. The flight was treetop level, ninety knots and closed up tightly with one-rotor-blade separation. The battalion commander was in the C&C aircraft at about three thousand feet above, giving navigation guidance and controlling artillery fire on the LZ when it was time. I had a light touch on the cyclic and was glued to watching Yellow One.

"Owner Yellow One is Tango," he called out as he crossed the border into Cambodia. Minus the bomb craters that pockmarked Vietnam, it looked pretty much the same. That changed as we flew across a dirt road just over the border. It was perpendicular to our flight path and as straight as an arrow. As far as I could see out my side window, there were NVA soldiers walking down both sides of the road, heading northeast with their weapons over their shoulders. I was sure they were surprised as hell to see and hear this thunderous display of aviation might. They didn't shoot at us. Our LZ was located in a large open dried-up rice paddy south of the town of Snuol. As in all operations, artillery impacted prior to our landing but was of shorter duration. The lack of artillery support was made up for by Blue Max releasing all their rockets with pinpoint accuracy. For the first time, our smoke aircraft proceeded us and laid a smokescreen over the tree line once the Cobras had laid in their rockets. Before we even touched the ground, the Vietnamese grunts were out of the aircraft and pushing to the tree line.

"Owner Yellow One is on the go" was heard probably before the last aircraft was over the LZ, but there was no need for empty aircraft to be sitting. As we came out, Grandpa took the controls. There were no calls of anyone taking fire.

"Lovelace, how's it look back there?" I asked as we cleared the LZ and I could see that Chalk Three and Four were with us.

"Sir, they're all coming out as fast as they're going in. I will bet this is the least amount of time in an LZ. Everything looks good. The grunts are really close together and moving out already."

"Okay, heads up back there. We've got gooks on that road and we have to cross that thing again. They'll be waiting for us." Evidently someone had thought about this already, as Lobo moved out ahead of the flight slightly and began hitting the edges of the road at the appropriate time. As we rolled over, we could see the effect of Lobo's work. Besides broken bodies lying in the road, a hornet's nest of fire came up and greeted us. Without saying a word, Lovelace and Peters opened fire. Just as fast as we came upon the road, we were gone and breathing easy. No one reported any hits. Refueling before the next lift took some time, and as an aircraft would complete refueling, it would move off and shut down until all aircraft were refueled. We then proceeded to a new PZ and repeated the process again, with equal results, into a new LZ. There would be a third lift for the day as briefed.

On the way back to the Chicken Pen that evening, the CO, flying Yellow One, took us over Lai Khe in formation at five hundred feet. As we reached the end of the runway, we changed formation and came up trail, circling back into a downwind leg, base to final leg, and finally turning onto final. Our transition from staggered right to trail was as sharp as any flying in a precision performance. We were showing off. The formation reflected the pride of the unit. The runway was lined with ground crews watching the demonstration. As we pulled into individual revetments, someone from maintenance guided us in, waiting to see what work needed to be done. The maintenance platoon was ready to work all night to get the aircraft back in the air, fully expecting to find multiple bullet holes in each aircraft. There were none! The operation had been a complete surprise from our standpoint. As crews finished post-flight inspections on the aircraft and began walking back to Flight Ops, high fives were exchanged. We felt like, for once, we had really taken the fight to the NVA.

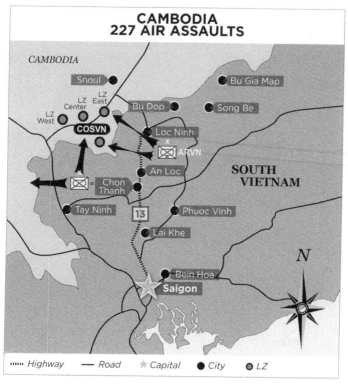

*Map created by Infidium LLC for Matt Jackson Books.*

2

# 40

## THINGS HEAT UP

Surprise may have been achieved on day one of the Cambodia campaign, but the NVA recovered quickly and May 2 was the day it started.

"Mayday, mayday, Dragon Breath Two-Three is bailing out and going down, vicinity." He gave his coordinates.

"Chicken-man One-Seven, Bulldog Six, over." Bulldog Six was a ground company commander, and Chicken-man One-Seven was flown by Captain Beauchamp, who was working for Bulldog Six flying resupply.

"Bulldog Six, Chicken-man One-Seven."

"Chicken-man, the forward air controller is going down. Do you have him?" At about this moment, the crew chief, Specialist West, spoke up.

"Hey, Captain, I have a parachute at four o'clock and about a mile away. Also a black cloud of smoke not far from the chute." Turning the aircraft to the right, the captain spotted the chute as well.

"Bulldog Six, I have him in sight and going for him."

"Okay, crew, be on your toes. There's an antiaircraft gun around here, and we need to get that pilot before the gooks do." Captain Beauchamp continued to fly to the chute, which was just entering the trees. "We're going in low and fast until we can pinpoint his location." He dropped to treetop level, heading for the location of the chute, which he could no longer see.

Flying at ninety knots and treetop level, West called out, "Got him! He's in the trees. Three o'clock."

Rene lowered his collective rapidly while raising the nose, resulting in no loss of altitude but rapid deceleration of the aircraft while executing a tight turn to the right. As he came around, he could see the chute tangled in the treetops. He approached slowly, very much aware that there was an antiaircraft gun somewhere around here. Small-arms fire was beginning to place green tracers in the aircraft's vicinity with no hits, yet. Rene also didn't want to create a lot of wind and have the chute reinflate into the rotors. Crew chief and door gunner had guns up and were scanning the jungle. The door gunner was picking his targets and engaging.

As Captain Beauchamp slid the aircraft over the pilot, West informed him, "Sir, the pilot appears to be out cold. He's just hanging in the tree there."

"Okay, we have to get him quick," Captain Beauchamp said, surveying the ground for a place to land. There wasn't one, as the vegetation wasn't dense but the trees were thirty feet high and close enough together that they didn't offer a clearing big enough to land in.

West had already climbed into the cabin area and was preparing a two-hundred-foot rappelling rope that was maintained in the aircraft.

"Sir, I can get him." And with that, he dropped the rope and was preparing to go down.

"Okay but..." And West was gone. He'd forgotten to put on gloves, and his hands were paying for that mistake.

"How am I going to get him out?" he said, more to himself than anyone in particular.

"Jamison, you keep an eye on him and keep him covered," Captain Beauchamp said to the door gunner.

Dropping the seventy or so feet, West sprinted to the pilot, who was still unconscious and hanging in the tree only a few feet off the ground. Small tufts of grass and dirt were being kicked up around West as small-arms fire was directed in his direction.

*Damn parachute release won't release. Son of a bitch.* "Damn it, come on!" West screamed, hoping the pilot would wake and give some assistance. He did not. *Got to get a knife.* Pausing at a low crouch, West waited a moment before he sprinted back to the aircraft, which was still at a hover, engaging the NVA position. As he ran, West made a cutting motion, hoping the gunner or copilot would recognize the signal and drop a knife. They did.

Picking the knife up, West didn't hesitate to sprint back to the hanging pilot, cut him free and throw him over his shoulder. Just then, an RPG round slammed into the tree the pilot had been hanging in. With the pilot over his shoulder in a fireman carry position, West ran for the aircraft and the dangling rope. Grabbing the rope, he wrapped it around the pilot and himself and motioned for the aircraft to take off. West didn't have time to tie a knot but only had the rope wrapped around himself and the pilot. Because of his rope-burned hands, West couldn't climb the rope but prayed he could hold on long enough to get safely back to the ground.

As the aircraft climbed out and built up some speed, the small-arms fire continued. Captain Beauchamp couldn't fly with any speed as the drag on West and the pilot would be too great and pull them off the rope. West was dangling about seventy feet below the aircraft, which was flying over the jungle at two to three hundred feet. Helicopter crews did not have parachutes. As West cleared the trees, Captain Beauchamp nosed the aircraft over and began picking up speed, all the while praying West didn't fall. Everyone was well aware that if they had an engine failure or any other emergency, West and the pilot wouldn't survive.

Arriving over a clearing, Captain Beauchamp lowered the aircraft to place West and the pilot on the ground and then the aircraft. This was an unsecured clearing only about fifteen hundred meters from where they'd picked up the pilot. Detaching the rope, West and Jamison quickly loaded the pilot into the aircraft and departed for LZ Center, where the unconscious pilot was quickly transferred to a medivac aircraft that had been requested. West resumed his duties as a crew chief.[1]

Huge cache sites were being located across the area because the NVA were using trucks to move supplies in Cambodia from a port in Cambodia where ships would deliver the supplies. In South Vietnam, cache sites were seldom found, and they were never very large, because there, bicycles were used to distribute small quantities of supplies to the NVA as soon as they entered the country. The use of trucks led to large three- and four-acre supply depots, and the NVA were determined to protect these huge cache sites. The division didn't change its tactics of rapidly moving company-sized units that were lightly equipped. As each cache site was discovered, grunts inventoried the contents and either removed the materiel or blew it in place. In order to remove it, helicopters were called upon. Between combat assaults, resupply of our own grunts, and now the Vietnamese Army units that were attached to the division, as well as backhauling the captured materiel, we were flying more than ever. And now the press wanted stories.

Up until this point, the press was never seen, at least by us, unless they wanted a ride someplace. The only "press" I recalled seeing in the Chicken Coop was an actor who was visiting us for the day. He was the guy that played Tarzan in a television series at the time. Hell, he wouldn't even fight our rooster! With the assault into Cambodia, the press now found everything about us interesting.

"Wake up, Mr. Cory, you have a zero six hundred launch to Camp Gorvad," the ops clerk informed me. "The rest of your crew is up and moving."

"Okay, I'm awake." I started rolling out from under my mosquito net. "What's the mission for today?"

"You'll love this one. You're flying some public affairs officer and the press around."

"What did I ever do to piss off you guys in Ops?" I asked. He just laughed as he walked out of the hooch.

Flying over, we were directed to land at the VIP pad at Camp Gorvad. *Why the hell isn't Eleventh Aviation Group VIP flight platoon handling this? Bill, where the hell are you?* I wondered. Could it be that we had so many VIPs, they'd run out of aircraft? Sad that the division was of no interest when we were operating in Vietnam, but something like this suddenly had everyone interested. As we were waiting, a clerk came out and said it would be a couple of minutes, so we rolled the throttle back and waited.

"Here they come, Mr. Cory. Holy shit, I know this guy! I mean, I've watched him on TV," Lovelace said.

"Yeah, who is it?" my copilot asked as they were approaching from the rear.

"It's Harry Reasoner," Lovelace responded. Mr. Reasoner introduced himself to each of us as he climbed into the aircraft. The guy was so down to earth right from the start. Not at all what I'd expected. The major from the public affairs office gave us a rundown of what Harry wanted to see as well as do, and I said okay to all of it. Pretty standard stuff, as he wanted to go to a couple of firebases, one US and one Vietnamese, as well as tag along on a combat assault. I had to make some calls to find where one was going down. For us, it was an easy day, which we would pay for the next morning.

Again we were hauling reporters, but not Harry. This time it was a news crew of three guys with cameras, recorders and an announcer. I had never seen these guys before, nor did they give us a clue who they worked for. Their egos were getting in the way. They wanted to go in on a combat assault, and we found one for them. The flight was a six-two combination. I suggested that they fly in on the initial assault, get on the ground and film the second lift come in and depart on the third lift. I would take them in, drop them off, bring troops in on the second and third lift and haul them out after the third lift. From there it would be back to Camp Gorvad, where they would catch a fixed-wing aircraft back to Saigon and they could file their story. They thought it was a great idea, and I finalized it with the flight leader for the mission.

Initially everything went as planned. Artillery went in; gunships rolled hot; slicks touched down; slicks came out to pick up second lift. We arrived back at the PZ, and grunts on the second turn around jumped in the aircraft and we proceeded to the LZ. As the aircraft were on final approaching the LZ, gunfire started hitting aircraft, intense small-arms fire. The ground commander waved the second liftoff and directed us to a new LZ that was about two klicks from the original intended LZ. Ground contact intensified, and for the next two days, that company was in heavy contact. The press crew couldn't be lifted out. Within the first thirty minutes of the fighting, they had used all their film. They had no water or food with them. They remained with the grunts for those two days until everyone could be extracted. After two days of flying the press pool around, I was back to flying normal slick missions, thankfully.

As the days wore on, aircraft continued to take hits and so

did crew members. The initial assault on May 1, 1970, might have been a surprise to the NVA, but they bounced back quickly, and on May 7, they had a surprise for us. Four of our aircraft, led by one of our experienced captains as flight leader, were directed to join a flight of three from our sister company, Bravo. As their company commander was in the flight, he assumed command of the flight as flight leader.

"Flight, this is Green One. I will be leading this flight. Chickenman Two-Four, are your aircraft all up on frequency?" he asked of our flight leader. Green One was the same flight leader who had taken Lou and me through an artillery strike a couple of months before. I was not a happy camper about following him around again.

"Roger, Green One, all Chicken-men are monitoring," Chicken-man Two-Four responded.

"Roger, Flight. We have a fourteen-sortie lift and will do it in two turns. Enemy situation is that Night Hunter took eleven hits last night crossing this LZ. Enemy strength is unknown at this time. We're inserting a rifle company initially and may have to reinforce later. We have three aircraft from my unit, and they'll be Chalks Two and Three, with Chicken-man being Four through Seven. Lobo is providing two aircraft and Blue Max will provide four. The LZ is outside of artillery range, which is why we're heavy with Cobras. Formation will be staggered right," he briefed us as the grunts climbed aboard. They didn't look happy.

Chief Warrant Officer Second Class Bill Hess was an experienced AC, but today he was playing copilot to a brand-new AC, First Lieutenant Jaquoff. Major Sundstrum had asked Bill to fly right seat with him since it was his first time out as an AC. Bill was in his fifteenth month flying in-country.

"Is someone nuts or what? We're going into an LZ that the Night Hunter took fire from, and without artillery coverage?" Bill said. He knew it wasn't smart to operate outside of artillery range and with only six Cobra gunships.

The new AC, a lieutenant with all of four months in-country, told Bill, "The major knows what he's doing. Don't worry about it." In the opinion of most of the warrant officers, this lieutenant was a twin to Lieutenant Dick Weed. Get rid of one and another pops up. As the flight lifted off with the troops on board, a staggered right formation was taken up with Cobras on the flanks.

En route to the LZ, Blue Max called Green One. "Green One, Blue Max Two-Zero."

"Blue Max Two-Zero, Green One, go ahead."

"Green One, we've just been pulled from this mission to cover a unit in heavy contact. Sorry, but we're leaving your formation. Lobo's staying with you. Good luck."

Chicken-man Two-Four came up immediately. "Green One, Chicken-man Two-Four."

"Go ahead, Chicken-man Two-Four."

"Green One, what are your intentions now that we have only two gunships with us?"

"Chicken-man Two-Four, this doesn't change the mission. We will continue," Green One responded.

"Green One, that doesn't make any sense. This LZ was hot less than eight hours ago, and we have no artillery support and only two gunships. Does the ground commander know we're down to just two Cobras?" Chicken-man Two-Four asked.[2]

"Chicken-man Two-Four, this mission is a go. At one minute out, we will engage. Green One out." The irritation in Green One's voice was obvious.

Shortly thereafter, the LZ came into view. It was larger than three football fields, with a small clump of brush in the middle. Seven aircraft in staggered right formation could easily fit. That was the good news. At H minus one, Lobo rolled hot, expending his rockets, and the door gunners opened fire, as did two .51-caliber machine guns and three .30-caliber machine guns from the tree line and one .51-caliber machine gun from the clump of brush in the middle of the LZ. Before the aircraft could land, all were taking hits. Battalion policy had always been that when aircraft were taking intense fire before even getting to the ground, the insertion would be aborted. Green One couldn't rise in rank to make general by observing this policy, though. He did not abort.

"Chalk Three is hit. I'm going in!" The AC was shot in the ankle and crash-landed, spreading the skids of the aircraft. No one told him or his copilot a helicopter could fly with the skids crushed. The aircraft was flyable. Chalk Five, a Chicken-man aircraft, moved up to pick up the crew. Green One had already left the LZ with his remaining aircraft, leaving only Chicken-man aircraft to cover Chalk Five, attempting to rescue Green One's crews. As the downed crew was loading Chalk Five, the remaining Chicken-man aircraft initiated their departure.

"Chicken-man Two-Six, Chicken-man Two-Four. Where are you?"

"Chicken-man Two-Four, I'm still in the LZ. The grunts need a medevac for a guy with a sucking chest wound. I can get him."

"Roger, but don't linger in there," Chicken-man Two-Four instructed him. Within a minute, Chicken-man Two-Six was on the radio.

"Chicken-man Two-Four, we're hit! My AC just took it through both legs. We're coming out." At that instant, Lieutenant Jaquoff leaned forward, in intense pain from a round in his calf and one in his groin. As he did, the front door post exploded from the impact of a .51-caliber round going through it. If he hadn't leaned forward, the round would have hit him in the head. The result of the first lift was that all seven aircraft had been hit, with six in un-flyable condition once they reached Song Be. Another lift had been scrambled together for the follow-on insertions. Chickenman Two Four returned twice more to the LZ, taking in ammo and extracting wounded soldiers. Chickenman Two-Four had 107 bullet holes and was still able to limp back to safety.

Our sister companies were having it equally tough. On or about May 18, while refueling at Quan Loi, a Charlie Company aircraft came in and shut down. The pilot exited the aircraft and I could tell he was upset about something. Walking over to him, I saw that the entire crew was upset. I knew the pilot from having flown with Charlie Company on previous missions.

"Hey, Tom, you okay?" I asked as I approached.

"No, I'm not. We just lost a bird up past Bu Dop. It was flying a sniffer mission. Warrant Officer 1 Riley and Captain Larson were killed as well as the crew chief, Specialist Abler, and the gunner, Private Mehlhaff."

"What happened? Was it shot down? Did the sniffer team make out?"

"No one knows. At this point we just know it went down. Lobo was covering him and said there was no call of taking fire or engine failure. The aircraft just crashed." Tom stated.

Placing my hand on his shoulder, I said, "Sorry for your loss. I know this hurts. You take care," and I walked back to my aircraft to inform my crew.

Things did not improve for Charlie Company.

Four days later, tragedy struck them again. That night at our club, Mike George was at the bar, looking as if he was attempting to clean out all the liquor. Mike was on an extension in-country.

"So Mike, how was your day?" I asked as I planted my butt on a seat next to him.

"It was crap, if you really want to know. Pure crap." I could quickly tell Mike was not in a good mood.

"Hey, what happened? Can I do anything?" I asked.

"Can you bring six guys back from the dead?"

"Oh, shit, did we lose a bird today?"

"No, we didn't, but Charlie Company did—and a medevac." Mike took another shot of Jack Daniels, and he normally didn't drink hard liquor.

"What happened?" I inquired. "Hell, they just lost a bird last week on a sniffer mission."

"I was up by Loc Ninh and a call came out to join an emergency lift of ARVNs into an LZ. Charlie Company was flight lead, with Captain Dan Foley and Captain Ellis Greene as flight lead—nothing planned but just thrown together due to the situation. The first and second lift went off smoothly. However, the ARVN grunts from the first two lifts only secured one side of the landing zone. As the third lift approached, we came under fire. As the aircraft touched down, an RPG round impacted on Captain Foley's chair, killing him instantly, I suspect, and seriously wounding Captain Greene. A medevac aircraft couldn't get in to extract Captain Greene for over an hour. Finally, when they were safely aboard the medevac aircraft, they left to get Greene to a hospital. En route, the aircraft experienced an engine failure over thick jungle and crashed, killing all on board." Mike took another shot of Jack. We sat in silence, thinking too much.

Each night we would fly our aircraft back to Song Be to refuel before continuing on to Lai Khe. And then the weather started to turn against us. Few of our aircraft were equipped to fly on instruments in overcast and rainy conditions. Back in Lai Khe, the mess hall would remain open until the last crew came in as well as have food placed in the EM Club and the Officers' Club for the maintenance crews that worked through the night. Besides late chow for everyone, we were running out of beer because of the PX at Lai Khe being closed. Major Sundstrum called me over to his hooch.

"Sir, you wanted to see me?" I asked.

"Yeah, Dan, I have a special mission for you for tomorrow." He handed me a stack of ration cards. "Take an aircraft tomorrow and fly to Saigon and get a load of beer. These are the ration cards of everyone in the unit, so you should be able to get a hundred cases. Try and get some soda as well. Take Grandpa with you—he could use a break. Any questions?" he asked.

"No, sir."

The next day, Grandpa and I headed south to the Saigon airport, Tan Son Nhat, instead of north with everyone else. I didn't think this broke Lovelace's or Peter's hearts. The PX was across the street from the helipad, which was convenient for helicopter crews. Going in, I approached an Air Force master sergeant who appeared to be working there. He was clean-shaven and smelled of cheap aftershave, and he wore a pressed uniform.

"Excuse me, Master Sergeant. Do you work here?" I asked. He looked me over, noticing my filthy flight suit, unshaven facial hair and body odor.

"Yes, sir. I'm the PX manager."

"Just the man I need to talk with. I need one hundred cases of beer and ten cases of soda. Here are our unit's ration cards." I handed him the cards. He took them but didn't even look at them.

"Sir, there's no way in hell I'm selling you one hundred cases of beer. They'll only wind up on the black market. No, sir. I don't care if you have a hundred ration cards. You get one case. That's it." He handed the stack of cards to me.

"Oh, really? We'll see about that."

Grandpa and I left. At this time we were operating in some intense flying, with aircraft taking hits every day. We were flying long hours each day. I was in no mood to deal with some Air Force NCO in clean clothes who probably had a hot shower and hot meal and smelled like a perfume princess. I played my trump card and called my dad. A jeep picked me up, and twenty minutes later, Grandpa and I were standing in front of a two-star general, explaining my story. He told me to go back to my aircraft and have a nice day as he picked up a phone.

When I got back to the aircraft, the beer was not only there but was being loaded onto the aircraft by PX workers under the supervision of the Air Force master sergeant, who was under the supervision of Specialist Lovelace, who was showing the master sergeant how he wanted the aircraft loaded.

"Any problems, Specialist?" I asked Lovelace.

"No, sir. All is good."

The Air Force master sergeant had more intelligence than I thought, because he kept his mouth shut. The general must have told him something else, because he didn't even charge us for the beer.

When we were fully loaded, I called for clearance from the heliport control and received it. The heliport was an open area about the length of two football fields. As I was pulling in the power, we weren't lifting off the ground before the engine would start to lose engine rpm! We were overloaded, but I wasn't giving up the beer. At full power, we were able to get the aircraft light on the skids and begin sliding forward, slowly at first but building up airspeed to attain translational lift. Like an airplane at a certain speed, air passing over the wing, or in this case, the rotor blades, creates lift and the aircraft flies. The aircraft lifted up only to settle back down on the ground but still moving forward and building speed.

"Chicken-man One-Niner, Tan Son Nhat Heliport."

"Tan Son Nhat Heliport, Chicken-man One-Niner, over."

"Chicken-man One-Niner, are you okay?" the tower controller asked.

"Tan Son Nhat Heliport, we're good. Practicing a heavy takeoff with a new pilot," I replied.

I didn't lie. We were heavy, and he was a new pilot. We climbed a bit higher this time, only to bounce down again, but with more speed and moving forward. Translational lift usually kicked in at about ten knots airspeed. After the third bounce, Tower was telling me to abort as there was a five-foot-high berm rapidly approaching the aircraft, or we were approaching it.

"Chicken-man One-Niner, Tan Son Nhat Heliport. Abort, abort!" We had good speed and translational lift kicked in. We were airborne, clearing the berm by at least two feet.

"Tan Son Nhat Heliport, Chicken-man One-Niner. No need, we're good. Just a bit of training. Chicken-man leaving your area. Good day, sir." And I quickly changed the frequency so I didn't have to answer any questions. As we continued the hundred miles to home, we were burning off fuel, which gave us more power to play with, and we were at a comfortable hover when we arrived at Lai Khe. We had cold beer that night and were in the air the next morning before the sun came up. The next day.....

"Chicken-man One-Niner, Chicken-man Two-Three, over."

"Yeah, Two-Three, go ahead."

"Hey, One-Niner, I heard you were leaving, going to Battalion. Over."

"Two-Three, that's bull. I'm not going anywhere." Now how the hell did that rumor get started? I was an old-timer, having extended, but I had no intention of going up to be on Battalion staff. That wasn't what I'd extended for. We continued on with our resupply mission, but the conversation didn't stop. Another aircraft called me.

"Chicken-man One-Niner, Chicken-man One-Four, over."

"One-Four, go ahead," I answered.

"One-Niner, hate to see you leaving us. Be sure and come back and visit once in a while. Over."

"One-Four, I'm not going anywhere. Who told you I was? Over."

"One-Niner, I heard it in Flight Ops before I left. I got off late today because of a maintenance issue and they were talking about it."

I said nothing. Crap, this could be more than just a rumor. Even later in the day, while sitting in a refuel point, my platoon leader hopped up on my skid.

"Hey, Dan, going to miss you, buddy. When you get to Battalion, be sure and send the good missions to us and not those other guys." With that, he patted my shoulder and was off back to his aircraft. I sank lower in my seat. This had come from my platoon leader, and therefore I knew I was sunk. The rest of the day's flying was almost depressing. I couldn't believe the CO couldn't save me from this.

That night, we got back in and I dropped my gear and headed for the club. I figured I had flown my last mission and would be flying a desk in the coming days, so I might as well have a drink, or two. Almost everyone that was back from flying was in the club eating dinner and having a drink, as we always did. The CO came in and took center stage.

"Let me have your attention. I got some good news and some not so good, which I will give you first." I knew what was coming.

"Mr. Cory, come up here." I hopped off the barstool my ass had been planted to for the past two beers and with a low-hanging head walked up to him. He towered over me.

"You all know that Mr. Cory, Dan, has been with us for the past—what, sixteen months?"

I mumbled, "Yes, sir."

"In that time, he has flown with everyone in this room and done all that has been asked of him and a lot more. Well, it's time for him to move on. Dan, you will be missed." And with that, he shook my hand and motioned for me to take my seat.

A couple of guys patted me on the back as I dragged my sorry ass back to my stool, where another fresh beer was waiting for me. I was at a low point in my life.

"Now for some good news. We're starting to see the replacement pool pick up as we have a new pilot in today. He's a bit unique as he has about seventeen hundred hours of combat flight time already and has been in-country for some time. Join me in welcoming First Lieutenant Cory." As I hunkered over my beer, I was thinking, *This poor bastard has the same last name as me. Wonder where he's from.* I turned to see him, and everyone was looking at me with shit-eating grins and started clapping.

"Come up here, Lieutenant Cory," the CO said and pointed at me. I got off my ass, not sure what was going on. All I could say was, "Sir?"

"Attention to Orders," bellowed Captain Wehr, and everyone stood at attention. "By order of the President of the United States, Chief Warrant Officer 2 Cory is promoted to First Lieutenant, Infantry, United States Army. Signed..."

Without my knowledge, someone had put me in for a commission and it had been approved. That was an expensive night as I had to buy the beer for everyone. Later, I was informed by some of the warrant officers that I had to move out of the warrant officer hooch and into the RLO hooch, but I managed to negotiate into staying, with a promise that I wouldn't pull rank on anyone.

# 41

## RISE TO THE OCCASION

THE NEXT MORNING, THE MISSIONS WERE PASSED out regardless of rank, and just like the day before, I was handed a resupply mission. As we pulled out of the revetment and started down the runway before the sun came up, I began briefing the crew.

"We have a log mission working out of LZ Snuffy. They found a bunker complex up there that they're emptying, and will be for some time I understand. Forty-two bunkers, and it's taking an infantry company a day to inventory and remove stuff from just one bunker. We'll be backhauling a lot today, so get comfortable. We will refuel at Song Be and then push up to Snuffy. There's supposed to be a refuel point being set up at LZ Jamie. You have the aircraft, Rick."

"I have the aircraft," Rick responded.

It was a quiet morning on the radios as it was too early for aircraft to be in the thick of things, yet. Most aircraft were calling for artillery clearances up to Song Be, Bu Gia Map and Bu Dop with almost everyone stopping off at Quan Loi or Song Be for fuel before pressing on. The sun was just beginning to come up in the east, so we had no turbulence and cloud cover was well above the twenty-five hundred feet we were cruising at. The aircraft was sounding normal and the instruments were all in the green. I enjoyed this time, as no decisions had to be made and I could just enjoy the ride.

I started to realize that now I was a commissioned officer, and an infantry officer at that. What did the future hold?

Warrant Officer Branch was willing to send me back to college: I wondered if Infantry Branch would offer the same. And my next assignment, I was sure, would be the Infantry Officers Basic Course, which might have a couple of aviators like me, but the rest would be recent ROTC graduates. As a first lieutenant, I'd probably get stuck with some leadership position as all the others would be second lieutenants. I needed to think about an assignment when I got out of school. I wondered if they'd send me back here as a grunt. I knew I would be required to maintain flying proficiency even in a ground assignment, and I would need to balance my career between aviation assignments and infantry assignments. One thing I needed to do was get an infantry company commander assignment, as I might already be behind my contemporaries, who would all have been platoon leaders over here. A thousand questions were creeping through my mind, and I had no answers at this point.

Rick had been in the unit for over six months now and hadn't made aircraft commander. At the monthly AC meetings, Rick had never received one positive vote. About two months ago, he had gone to the CO, wanting to know why he hadn't made AC. He felt that the ACs had something in for him. The CO had come to me as the unit IP.

"Dan, I want you to fly with Rick tomorrow and give him an AC check ride."

"Sir, no one has voted for him becoming an AC. He's just not ready. He doesn't think. He makes the same mistakes every time with every AC. Sir, if I tell Rick to fly at three thousand feet, ninety knots on a three-sixty heading, he does it perfectly regardless of what gets in his way—artillery, another aircraft, Song Be Mountain. Unless you tell him to avoid those things, he'll fly right into them."

"I know, but I want an impartial honest check ride tomorrow. I want every mistake documented and every good point as well. I want you to give him a through critique afterwards and then come to me. Understood?"

"Yes, sir. I would like a log mission with an assault if possible. Those are our bread and butter, and he's got to be able to handle them."

"I'll talk to Ops and see that you have that." With that, he left. Great, just the guy I wanted to fly with. Okay, this should be fun. Best go tell Rick the good news.

I found him in his room, doing what we all did when sitting in our rooms, writing a letter. "Hey, Rick. How you doing?"

Looking up, he said, "Good, what's up?" I was still a warrant officer at the time, and while technically I did outrank him as I was a W2 and he was a W1, rank between warrant officers is like virtue between whores.

"What's up is you're taking an AC check ride tomorrow with me. We'll have a log mission followed by an assault. We'll use my aircraft, but you're left seat. From the time we wake up until we're back in the Chicken Coop, shut down and back in Flight Ops, you are the AC, unless you really blow it. Understood?"

His facial expression didn't change. He held that blank stare as always, which made you wonder if anyone was home. "Okay," he finally said, and he went back to writing his letter. I just walked off, knowing it was going to be a long day tomorrow.

"Wake up, Mr. Cory. You have a zero six hundred launch," said the ops clerk.

"What kind of mission?" I asked through the haze of sleep.

"Log and assault, out of Camp Gorvad," he answered. *Hmm*, I thought as I dragged my ass out to take a piss. The terrain around Gorvad was fairly flat and had low vegetation, mostly tall brush and few big trees. PZ and LZs were plentiful. No hover holes, though, and I wished we were going to have at least one of those. Did I really want one of those with Big Rick? Who was I kidding? I headed back to get dressed and grab my gear. I walked over to Flight Ops, and Rick came out of his hooch and walked with me.

"Morning, Rick," I said. I might as well be civil to the guy. Maybe he would surprise me.

"Hey, Dan," he responded. Man of few words.

"Okay, once we get to the door at Flight Ops, you are the AC and take the lead. Got it?"

"Got it," he responded flatly. In Flight Ops, the assistant ops officer began his brief, addressing me. I stopped him.

"Rick is AC today. Need to talk to him." The look of surprise was obvious, but Rick didn't see it because Rick was looking at the area of operations map.

"Hey, Rick, you want this brief?" Mr. Stevens asked.

"Yeah, sure." And Rick rejoined the conversation as I stepped back and made my own notes. Arriving at the aircraft, we began our preflight and Rick was putting his stuff in the right seat.

"Rick, you're left seat today," I reminded him.

"Yeah, but I like the right seat. I'll fly it today." Unusual in our unit, but okay if he wanted to fly right seat. No big thing. We climbed in and got ourselves adjusted, and he started going through his start-up procedure. Before we got out of the revetment, he made a major mistake. He forgot to do the hydraulics check. Pick up the aircraft with no hydraulics and you could have a major accident. I made a note of that.

"Okay, take us out," he said, turning to me. So he wasn't

going to pick us up to a hover in the revetment, which was a problem for him, as I had seen and others had pointed out. Smart on his part; he was the AC after all.

"I have the aircraft," I said and commenced with the hydraulics check.

The crew cleared us. I applied power, eased us out of the revetment and turned towards the runway.

"I have the aircraft," Rick said, taking the controls. "Get us clearance for takeoff." I did, and we hovered out. Rick applied power down the runway and climbed out. As we cleared the trees, he directed me, "Take the controls and give me a heading to Camp Gorvad at fifteen hundred feet."

"I have the aircraft," I responded and took up a heading to our destination. *Does he not know the way to Camp Gorvad?* Normally an AC would climb out and take up his heading to the destination and even fly for a bit to get the feel of the aircraft.

The flight over was uneventful and quiet, without the normal early-morning banter between the crew, each lost in his own thoughts. That was okay. *Oops! Rick didn't get us arty clearance to Camp Gorvad. Major mistake. Noted.*

As we approached Camp Gorvad, Rick asked for the controls and told me to contact the unit and get us our clearances, which I did and relayed it to him. The unit's instructions were to shut down on the log pad and come in for a briefing. So far Big Rick was doing okay—two major mistakes and a couple of little things. Rick retained control of the aircraft and landed on the unit's log pad, which was the same log pad that had been used since I'd arrived in-country over a year ago. We headed into the brief, which was conducted by the S-3 air. They had three morning resupply runs for us right away. *Good*, I thought.

Rick asked, "What's the call sign and freq of each and where are they?" Reasonable question, I was thinking. The S-3 air handed Rick a piece of paper with the information and we left. So far so good.

Arriving at the aircraft, we saw that it had been loaded with cases of C rations. I looked around and didn't see any water cans. Unit must have been resupplied the night before with water. Rick spread his map out and hunkered over it. I looked over his shoulder. *Oh shit!* He was not only marking the location of each unit on the map, which in itself was okay, but he was writing the call sign and frequency of each unit next to each mark. Major no-no. I said nothing but made a note. We cranked the aircraft, and Rick pulled in the power for the takeoff, with no announcement of coming up, leaving the crew chief standing on the ground. Poor Lovelace was attempting to climb onto the aircraft by grabbing the machine-gun mount and hanging on.

"Stop! Stop! I'm not on board," Lovelace howled. And Rick did, but he put the collective down so fast that it almost landed on Lovelace's foot and banged us hard.

"Sir, you have to let us know you're coming up and give us a chance to respond." I could tell that Lovelace was pissed.

"I thought you were on board." Rick's voice was a bit testy. "Don't get out of the aircraft unless I tell you to."

"Sir, we were shut down on the log pad. Do you want us to stay in our seats when we're shut down?" Now Peters was entering the fray. This was going south real quick.

"I think the ground guide is signaling you, Rick," I said to get the mission going.

My crew had only so much patience. Rick turned his attention to the ground guide, who was signaling all clear to come up. Again Rick pulled up on the collective without notifying the crew. *Okay, that's how it's going to be.* I knew my crew. They were professional enough that they weren't going to do anything that would endanger us or damage the aircraft, but they were probably not going to do anything to help out

Rick either. Rick flew us out to the first location. Arriving overhead, we could see troops on the ground. He began his approach.

"Rick, don't you think we should call and ask for smoke?"

"I can see them. I don't need smoke," he responded.

"Just because you can see troops on the ground doesn't mean they're friendly." I was trying to coach him to do the right thing without directing him to do the right thing.

"Okay, you call them," he directed.

"Badger Six, Chicken-man One-Niner, over."

"Chicken-man One-Niner, I have you in sight, smoke out."

"Badger Six, Chicken-man One-Niner, I have Rosy Red."

"Chicken-man One-Niner, that's affirmative. Recommend you land north to south. Over."

"Badger Six, roger.

Got that, Rick?" I asked.

"Got it."

And Rick set up his approach to land south to north. The smoke clearly showed a breeze from the south, and the recommendation from the ground unit was land to the south, so why was he setting up for a downwind landing? He was flying, so I kept my mouth shut. I made a note. The LZ was a good long clearing devoid of small trees and brush. Rick made his approach, passing directly over the troops on the ground with plenty of airspeed as the wind was pushing the aircraft along and he was using maximum power to come to a hover. As we had speed coming over the southern end of the clearing, we used the entire clearing to stop the aircraft and turn around. If there were any unfriendly troops on the north end of the LZ, we would have been a tempting target. We hovered back to the troops and unloaded the C-rations and took on empty water cans.

"You have the aircraft," Rick instructed me. Lovelace and

Peters were still in their seats, not helping the grunts load—doing what they had been told. As the unloading of the C-rations was complete and the empty water cans loaded, Rick instructed the crew,

"Close the doors. I don't want any of the water cans to blow out." This was unheard of.

"Sir, we close the doors, we can't fire our guns if we need to," Lovelace stated, almost pleading.

"I don't care, I don't want any of those water cans to blow out."

I looked at Rick, glad that my sun visor was down so he couldn't see my eyes, which must have been the size of saucers. I made another note. If the aircraft was properly flown, water cans didn't blow out of the cargo area.

I flew us back to the log pad and picked up the next load, returning to the LZ and making a north-to-south approach. After we were offloaded, Rick instructed me to take off and return to the log pad while he studied his map. We were halfway back when he put his map on the top of the instrument panel and took the aircraft controls. Maps did not go on top of instrument panels because maps in that location were above the open side window and had a tendency to blow out. Rick's map was no exception, and out the window it went.

"I have the aircraft," I stated and turned immediately to keep an eye on the map as it drifted downward.

"Peters, keep an eye on that map. Rick, this ride is over. I'm AC for the rest of the day. We'll talk when we get to the log pad. Watch that map." He said nothing and continued to watch. Finally the map landed.

"Mr. Cory, it's down. There's a clearing about twenty meters from where it landed," said Peters.

"Roger. Lovelace, pass up your M-16 to Rick. Here's the deal, Rick. I'm going to land in that clearing and drop you off. You're going to retrieve that map and come back to the clearing, where I am going to pick you up, and you will jump into the cargo area so I'm on the ground for only a few seconds. I'll orbit low over you and cover you with the guns. Any questions?"

Rick just stared at me like I was nuts. I wasn't. I was pissed. Stupid to let the map fly out, but what was worse was putting call signs, frequencies and locations on the map. Locations, okay, but not all the other stuff.

We flew around in a circle several times to see if we could spot anyone on the ground. Finally I set up the approach and landed. It was this sort of thing that had gotten Dave killed. Reluctantly, Rick got out with the M-16 and moved away from the aircraft. As soon as he was clear, we were back in the air. As I circled above him, his movements reminded me of Elmer Fudd hunting the elusive Bugs Bunny.

"Damn, sir, why doesn't he just haul ass over and get it?" Peters asked.

"Because he's scared, that's why," I answered.

Lovelace had moved over to the right side of the aircraft and was holding Peters's M-16 and searching the brush. Finally Rick got to the map and this time sprinted as fast as his fat little body would carry him to the clearing, waving his arms frantically as we made our approach as if we didn't see him. The aircraft hadn't touched the ground, and he was on board and we were coming out. At the log pad, he resumed his position in the right seat.

"Okay, I have the aircraft," he said, as if he didn't understand his situation.

"No, Rick. You do not. I am now the AC." And with that, I put us on private on the intercom.

"Rick, you have bused this check ride. First you left this morning without doing a hydraulics check. That's a major mistake. If all else had gone well, I would have overlooked that. Getting here, you didn't know the heading, and yet you've been flying for, what, six months now? You still don't know your way around the AO. You never got us clearance from Arty, another major mistake. Then you plot unit locations, which in itself is okay, but you put the call sign and frequencies on your map, which is a major mistake. And where does your map go? Out the window. A major mistake. Let's not forget you left your crew chief standing on the ground when you picked up and then nearly set the aircraft back down on him. You instructed the crew to close the doors, which in essence left the aircraft defenseless. Rick, I can't sign you off for AC. Look, you're an okay guy and no one has it in for you, but there's something about you. You aren't ready for AC. You're an okay copilot but not thinking like an AC."

"You going to tell the CO?" was his only response.

"I got to tell him something. He ordered this check ride. I tell you what. I'll say nothing to the other ACs, and I'll tell these two not to say anything about this being a check ride. That's the best I can do, but word will eventually get out, I'm sure."

"Okay. Thanks." Rick remained quiet for the rest of the flight and performed his duties in a satisfactory manner. In fact, he was more relaxed and did better. In fairness to him, I told the CO that it may have just been nerves that caused him to make some major mistakes, but the CO didn't buy it. Plotting frequencies and call signs along with unit locations on your map isn't nerves, and what would he do under fire?

I was about to find out.

Landing at LZ Snuffy, Rick and I went into the TOC and met with the S-3.

"Morning, Mr. Cory." Looking up, he saw me. "Wow, what's this? Lieutenant Cory now?"

"Yes, sir, I've come over to the RLO side as of last night."

"Well, congratulations. What branch?"

"Infantry, sir."

"Oh shit, you're going to be a grunt. Different world. I'll see if I can get you assigned here."

"Sir, I still have to go to Benning School for Boys, and that won't be until I rotate back."

"Too bad. I could use you here as S-3 air. Okay, here's what we got today. Backhauling a ton of crap. We have a medical supply bunker that's full of new medical instruments. I mean new in the packing crates from Europe. I have a bunker packed with new Chinese Communist SKS rifles still wrapped in grease and paper. I have a couple of bunkers of rice. I need to resupply three rifle companies. That should keep you busy for today. Might toss in a C&C flight as well," he added.

"Sounds like we're not going to get bored today. If your guys are ready, we'll head out for the first load."

"Alpha is standing by with a load of rice for you. I'll call them and let them know you're coming."

We headed back to the aircraft, which was already loaded with thirty water cans to take to Alpha. Lovelace had supervised the loading, so the aircraft was ready to go. As Rick was going through the start-up procedures, I was tuning the radio to Alpha Company's frequency on the FM radio.

"I have the aircraft." I took the controls from Rick.

"You have the aircraft," he responded.

The crew cleared us, and I pulled in forty pounds of torque. The bird responded beautifully, and I had to decrease some torque to keep us from leaping into the air. Clearing the firebase, we headed in the general direction of the Alpha Company LZ. Flying out, I called Alpha Company.

"Sidewinder Six, this is Chicken-man One-Niner, the wonderful white-winged wicked weekend warrior. Over," I said, taking a line from the radio show.

"Chicken-man One-Niner, good morning, Sidewinder Six India, over."

"Sidewinder, good morning. The wonderful white-winged wicked weekend warrior is here to serve you this fine day," I joked with him.

"Chicken man One-Niner, smoke is out." I could hear him and someone else laughing in the background.

"Roger, I have Goofy Grape."

"Chicken-man One-Niner, that is affirmative."

A moment later, as I was descending and setting up my approach to the smoke, Lovelace chimed in.

"Ah, sir, I have purple smoke behind us at eight o'clock." I was looking at two o'clock. Something was wrong, and I increased power to get altitude.

"Sidewinder Six, Chicken-man One-Niner, I'm a bit confused. Can you pop another smoke for me? Give me a Mellow Yellow." There was a long pause.

"Roger, Chicken-man One-Niner, I understand you want a yellow smoke. Wait one." Since our last sighting of the smoke, we had executed a 180-degree turn and were facing the second purple smoke location. Now we were seeing yellow smoke mingling with the second plume of purple smoke.

"Sidewinder Six, Chicken-man One-Niner, I have your yellow smoke."

"Negative, Chicken-man! I did not, repeat, did not pop yellow smoke."

"Roger, Sidewinder Six! Wait one." And I switched to FM number 2.

"Song Be Arty, fire mission, troops in the open, coordinates..."

Shortly afterwards, I heard, "Chicken-man One-Niner, shot out."

Turning to Rick, I said, "Take over adjusting the artillery, I'll fly." And he did, hitting the target with one adjustment.

"Nice shooting, Rick," I complimented him. I received his usual stoic reaction.

It was a trick of the NVA to monitor the radio frequency that the grunts were using to communicate with the aircraft and if possible lure an aircraft to the wrong location by popping the color of smoke identified by the aircraft, only for it to be greeted by antiaircraft fire. Aircraft never called for a particular color of smoke but always identified the smoke that the grunts had chosen. We returned to Sidewinder's location and began an approach to his PZ.

"Chicken-man One-Niner, break off. Break off, we are in contact. RPGs!" The aircraft nosed over and banked hard left to terminate the approach and gain speed and altitude.

"Sir, I can see where it's coming from. They're in the tree-tops," Peters said.

"Sidewinder Six, you have snipers in the treetops with RPGs."

"Roger," came his response over the sound of heavy automatic weapons fire and explosions. With each explosion, we could see a puff of black smoke as the RPG was launched, indicating the shooters' positions.

"Sidewinder Six, Chicken-man here. I can see their positions. Do you want me to make a gun run and distract them from you?"

"Chicken-man One-Niner, go ahead, but just don't shoot us."

"What heading are you facing?"

"Facing due east, over."

"I'll make my run north-south. Okay, crew, I want both guns firing straight ahead and swinging straight down unless you see an identified target. Got it?"

"Got it, understood," the crew replied.

Into a shallow dive we went with both guns firing to the front and down. The RPG fire stopped, and I could see tracers from the grunts' automatic weapons passing under me. *Hope they don't shoot us*, I was thinking when Peters broke my train of thought.

"Shit, RPG! Sir, they're shooting those things at us." His comment was confirmed almost immediately by Sidewinder Six as an RPG streaked behind the aircraft.

"Chicken-man One-Niner, you almost took an RPG in the ass. Clear the area. We have arty coming in soon."

"Roger. Chicken-man is clear of the area and standing by. Rick, you have it."

"I have the aircraft," Rick said as we pulled up and moved out of the way of incoming artillery. During the whole time, Rick just sat there, appearing to be bored with the whole thing.

After a few minutes, during which several artillery rounds landed in the vicinity of the RPG fire, we heard, "Chickenman One-Niner, Sidewinder Six, over."

"Sidewinder Six, Chicken-man, go."

"Chicken-man One-Niner, PZ is secure. Can you take out our wounded?"

"Sidewinder Six, that's affirmative. How many?" I asked as Rick set up our approach.

"Chicken-man, we have seven. Medivac is coming, but if you take them to LZ Snuffy, it'll be quicker for them."

"Roger. We are one minute out. Pop smoke."

Almost immediately, smoke was blowing across the PZ. Rick brought the aircraft in fast and stopped on a dime, troops climbing aboard right away. None had on their load-bearing equipment or rucksacks. Most were walking wounded, but one was missing a foot and had a tourniquet around his leg. Most looked to have shrapnel wounds from RPGs.

As the last was loaded, I gave Rick a thumbs-up. "Let's go."

As we approached the log pad, medics were standing by with a stretcher for our soldier with the missing foot. As much pain as he was in, he was high-fiving guys because he knew he was going home. I could see the morphine needle sticking through his shirt collar and a bloody red "M" on his forehead indicating he was on morphine. The others would be back in the field in a couple of weeks from the looks of things. As we were loading some ammo to take back, I saw a medivac chopper approaching. For the next five hours, we were flying steady, hauling in supplies and backhauling all manner of materiel. Finally we got a chance to shut down and eat some C-rations. Lovelace grabbed a five-gallon can of water, and we all helped wash the blood out of the aircraft. I saw the S-3 approaching, and he was not smiling.

"Hey, Dan, I need you to get out to Bravo for a backhaul to Song Be."

"Okay, what we got?" I asked.

"We just lost two to another RPG attack. The bodies need to go back there. Medivac won't take them."

"Yeah, I know," I mumbled. "They take the living but... okay, let the unit know we are on our way. Mount up, guys, we have a pickup."

As the crew policed up our garbage and closed up the C-ration box, I explained to them our cargo for this trip. This wasn't the first time, but we never got used to hauling the dead out. From Song Be, someone else would fly these grunts to Camp Gorvad for their final trip home.

As we approached the PZ, Rick called for the smoke and made our landing with a ground guide. When we touched down, there were two groups of four standing soldiers, one group on each side of the aircraft. With each group was a wrapped poncho lying on the ground. The ponchos were tied, but it was obvious that these were boys making their final trip home. I wondered what their families were doing right now. Soon they would have a visit from an officer, who was normally accompanied by a chaplain. Casualty notification officer was not an assignment that anyone volunteered for. The days of just a telegram from the Pentagon had ended in early 1967.

The crew concentrated on watching the ground and rear of the aircraft as we flew back. They didn't like seeing the dead on the aircraft.

I mumbled a prayer that I had written. "May they soar with the angels on wings of eagles; may they watch over those they loved and those who loved them; may they rest in peace until we all gather for the final formation."

Returning to LZ Snuffy, we resumed our backhaul and resupply, and when finally released, we had racked up another twelve-hour day with a hour-and-forty-five-minute flight to get home. Rick had done good today and had risen to the occasion, I was glad to tell the CO that night.

# 42

## AND THE BEAT GOES ON

THE NEXT DAY WE WERE BACK, BUT THIS TIME TO LZ Jamie with a six-two package. We were going to be doing combat assaults all day, it appeared, and the brigade was controlling it all. The Third Brigade was a good outfit to work for, and I had done so many times in the past sixteen months. As we were waiting to refuel our aircraft at the refuel/rearm point that had been established, two helicopters landed, but I couldn't tell what make or model they were. They weren't Army aircraft but Navy, and painted blue. Everyone's curiosity was piqued. What the hell was the Navy doing so far from the ocean, which was at least a hundred and fifty miles away? Had they really gotten that lost?

After they shut down, the pilots came over and asked who was in charge.

"In charge of what?" I asked.

"This whole operation," the lieutenant junior grade answered, attempting to muster some authority. His rank was the same as first lieutenant in the Army.

"That'd be the TOC. I'll take you up there. I'm Lieutenant Cory. What are you guys doing here?" I asked as we started walking.

"We were told to fly up here and help find cache sites. Normally we're dropping sonar buoys and listening for subs, but we have the capability to drop magnetometers and pick up metal."

"How 'bout that? How does that work, and what kind of aircraft is that?" I asked.

"Our aircraft are Sikorsky SH-3As, Sea Kings. We fly off the ship and they direct us to where they think a sub may be. We come to a hover and drop the magnetometers on a cable into the water and watch for a reading on the oscilloscope. If we get a hit, we drop a torpedo."

"Let me get this straight—you're going to fly to a point and hover while you drop that thing into the jungle. Is that right?"

"Yeah." And we continued to walk. I was thinking, *Buddy, you have no idea about this, do you?* When he was hovering over the water, no one was hiding and shooting an AK-47 up his ass. It didn't take him long to learn, however. Very first time out, Charlie let him know that there would be no hovering with a magnetometer hanging down into the jungle. They were going to have to develop a new tactic for this to work. And they did. The next day they were back, and while they continued to operate for a couple of more days, the magnetometer was strapped to the wheel struts of the aircraft and they flew at sixty knots over the jungle. Don't know how effective they were, but at least the Navy was with us in spirit.

A few days later, things didn't go as well. Coming out of a hot LZ, a door gunner, PFC Kittleson, took a round in the armpit, which wasn't covered by the chicken plate, and died before he could receive medical attention. A couple of days later, a formal memorial service was held in the afternoon. It was the only time I ever recalled the unit hosting such a service. PFC Kittleson was a very popular kid, and his loss was felt throughout the company. But the missions continued.

"Lieutenant Cory, you have Night Hawk tonight," the ops clerk informed me as I returned to Lai Khe with a damaged aircraft around noon. "We just got the mission, and you're the only AC back here with experience flying that mission. You best get some sleep this afternoon. I'll wake you around eighteen hundred."

"Okay, but my aircraft is done for today, so it's going to have to be another with crew."

"I'll get with maintenance and see what they have. I'll try to get it instrument equipped in case you hit bad weather," he added as I walked out.

At 1800 hours, I was deep in a pleasant dream when it was interrupted by the ops clerk. "Lieutenant Cory, you have a nineteen hundred departure. Specialist Grossman is getting the aircraft ready now."

"Okay, I'm awake," I stated as I rolled out of bed and started getting dressed. When I arrived at the aircraft, Specialist Grossman had it ready with the M2 .50-cal mounted and the searchlight and starlight scope in the cargo door. Specialist Jones was on the searchlight tonight with Specialist Leonard on the .50-cal. Grandpa was occupying the copilot seat, which I found reassuring.

"Evening, gents, are we ready?" I asked as I climbed up to inspect the rotor head.

"Everything looks good," Grandpa came back. "Did you bring any cigarettes?" I ignored him. Grossman gave me a thumbs-up, as did Leonard.

"Okay, we're going to Song Be to refuel and then out to LZ Jamie to work with Third Brigade. We'll meet up with Lobo and a flare ship up there. The flare ship is coming from Bravo Company. Not sure who's flying Lobo tonight," I explained to the crew. In the Snake Pit, I could see someone preflighting an aircraft and assumed it was our cover bird for the night. The Cobra was a much faster aircraft, so he could launch later and still get to Jamie before me.

The flight to LZ Jamie was uneventful, much to my pleasure. At LZ Jamie, we shut down just as Lobo and the flare ship arrived. When they were ready, the pilots all headed into the TOC for the mission brief.

"Evening, Lieutenant Cory," greeted the operations officer S-3.

"Evening, sir. Let me introduce the other pilots tonight." And I proceeded to introduce everyone. Seldom did Cobra pilots meet with operations officers as the Cobra was generally in a support role to the lift aircraft and generally arrived after the mission brief was given to flight leaders.

"Here's what we have for you tonight." He pointed at the map of the area. "We have indications of vehicle movement on this road and want you to check it out. Start where this bridge crosses the river and go northeast."

"How far northeast do you want us to go?" I asked.

"Until you need to come back for fuel, unless you can find a refuel point out there somewhere." He thought he was funny.

"Sir, where are the nearest friendlies?" Mr. Beckman, the Cobra AC, asked.

"South of the bridge," the S-3 responded.

"What's the enemy situation along the road?" I asked.

"Well, we have vehicle traffic moving on that road, according to sensor readings."

"What about troops or antiaircraft positions?" Mr. Cosby asked.

"Not aware of any," the S-3 sort of mumbled.

"Let me understand this. We start at the bridge and follow this road, the only road in this part of Cambodia of any size. We fly northeast until we have to return for fuel. You have no intel except that there's vehicle traffic along the road. You have no idea about enemy antiaircraft positions or troop concentrations. And if we go down, there's no way you can get anyone up to help us out. Is this what I'm hearing?"

"That's about it, Mr. Beckman," the S-3 said while moving his eyes to the floor. I could see that Mr. Beckman was about to explode, but I cut in.

"Sir, where are the nearest artillery positions and what is their coverage up that road?" I asked.

"The nearest artillery position is here, and they're 105 howitzers," said the S-3, pointing at the map.

"You're shitting me," Mr. Beckman interrupted. "That unit can only cover ten klicks beyond the bridge. We'll be out of his coverage in no time."

"Okay, sir, we'll give you a call when we lift off. Thank you, sir. Let's go, guys." I took Beckman by the shoulder and guided him out of the TOC. Walking back to our aircraft, Beckman was a bit upset.

"Dan, you up for this? You know this could be a shit sandwich for all of us. You're down low and we're up high at a perfect altitude for antiaircraft guns. You go over one troop concentration and you're going to have a hell of a lot of AK fire. I don't know about this," he grumbled.

"Look, we got the mission, so let's be smart and get it done. I'm not going to follow the road. I'll fly an S pattern up the road from one side to the other, crossing the road each time perpendicular. That'll give me minimum exposure over open ground. I suggest you guys fly circles clockwise and counterclockwise to switch it up. Flying an S pattern will use fuel and not put us too far up the road. I have no desire to follow that road to Hanoi, so I'm really going to concentrate on the area ten kilometers north of the bridge, within artillery range," I explained.

After a few more minutes of discussion, we went our separate ways and cranked the birds. There was a bit of apprehension in the aircraft as we lifted off. Grandpa reached in his pocket and put a fresh pack of cigarettes on the center console with his lighter. Three klicks off the firebase, we picked up the road and proceeded to follow it northeast to the bridge. Grandpa had the artillery frequency tuned in as well and had marked on his map the limit of the artillery range for the 105s. Mentally, that was my limit of advance for this night, and I told my crew that as well. I was not flying out of the range of artillery support. Approaching the bridge, I slowed the aircraft to sixty knots and dropped to treetop level while executing the beginning of an S flight pattern.

"Lobo Two-Six, Chicken-man One-Niner, commencing my run."

"Chicken-man One-Niner, roger, I have you covered. Good luck."

"Jones, how's the starlight scope working?" Secretly I was hoping he would tell me it wasn't and we would have to go back.

"Working fine, sir," Jones said. *Damn.* We continued up the road for another five minutes and saw nothing except jungle vegetation and the road.

"Sir, we have houses on the road ahead," Jones reported.

"What? How many?" I asked.

"Looks to be about six, and they're big. They're at nine o'clock now. Your next turn is going to put us right over them," Jones replied.

"Okay, any lights?" I asked as we started to make a left turn back to the road.

"Didn't see any. They're at your eleven now," he said as I started slowing the aircraft to forty knots. Grandpa was on the radio, calling Lobo to inform him of what we were looking at. As we approached the cluster of houses, they appeared to be on stilts and about thirty feet long and fifteen feet wide.

Thatched roofs and bamboo mat sides. One set of stairs up the front of each to a wraparound porch on each house. There were no signs of life, not even chickens or pigs. Just deserted. We passed it by and did not engage. Continuing up the road, we came upon a second village, which looked to be deserted like the last. These appeared to be Montagnard villages. The Montagnards were the indigenous people of the region. These people were generally friendly to US forces but not so with the Vietnamese. Good to know if we went down and had to exercise our SERE training.

Moving further northeast, we came upon a third village. Again I slowed the aircraft to forty knots as I came over the village, almost hoping to take fire as the evening was becoming boring. As I passed over, Jones spoke up.

"Sir, I have someone in the village!"

"Where?" I asked excitedly.

"Right in the middle of the buildings. He's just standing there." Grandpa had his grenade launcher cocked and loaded and was peering down as he was talking to Lobo. I slowly brought the aircraft back around.

"Jones, hit the searchlight. Everyone, get ready."

The searchlight came on, lighting up the town, which wasn't necessary as the flare ship had dropped a flare and the entire village was bathed in white light. The gentleman standing in the middle of the village was naked except for a loin cloth and a Montagnard crossbow he was holding.

"Sir, should I engage?" Leonard asked.

"No, not yet. We'll hold off unless we take fire. Grandpa, tell Lobo to hold off, but keep us covered." As we were at a hover at fifty feet right over the village, people started appearing. First it was just a couple of guys, then women and children. Within a minute, we had maybe one hundred Montagnards standing in the village center, but we didn't take fire. I was calling this in.

"Wrangler Six, Chicken-man One-Niner, over."

"Chicken-man One-Niner, Wrangler Six India, over."

"Wrangler Six, Chicken-man. I have a village with approximately one hundred people that appear to be Montagnards." I gave him the coordinates. "We have not taken fire, and they're just standing here. Over."

"Chicken-man, understand you have a village with one hundred people, is that correct?"

"Wrangler Six, that is affirmative," I responded.

"Roger, Chicken-man One-Niner, engage." *What did I just hear?*

"Wrangler Six, did you just tell me to engage?"

"Roger, Chicken-man, you are to engage."

"Wrangler Six, you must have misunderstood. These are Montagnard villagers and not, repeat, not November Victor Alphas. We are not taking fire nor hostile actions. Over."

"Roger, Chicken-man, understood and you are to engage." Grandpa was looking at me with a shocked expression.

"What are we going to do?" he asked me.

"Not sure, but we're not going to engage. I can tell you that. Guys, nobody shoots. Understood? Unless we take fire," I told them. They all responded with an affirmative and I believe a sigh of relief.

"Lobo, Chicken-man One-Niner."

"Go ahead, Chicken-man."

"Lobo, are you seeing what I'm seeing in the village?"

"Sure am, and they look like civilians. What are we going to do?"

"We are not engaging. Repeat, not. We did not take fire."

"Roger, sounds good to us. Let's continue up the road."

And we did, which paid off nicely as five minutes later, Jones reported, "Sir, I have a light, very faint, up the road maybe three hundred yards." Grandpa was flying now, with the road on the left side of the aircraft.

"Grandpa, let's parallel the road until that light's at our ten o'clock. Jones, do you still see it?"

"Yes, sir. I'll bet it's someone smoking a cigarette."

"When we get it at nine o'clock, hit it with the searchlight. Leonard, are you ready?"

"Yes, sir. Target will be at ten o'clock." And he pointed his gun to the ten o'clock position. Suddenly the searchlight came on and there stood a guy next to a truck, smoking a cigarette. Leonard depressed the butterfly trigger on the .50-cal and laid rounds into the truck.

"Lobo, Chicken-man, engage!" My call was unnecessary as Lobo went into a dive as soon as the light came on and was delivering rockets when a secondary explosion occurred on the other side of the truck. On cue and without request, flares began to light up the area. It immediately became obvious that we needed to get out of there as we were sitting over a truck park with several trucks along the road and more under the trees.

"Chicken-man, Lobo, I'm expended." The number of explosions and the secondary explosions left no doubt in my mind that he had punched off every rocket he was carrying.

"Roger, Flight. Let's head south back to Jamie," I called out.

"Song Be Arty, Chicken-man One-Niner, fire mission?"

And we turned the rest of the destruction over to the King of Battle, after we told him where to place his balls. Returning to the TOC, we briefed the S-3 on the mission and told him we were done for the night as the weather was starting to turn for the worse and the flare ship wasn't instrument equipped to fly in bad weather. We had a good night.

The next day, others did not fare so well. Bill Hess was breaking in a new platoon leader, an RLO, in to flying in

Cambodia. The mission was a resupply with fifteen water cans and two priests on board. Chaplains in general and priests in particular were not seen very often going into company locations. Bill was letting the lieutenant make the first approach into a hover hole that was really not much of a problem as it was a natural clearing surrounded by bamboo, which was also surrounding a small metal-roofed house.

"Slow your approach, you're coming in a bit hot," Bill instructed the lieutenant.

As the lieutenant started to decelerate, the aircraft experienced a low side compressor stall and began to lose power, settling rapidly. The lieutenant was pulling up the collective, trying to keep from crashing, which only increased the loss of power and the rapid descent. Bill didn't have time to react as they were running out of airspeed and altitude and were inside the dead man's curve. They crashed into the roof of the house and rolled over, with the rotor blades chopping bamboo like a giant lawn mower. When things stopped, everyone was hanging upside down and suspended about ten feet in the air on a pillow of bamboo. The biggest fears were fire and being impaled on a bamboo spear when they released their seat belts. Eventually everyone got out okay. It must have been the fact that priests were hard to come by and God did not want to lose two to Bill and the lieutenant.

# 43

## ROCK ISLAND EAST

Almost every day, new cache sites were being discovered and they were huge, covering three and four acres in size. One was so large it was named Rock Island East. Located north of Loc Ninh, the amount of materiel in each site was too much to haul out so it had to be destroyed in place. Tons of rice; million rounds of small-arms ammunition; new medical supplies that had been flown into Cambodia on Air France and then trucked to these sites. There were twenty-seven bunkers on Rock Island East and each was so large that it took an eighty-man unit one day to clean out just one of these bunkers. This was just too much to evacuate, and it had to be destroyed. The seven-man demolition team brought three hundred cases of C-4 plastic explosives, with thirty sticks to a case; twelve cases of det cord with three rolls to a case and one thousand feet per roll. In addition, the NVA were not far away and were probing the demolition crew's work.

From Bu Dop, a loud rumbling noise could be heard in the distance. Unlike an arc light bombing run, which rumbled for a good minute, this was just one noise that dissipated quickly. About thirty minutes later, four aircraft from C

Company arrived with their commander, Major Lawson, as the flight leader.

I had flown with his company before on a couple of air assault insertions. He led all his company's air assault missions. I liked flying with this group as he was a squared-away commander in my book and kept the mission as well as the safety of the flight crews in mind, maintaining a balance. I was supposed to join his flight for an assault later in the day and would just be waiting here for that mission to kick off. Might as well let him know I was here, so I walked over to his aircraft, where he was just opening a C-ration meal.

"Hey, sir, Chicken-man One-Nine, attached to you for this afternoon's flight." Naturally I saluted as I approached.

Returning my salute, he said, "Dan, how you doing? Glad to have you with us today. Want a C?"

"I think I'll pass on that, sir." Looking over the aircraft that came in with him, I noticed only four. "Sir, I thought this was going to be a six-ship lift. We missing someone?" I asked.

"Yeah, I had a bird earlier go down for maintenance and am waiting for a replacement to get up here." He started chuckling. "I got to tell you the damnedest story. Sit down." He slid over a foot so we both could sit in the cargo door.

"Do you remember watching Keystone Cops when you were a kid?"

"Yeah."

"Well, this morning it was that, Keystone Cops. We had five ships to pick up the demo team located at Rock Island East. The PZ was a three-ship, so we went in three and two. The demo charges were all set, and the NCOIC of the demo team, MSG Land, lit the fuses as the last two aircraft came in. Not a problem, the fuses had a ten-minute burn.

"MSG Land strolls back and climbs aboard Chalk Four and they start to come out. As Four pulls power, it starts bleeding off. He can't get off the ground with his load, and he is not overloaded. I'm sitting up at twenty-five hundred and watching this. Land jumps out of the aircraft and walks—walks, mind you—over to the burning fuses, about twenty-five yards, and starts cutting them. In the meantime the crew chief is our working on the engine.

"As Land walks back to the aircraft, the crew chief closes the cowling and tells the pilot they're good to go. Land gets to the aircraft and the pilot tells him to light the fuses, so he walks back, lights them and moves back to the aircraft, only now the fuses will blow in seven minutes. He gets in the aircraft; they start to lift and again no power. Pilot tells Land to cut the fuses. Land hops out, and as he does, the crew chief appears, and this time Land is trotting over to the fuses.

"About this time a charge that was set to blow, keeping the NVA away, goes off on the far side of the site. Someone set it off. Land lights the fuses and trots back to the aircraft. They attempt to take off and still can't. Pilot sends Land back to cut the fuses again, and this time he's jogging over to the burning fuses. He cuts them and jogs back to the aircraft. Just as he gets to the aircraft, the pilot must have told him to go back and light the fuses because he takes off in a sprint back to the fuses.

"We can see some gooks on the far side of the site, moving cautiously as another charge went off that was booby-trapped. Land gets to the fuses, which now only have a four-minute burn because he's cut them three times. He lights them and is sprinting back to the aircraft. They try to come out, but still the bird won't get off the ground, so the pilot kicks him off with two other and they go back to Chalk Five. They climb in and Chalk Five can't get off now because he's overloaded, so he kicks those three out and tells them he'll come back.

"As he's coming out of the PZ, and without telling anyone, Chalk Three, who dropped his pax off, comes over the trees and lands. Land and team jump in, and Land tells the pilot he has one minute before it blows. Land had figured he was going to die right there from the blast with everything going off at once. That aircraft with only three pax came out of the PZ so fast it had to be a record. Pilot said he pulled forty-three pounds of torque and the aircraft shot out of there. He figured that the shock wave was going to kill them even in flight."

"Did they get out of there okay?" I asked, my eyes the size of saucers.

"Yeah, they were fine. When we got to Firebase Buttons and dropped everyone off, people there said they saw the mushroom cloud over Rock Island East, fifty klicks away."

"Sir, I think we heard it here and we're about that far as well. Must have been a hell of an explosion," I said, shaking my head.

"It was, and one that I don't ever want to be around again," Major Lawson said. "Well, I have a flight brief to get up at the TOC. See you later." And he stood and headed to the Brigade TOC.

Walking back to my aircraft, I was wondering why they just didn't drop a stick of B-52 bombs on the place. Wouldn't be much left after that.

## 44

## GAME CHANGER

THE PRESIDENT HAD ORDERED THAT ALL FORCES BE withdrawn from Cambodia by the end of June. On that day, I was Yellow One for a six-two working out of Bu Gia Map, where a firebase had been established at the old Special Forces camp. We were scheduled to insert a rifle company around noon from the firebase and extract the final elements of the division later that day from Cambodia to the firebase. As the rifle company wasn't ready for insertion, I instructed the flight to shut down. Blue Max arrived with two aircraft and shut down as well. Seldom did we meet Blue Max pilots, as they would arrive to support the mission in flight to the LZ and leave for their next mission without a chance to meet. The front seater was brand-new in-country, first mission. The back seater was an older pilot that would be rotating home soon. As we were talking, the sound of an AK-47 could be heard in the distance, along with the sounds of an approaching CH-47 Chinook helicopter. A grunt came out from the TOC and signaled me to come in.

"Sir," I said upon entering and seeing the battalion commander looking over the map.

"Change in plans, Lieutenant Cory. The CH-47 just took fire here." He indicated a location on a ridge due west of our location. "We're going to insert a rifle company here. It's the only clearing, as the ridge is covered in bamboo."

"Sir, we can go in there with six aircraft in staggered trail formation. Landing should be south to north, paralleling the ridge and in line with the valley. I know exactly what clearing that is. And you're right, it is the only clearing. Charlie may have it zeroed in for mortars. This could be a trap," I responded.

"Let's set H-Hour for half past the hour, and we'll give a six-minute artillery prep with a white phosphorous to clear the tubes, just in case he's there waiting."

"Sounds good, sir. I'll brief my crews, and we'll be off as soon as the grunts arrive."

As I finished the briefing for the pilots, the grunts began arriving. They were traveling light with light rucksacks, which made placing seven on each aircraft easy, leaving us with plenty of power. At the appointed time, we lifted off and the artillery opened with the prep. Flight time to the LZ was only about eight minutes, as it was just down in a valley below the firebase and the ridge on the other side that the fire had come from. At H minus two, the artillery fired the last round. The slicks were about three hundred feet above the trees. Blue Max nosed over into their gun run from one thousand feet.

"Jesus, what is that!" came a cry over the radio.

"Blue Max is down!" came another call.

"What the hell was that?" another aircraft called.

"Yellow One, get out of there!"

"Chalk Two taking fire. Smoke out."

"Chalk Three taking fire. Smoke out."[1]

"Flight, Yellow One, abort. I say again, abort. Return to PZ. Chalk Two, take the flight back to PZ."

"Yellow One, roger. Where are you going?"

"Yellow One is going to look over Blue Max." The aircraft broke formation and accelerated in a tight turn to locate the downed Blue Max. It became obvious very quickly where he was, as the column of black smoke rising from the bamboo marked his spot. Passing over the location at one hundred feet, it was apparent that neither pilot had survived the crash, as the tail boom was separated from the aircraft by some distance and the nose was caved in. The body of the aircraft was on fire from burning fuel and exploding rockets. A flight crew's worst nightmare is burning to death in a crash. A quick look indicated that neither pilot had burned to death; they had died on impact. We returned to the PZ, where the other ACs were standing waiting for word. It wasn't good. The remaining Blue Max and the two Cobras from Lobo were expending every rocket and minigun they had on board at the top of the ridge that the fire had come from.

"Who saw what took him out?" I asked after we shut down.

Mike spoke first. "I never seen anything like that. It was some sort of rocket that came off the ridge. Son of a bitch streaked up and hit him about four feet down the tail boom. Took it right off. The rotor head came off and just flew away like a giant fan. His nose went low and he just fell. Son of a bitch. Damn!"

"Christ, those guys never had a chance," another pilot spoke up.

"Are you sure it was a rocket? An RPG?" I asked.

"Shit, no. I've seen RPGs and this was not that," said Ron Fender, who'd had an RPG round come though his windshield when Mr. Young had been killed. "This thing had a white smoke trail like I've never seen before. It was more of a missile than a rocket," he added. "It initially wasn't even coming at him, and then it turned on him. An RPG wouldn't do that. This was a missile."

The grunts were leaving the aircraft and forming up. Seeing their company commander, I approached him. "Where are you going?"

"We're going to hump down to the aircraft and then up that ridge and see if we can find them. We're real sorry for you losing those guys. Never seen a Cobra go down before. What the hell was it that got him?"

"I have no idea. I didn't see it from where I was. The guys tell me it was some sort of missile. I hope you find the little bastards. They really set us up for this one. They were gunning for a Cobra."

"What do you mean?" he asked.

"Look, they fire an AK-47 at a CH-47. Nice and loud and he's coming in here fast and low. They know there are six UH-1s here and two Cobras, possibly four. They know that the LZ is the only usable LZ over there. So they're up on the ridge overlooking the LZ. We fire the artillery around the LZ but don't cover the ridge as it doesn't offer any direct fire on the LZ, and the artillery is to protect the assault on landing. They knew the UH-1s would be below the ridge on the approach, but the Cobras would be making their run from up high, and a missile shoots up, not down. An RPG would be fired down and not leave a white smoke trail. We walked right into their ambush."

"Have you ever seen a missile fired before?" he asked.

"No, and I hope I don't see another. This is going to change things. I need to get up to the TOC." I walked off. At the TOC, the battalion commander offered his condolences and told me that a report had been sent to higher. He said Blue Max was coming in force to work over the ridge. A lot of good that was going to do at this point. The shooters were long gone. We were on standby for any other missions until we had to depart for our last lift, which would be the final extraction out of Cambodia that the president had ordered.

Sitting back at my aircraft, I was bothered by the events of the morning. Had I screwed up? I should have insisted that the artillery shift to that ridge at H minus two. I knew nothing about missiles and had never seen one. Why the hell didn't we have any intel on these things? What was their range? How low did we have to fly to avoid them? How could we throw them off? Too many questions and no answers. In the distance, I could hear a Huey approaching. I hoped the TOC had told him to avoid the ridge, although several Blue Max aircraft were out there pounding the ridge with rockets. The arriving Huey came in to land next to my aircraft and I saw Major Sundstrum at the controls. He climbed out and with all his gear approached me.

"Dan, have your copilot get in my aircraft. I'm flying with you for this last mission." Shit, someone had lost confidence in my ability to be flight leader. My spirits plunged to the bottom of my gut, and at this point I didn't think it possible to go any lower. I informed my copilot that he was going back in the CO's aircraft, and he removed his gear. The major didn't appear to be happy, and I suspected that someone had gotten on to him about me screwing this operation up. It was time to launch for this last mission.

"Sir, you want the left seat?" I asked.

"No, you're AC. I'll right seat on this one." He began placing his gear in the right seat, giving the "crank them up" signal. The other crews began preparing their aircraft. When all was ready, I made the call.

"Flight, this is Yellow One on the go."

Off to the right, we could see that Blue Max wasn't letting up on pounding that ridge. More aircraft had joined the assault, and it appeared as if a hive of hornets had been unleashed. I wouldn't be surprised if an air strike had been called in on the place.

"Yellow One, Chalk Six, flight's up."

"Roger," I responded, my thoughts about the ridge interrupted.

"I got it if you please," the major said. A bit unusual for the right seater to ask to take the controls, but I let him have it. I guessed I should get it out as to why he was here and the ass chewing I knew was coming, so I switched our intercom to private.

"So, sir, how pissed is Battalion at me for this mess?"

"What are you talking about?" He looked at me with some degree of surprise. "What did you do?"

"Sir, I lost a bird this morning. A Blue Max got blown out of the sky on the lift this morning," I answered.

"I know nothing about it. What happened? Is that why Blue Max is working that ridge over?"

"Yes, sir. As he went into his dive, something— a rocket, a missile—came off that ridge and nailed him. Took the tail boom right off, I'm told."

"Did you see it?"

"No, sir, he was behind and above me."

"Well, that's not why I'm here. Battalion wanted me here for this last lift out of Cambodia. I told them you could handle it, but everyone is watching and it has to come off on time. Be thankful I'm here, because if it goes to hell, it'll be my ass, not yours, that they're going to be chewing on."

"Shit, sir, I thought Battalion sent you out here to relieve my ass because of the downed Cobra."

"Nope. Let's just pull off this last lift without any problems," he said before he switched off the private intercom. And we did pull it off.

# 45

## DARKER DAYS

"Flight, this is Yellow One. We have an eighteen-sortie mission in a two-ship LZ. We'll go in two, two and two with one-minute separation. With six aircraft, we'll do three turns. The LZ has some stumps in it, so be careful, and it's on a slope, so the grunts may have to jump a few feet. Our approach will put the upslope under the nose. You may not be able to touch down. Now for the bad news: we can't linger as it's expected to be a hot area. Gunners, be on your toes. Chalk Six, give me an up when all birds are loaded." To my crew, I said, "You guys have any questions?"

My copilot was a captain that was an AC also, and I had all the confidence in the world in his ability.

"Yellow One, Chalk Six, all birds are up."

"Roger, Chalk Six." Switching radios, I called the battalion commander for the mission.

"Sandbagger Six, Chicken-man One-Niner. All aircraft up and loaded. I have H minus ten and am departing. Over."

"Roger, Chicken-man One-Niner, H minus ten and departing," he came back to me as we were climbing out to head for our initial checkpoint, which should be H minus six and the start of the arty prep fires.

"Yellow One, all aircraft are up, staggered right," said Chalk Three.

"Roger. Chalk Three and Five, take up one-minute separations."

"Chalk Three, roger."

"Chalk Five, roger."

*This sucks. An eighteen-sortie insertion into a two-ship LZ with enemy contact highly probable. Charlie isn't stupid. He won't engage the first two aircraft but will wait for the next two or the last two. If he can knock a bird down in that LZ, the chances of other aircraft getting in are slim to none, and with only a few grunts on the ground, the enemy may be able to overrun them. This is not good. Someone isn't thinking.*

At H minus six, the first of the arty started hitting the LZ. At H minus two, the arty shifted to a ridge on the side of the LZ and the gunships rolled in. At H minus one, the door gunners opened fire and I got a clear view of the LZ. It was worse than I'd realized, having only seen it from the air at two thousand feet. Stumps everywhere, broken trees on the perimeter and no maneuver room with two aircraft in there. As we came to the high hover, the grunts started jumping. I'd always hated to have them jump with rucksacks on their backs. Good way to dislocate a knee or sprain an ankle. As my last grunt disappeared below the aircraft, Chalk Two called.

"Yellow One, are you clear?"

"Roger, Yellow One coming out."

"Chalk Three on short final." *Damn, that was about thirty seconds, but okay, the faster the better.* I turned the controls over to my copilot, and he began to take us back to get the next load when we heard a call over the radio.

"Bird down! Chalk Three is down in the LZ." It was Chalk Four on the radio.

"Chalk Four, what happened?" I asked with some apprehension.

"Looks like he came in too fast and fell through the hover. Some stumps have gone through the bottom and a skid is flattened. He's shutting down and un-assing the aircraft. I'll get him." Moments later, he said, "Chalk Four has him and is coming out."

"Chalk Five on short final."

"Chalk Six taking a one-minute separation."

Great, we now had a one-ship LZ with a downed bird in the forward portion. That bird being there meant not only minimum ground combat power, but also the grunts were going to have to stay there until a recovering crew could get in with a CH-47 and extract that aircraft or blow it in place. This was not good.

"Flight, this is Yellow One. On this next turn, everyone take a one-minute separation coming out of the PZ." The PZ was on the firebase, so only friendlies were there. I got my load on board, and we headed back with my copilot on the controls. I informed the battalion commander and he wasn't happy, but he understood. As we made our approach, I could see the downed aircraft had a bent skid but the rotor blades looked fine. Aside from the skid, I could see no damage. I had to clear this LZ. As we came to a low hover, I told my copilot to take the aircraft out once I got the downed bird airborne if I could, and I jumped out and ran to the other aircraft. Oops—it was on a stump, but nothing was leaking and all looked good. Shit, I could fly this out. I quickly started the aircraft. Reaching full power, I pulled up on the collective and the aircraft shook a bit as it came off a stump that I hadn't seen, impaling the bottom of the aircraft.

"Coming out," I reported. *Oh crap!* I had just gone from six hundred pounds of fuel to two hundred pounds! A fuel cell must be punctured. Two hundred was enough to get me to the firebase, and my copilot was following me. The aircraft was flying okay, and I stayed low. At the firebase, a pile of sandbags had been positioned to receive the aircraft and keep it off the ground. I noticed that it was Captain Copenhaver and a new pilot that had only been in the unit for a month or so. Captain Copenhaver's nickname was Lightning because he moved so slow with a long, slow stride. He sort of reminded us of Abraham Lincoln with his gangly features. Everyone liked him and his stories of riding across Europe on his BMW motorcycle while on leave.

As I climbed into my aircraft, my copilot looked at me and said, "You're either going to get a medal for that, or an ass chewing."

"My money is on the ass chewing," I said. I would have won. It was a very minor, fatherly reprimand from the major in my room that night after he calmly asked me what had happened and why I'd done it. He admitted he might have done the same thing in my shoes but told me not to do it again.

"Yes, sir."

There's something about some people that doesn't project confidence. Having been in the unit eighteen months now, I had seen all sorts of pilots. The overconfident, the quietly efficient, the risk-avoidant, the cowardly, to put it bluntly. And then there was a personality that you could just observe and something told you, *This guy is not going to make it.* Copenhaver's copilot that day was such a person. I really felt he wasn't going to make it. He was a new warrant, and I got a feeling about him the instant I met him. He proved to be very competent pilot and a good guy, but there was just something about him. Unfortunately, I was not proven wrong.

A week later, the company was conducting an extraction with Chalk Three having this young pilot flying as right seater for Lightning again. The PZ was large enough for all six aircraft in a staggered right formation with some dead trees located on the PZ, but well spaced for the flight to get around. To exit the PZ, however, we would have to use maximum power to climb over the trees on the departure end. Those that did not have enough power initially would have to fly between two trees, rolling the aircraft slightly while maintaining directional heading so the rotor blades could clear those trees as we gained altitude. The grunts were in the staggered formation and awaiting our arrival. They were being extracted and returning to Song Be for some downtime, hot food and hot showers—well, hot for being in Song Be. No enemy contact was expected on the extraction. Bill Hess had convinced the new maintenance officer, Captain Head, to fly as his copilot on this day as Captain Head usually bitched about us tearing up his aircraft, his aircraft, but seldom got to fly combat missions. This was going to be his opportunity to witness things firsthand. Bill was flying Chalk Five.

"Yellow One, Chalk Six, we're up," I said, indicating that all aircraft were loaded and Yellow One could depart.

"Roger, Yellow One is on the go." And he began his take-off, with each subsequent aircraft picking up as well. Chalk Three for some reason was slow in picking up, and when he did, it appeared he might be caught in the rotor wash of Yellow One, forcing him to use more power to get airborne.

On takeoff, Chalk Three attempted to fly through the opening in the trees as Chalk One and Two had done. We suddenly heard a scream over the radio.

"Chalk Three hit a tree!"

I was in the Chalk Two position and had just cleared the trees and really was paying no attention to Chalk Three, who attempted to fly between two trees and caught a rotor blade on one. To everyone's horror, the aircraft slowly rolled to the right, where the damaged rotor blade made contact with the ground. When it did, the rotor blades began to disintegrate, with pieces flying everywhere. Soldiers in the back began falling out of the aircraft, and they were the fortunate ones as the aircraft was now descending towards the ground. As the right side impacted, the transmission was ripped from its mounts and tore through the cargo compartment. As the aircraft came to a stop, the engine was still running, now at ever-increasing rpm as there was no rotor to turn or transmission connected. Fuel began to spill across the engine. At this time, the aircraft were not equipped with self-sealing fuel cells that would prevent a major fire. The aircraft began to burn and burn rapidly.

As Bill had been waiting for Chalk Three and Four to take off, he was only light on his skids when the accident happened. His crew chief, door gunner and Captain Head immediately jumped out and ran to pull people out of the aircraft. Soldiers on the ground also moved forward to assist. Lightning was attempting to climb out but was dazed and having difficulty. Moving quickly to assist Lightning, Captain Head was having difficulty as well, as the fire was now in the cockpit and spreading rapidly. The copilot was consumed in the flames, as was the crew chief. The gunner could not be seen as he was under the aircraft, having occupied the right side of the aircraft that day. Finally Lightning was extracted from the wreckage and fire.

Upon hearing the call that Chalk Three was down, Yellow One had aborted his takeoff, returning to the PZ, and was now sitting on the ground, facing the carnage. Aircraft were scattered around the PZ, not wanting to be too close to an aircraft on fire for fear of an explosion and ammo cooking off, which it was doing. Individuals were also lying prone or standing behind aircraft to avoid being hit by the superheated ammo. Smoke grenades as well as a hand grenade left in the aircraft exploded. Black, green and red smoke intermingled and rose above the burning metal.

"Chalk Five, Yellow One."

"Yellow One, Chalk Five, over," Bill answered as he watched Captain Head and some grunts carry Lightning back to Chalk Four.

"Chalk Five, how many casualties?" Yellow One couldn't really see what happened from his position.

"Yellow One, it appears to be just one person made it, and it's Lightning.[1] No one else got out. Some grunts are on the ground and being treated. Most of them were thrown out as the aircraft rolled."

"Roger, how's he look?"

"Yellow One, not good. From what I can see, I will bet he's going home." A grunt medic was kneeling over Lightning, administering what first aid he could, which at this point was only morphine and an IV. Lightning was placed in Chalk Four along with the medic and flown to Song Be, where a medivac aircraft was waiting to take him to an evacuation hospital.

No one was in good spirits that evening. Everyone, in both the Officers' Club and the EM Club, was in a sober mood. It hurt even more when we were informed that the division commander's aircraft was missing and presumed crashed. My good friend, Bill Michel, was the pilot. The division commander was Major General Casey, a very much liked division commander.

# 46

## HOMEWARD BOUND

Early August in the Pacific Northwest was refreshingly cool compared to the heat of Vietnam. Unusual for the Pacific Northwest was the clear skies, and no rain. I stood at attention and slowly raised my right arm to salute the folded flag that the second lieutenant had received from the pallbearers' burial detail after it was raised from the casket and smartly folded. As we stood facing each other, my mind raced back. It was the day after my last mission, when the CG's aircraft had been found on the side of a mountain. He had been on his way to visit wounded soldiers when they had flown into bad weather and crashed into the side of a mountain. The hurt I felt for Bill's family ate at me those days as we awaited some word. There were no survivors. Bill's little brother was in the middle of his "dooly" summer at the US Air Force Academy. Bill had been so proud of that fact.

It was a down day for me. I would be rotating home in a month, as I was advised not to extend again but get on to Fort Benning and the Infantry Officer Basic Course. Dad had left two weeks ago to return to the States to take command of the

Naval Facility at North Bend, Oregon. The orderly room clerk walked into my room.

"Lieutenant Cory, sir, I got your orders. You're going home. You're to report to Division Rear, no later than tomorrow. We have a bird waiting for you at fourteen hundred today to take you to Bien Hoa."

"What! What are you talking about?"

"Sir, you are to report to Division Rear casualty assistance office. You best get packing fast." It suddenly dawned on me. Bill's parents had requested that I bring Bill's remains home.

The next seventy-two hours were a blur. Grabbing what little I wanted to take back to the States, I tossed it into a half-full duffle bag. Shoulder holster and Ka-Bar knife, I gave to Mike George, who was out flying, so I tossed them on his bed. Refrigerator and fan, I left for Grandpa. A chopper ride to Bien Hoa; a night at Division Rear; a commercial flight back to the States seated with two other pilots from the company, Roy and Gill. Now the unit was down four experienced pilots and a newbie for the month. A total of five pilots leaving in one month was a blow to the unit.

Reaching Oakland Army Terminal in Oakland, California, I was briefed quickly on the duties of a casualty assistance/escort officer and taken to the airport for the flight to Seattle. Landing in Seattle, the stewardess asked me to accompany her and asked the other passengers to keep their seats. Two police officers were at the door and escorted me off the plane and down to the tarmac. This was not their first rodeo. As Bill's casket was the first item to come down the conveyor belt from the baggage hole, I came to attention, standing next to the conveyor belt. Raising my right arm slowly, I held my salute until the baggage handlers removed it from the conveyor belt. Then I draped the flag over the casket before it was loaded into the waiting hearse. People on the plane just stared out the window. Was his death worth it?

Arriving at the funeral home, I made sure Bill was settled in for the night, and then I was taken to Bill's parents' house in Monroe, Washington. Mom and Pop wanted me to stay with them, as they considered me family. Two other couples were there with Mom and Pop when I arrived. After putting my bags away in the upstairs bedroom, I came into the dining room, where they were all seated.

"Dan, what are you drinking?" Pop asked. I wasn't much of a drinker, except beer, but took a scotch on the rocks.

When I sat down, Mom placed her hand on mine and asked, "What happened? He was a VIP pilot." She was a tough woman, but I could see from the puffy eyes that she had been crying.

I tried to explain as calmly and in as much detail as I could what had happened—bad weather, bad maps—but didn't have the heart to say that the general was probably flying the aircraft. Generals could fly, but not in weather, and on top of that, Bill wasn't instrument-rated either but could handle the aircraft in weather conditions. Then the hard part came.

"Bill's in the casket, but I advise that it be a closed-casket ceremony," I said before taking a sip of scotch.

"Why is that?" asked Pop.

"Well, there was an explosion and fire. His body is in a plastic bag under a glass case. On the glass case is his uniform with all his decorations. The glass case is held down by three hundred screws. Opening the lid is easy, but not that glass case."

The rest of the evening was spent telling good stories of Bill from flight school and our one mission in Vietnam together. Between drinks and teary eyes, we got through the night.

The next day, I escorted Mom and Pop to the funeral home as it was the duty of the casualty assistance officer to do. The casualty assistance officer represented the government in these cases. Some guys didn't have it this easy, as the families were sometimes very bitter and took their rage out on casualty officer. I was fortunate.

Later that day, Mom asked me if I would drive down to SeaTac and pick up their younger son, Norm. The Air Force Academy had given him emergency leave to come home for the funeral. Norm was a tough kid but was hurting just the same. He and Bill were close, as was their older sister, Judy.

The day of the funeral came and Judy arrived early with her husband and children to cook breakfast. The ride to the church was quiet, and we all sat together in the front of the church. It was packed, as Monroe was a small town and everyone knew the Michels. The preacher stood and gave the eulogy, praising the work Bill had done in the community and for the nation. He said that Bill was not afraid of death but loved life. Few helicopter crews in Vietnam were afraid of death—it was part of the job—but they all loved life. They were some of this nation's finest. When the preacher finished, six Army pallbearers came forward, hoisted Bill's casket and solemnly moved outside to the hearse.

At the grave site, I lowered my salute and accepted the flag from the commander of the burial detail. Executing a smart about-face, I walked over to Mom, thinking that this was one strong woman, as I saw no tears. Standing in front of her, I knelt and said, "On behalf of a grateful nation, I present this flag." That was what I had been instructed to say, but in my heart, I had my doubts about this being a grateful nation.

Standing slowly, I came to attention and again raised a slow salute. In the distance, the commands for the firing squad could be heard, and three volleys of seven rounds each caused many to jump as the twenty-one-gun salute was fired. On the last volley of three, the distant sound of "Taps" was heard. No one held back tears at this point. I slowly lowered my salute, turned and walked to the side, my official duties concluded. As many started to leave, I came back, put my arms around Mom, and wept just like every other human there. And I weep to this day.

\* \* \*

**THE NEXT BOOK, *UNDAUNTED VALOR: MEDAL OF HONOR* IS AVAILABLE NOW**

**FIND IT ON *AMAZON* IN *KINDLE*, *PAPERBACK*, AND *AUDIO*!**

**SIGN UP TO RECEIVE UPDATES FROM MATT JACKSON BOOKS!**
https://frontlinepublishinginc.eo.page/mattjacksonbooks

**KEEP READING FOR A SAMPLE OF BOOK TWO**

# UNDAUNTED VALOR: MEDAL OF HONOR

# INTRODUCTION

*Undaunted Valor: Medal of Honor* is a follow-on to *Undaunted Valor: An Assault Helicopter Unit in Vietnam*. Continuing the exploits of Company A, 227th Assault Helicopter Battalion, 1st Air Cavalry Division, *Medal of Honor* tracks the company through the days after the Cambodian Incursion and the company's move north from Lai Khe to Camp Holloway in the II Corps region of Vietnam.[1]

I have attempted to present the events as factually as I can based on information provided by those that were there at the time. I have used the names of those that gave all in the hope that, in some small way, I have honored those individuals. Names of other individuals have been used with their permission. Some names are fictitious as the individuals were unknown or requested that I not use their name. Some names may appear that are similar to individuals, past and present, that I was not aware of and in those cases it is entirely coincidental.

In the early years in Vietnam, a pilot with the 227th AHB was the first Army aviator to receive the Medal of Honor. In the period depicted in this book, one member of the company posthumously received the Medal of Honor. Another individual working with the company and supporting the company in an action also received the Medal of Honor. Two Medals of Honor in such close proximity of time, distance and events is a clear indicator of the intensity of this conflict at that time and location. Another member of the company received the Distinguished Service Cross posthumously for his actions as well. Their stories need to be told somewhere besides the archives of the US Army Historical Center. This is my small attempt to tell their stories.

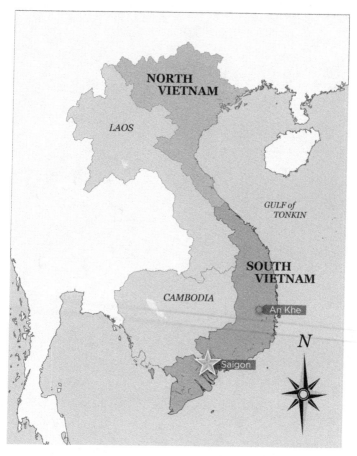

*South East Asia, 1969 - Map Created by Infidium LLC for Matt Jackson Books.*

23

# 1

## AUGUST 1970, LAI KHE

The southwest monsoon season was in full swing, with late-afternoon showers that seemed to take the oxygen out of the air. CW2 Mike George waited in his aircraft for it to let up after landing but finally said the hell with it and walked back to his hooch. By the time he arrived at his hooch, there was not a stitch of dry clothing on him.

"Anyone seen Cory?" Mike asked, coming through the door of the hooch soaking wet. First Lieutenant Dan Cory had been in the unit for the past eighteen months and had acquired over two thousand hours' combat flying time. He had previously been a warrant officer and had received a direct commission to first lieutenant. He had also served as a flight leader and the unit instructor pilot.

Mike had been flying all day in the Song Be region, one hundred miles north of Saigon. Days had become somewhat boring since the Cambodian Incursion had ended last month. The North Vietnamese Army (NVA) had not regrouped and weren't as active in the area as they had been before May 1, 1970, when the 1st Air Cavalry Division along with the 25th Infantry Division and 1st ARVN Airborne Division had made the incursion into sanctuaries in Cambodia in the Parrot Beak and Fish Hook regions north of Saigon. That incursion had destroyed numerous supply dumps, hospitals, transportation hubs and command centers that supported NVA forces in the III Corps area of South Vietnam. The feeling from higher headquarters was that it would take the NVA years to recover before they could launch another major attack into South Vietnam, which would give the South Vietnamese Army time to develop and the US the opportunity to withdraw ground forces from South Vietnam.

Mike's aviation company was Company A, 227th Assault Helicopter Battalion, part of the 1st Air Cavalry Division. The unit had been located at Lai Khe for almost two years now, having moved down from the Demilitarized Zone, or DMZ, of Vietnam, where it had been since early 1968. Prior to that the unit had been in the central highlands since arriving in Vietnam in 1965. The unit's aircraft, the UH-1H helicopter, lovingly referred to by everyone as the Huey, or Slick, was the workhorse of the Vietnam War. Capable of flying at just over one hundred miles an hour and carrying a combat load of six to seven fully equipped infantry soldiers, or grunts as they were called. The aircraft could fly for two hours with a twenty-minute fuel reserve. If all its instruments were working, it could fly in bad weather conditions as well, but seldom did the weather instruments work properly.

"Yeah, I saw him, just before he went home today," responded CW2 Bill Hess, a pilot walking down the center hall in their hooch. Bill was now flying an extension past his required one year in Vietnam, as was Mike.

"What'd you mean he went home?" Mike asked, opening his refrigerator and retrieving a cold soda. Mike seldom drank beer as most pilots did. Originally from Sacramento, California, Mike had been a fireman when he'd joined the Army. He was in his mid-twenties, a bit older than most pilots, and he looked it. You could always tell a pilot was a bit older by his well-developed mustache. Most pilots sported peach fuzz mustaches, but not the older guys. Fellow pilots would joke that Mike looked like a Hollywood actor, Richard Boone, the TV cowboy Paladin from the TV series, *Have Gun Will Travel*. Mike did not agree with that assessment.

Bill continued, "I guess the family of the CG's pilot requested that Cory escort the body home, and they sent him home today. Hell, the clerk came in at 0900 and told him to be on the bird at fourteen hundred to fly to Long Binh and report to Division Rear. I think he left his shoulder holster on your bed and his Ka-Bar knife on Lou's bed. His refrigerator he donated to Grampa." General Casey, the division commander or CG, had been killed two weeks before in a helicopter crash while en route to Cam Ranh Bay to visit troops in the hospital. His pilot, First Lieutenant William Michel, had been very close to Cory, and the family had requested that Cory bring their son's body home.

Grampa, as everyone called him, was WO1 David Fairweather. He was much older than everyone else, mid-thirties, and looked it too as he had been a sergeant first class when he'd volunteered for flight school. He had a respectable-looking mustache, dark with a sprinkle of gray. He had been Cory's roommate since he'd arrived. He let everyone know if they met his wife back in the States, they best not be referring to her as Grandma.

"Oh shit, we're going to be hurting for aircraft commanders, then. Cory left today, Gill and Roy left yesterday, and Copenhaver has been medevaced back to the States. We're down four ACs right away. That isn't going to be enough ACs. We're going to be flying our butts off until we can get some of the new guys checked out for left seat."[1] Mike fussed, shaking his head.

"I'm sure Major Sundstrum will be calling a meeting for

the ACs to select some candidates. Probably be looking for a new instructor pilot as well since Cory is gone. Do you want the job?" Bill asked Mike. Bill was from Newburgh, New York, and had joined the Army right after high school graduation. He bragged about his ability to play middle linebacker in football as he was built for that position. He talked about a girlfriend back home but had no pictures to pass around. The guys wondered about that. When he opened his mouth to speak, there was no doubt in anyone's mind where he was from.

Looking at Bill as if he had a third eye, Mike said, "Hell no! New guys scare the crap out of me. Hell, some of these guys are flying with their heads up their ass the way they fly. Have you flown with Captain Vargus? That guy has one thing on his mind—medals."

"Hey, Mike, let's get some chow," Lou called out. He'd just walked in after leaving the officers' club. "Oh, sorry, didn't see you standing there. You want to join us, Bill?" This was CW2 Lou Price's second time in Company A, having served in the unit from 1968 to 1969 before leaving to be a flight instructor at Fort Rucker. After nine months of instructor duty, he felt it was safer to come back to Vietnam and take his chances in combat than put up with student pilots. Originally from California, Lou had an immature mustache that matched almost every other warrant officer in Vietnam, and his hair length barely met military standards, as was pointed out on more than one occasion by the platoon leader.[2]

"Yeah, sure. I'll meet you over there," Bill said, heading to his room.

"Let me get some dry clothes and I'll walk over with Hess in a minute," Mike responded and headed into his room to change.

The mess hall was a metal building with concrete floors, fluorescent lighting and screen walls from about four feet up to the metal roof eaves. During the monsoon season with typical rain showers, it was hard to hear oneself think over the noise of the pounding rain. One half of the building was the kitchen area and the other half was the dining area, with the two separated by the steam table/serving line. Tables were arranged to seat four but could be pushed together if needed. Several large floor fans lined the walls and moved the air around as there was no air conditioning. The cooks took a lot of pride in what they did, and they did work some miracles. They were cooking by 0500 hours, and the mess hall stayed open until one hour after the last flight came in, which usually wasn't until 1900 hours. What they served was what the supply system sent them. How it was prepared and served was on them, and they did it pretty good. No one had to pull kitchen police, KP, as the company had hired Vietnamese ladies to perform those duties from profits made at the officers' and enlisted clubs.

Later that evening, the executive officer, Captain Wehr, came through the hooch and stuck his head into Mike and Lou's room. Captain Wehr was a very likable guy on his second tour in Nam. "CO wants to see the ACs in the club. Now," he said.[3]

"Yes, sir," they both responded, abandoning the unfinished letters they had been writing. Writing letters or reading a well-worn book was about all anyone did in the evening, when not in the club drinking.

When they arrived at the club, the CO, Major Sundstrum, had several tables pushed together and seats for the fourteen aircraft commanders. After each had a beer in hand and was settled, the CO brought the meeting to order. Most right-seat pilots knew what the meeting was about and knew enough to leave and return to their respective rooms, although Major Sundstrum didn't ask anyone to leave.

Standing up, the major started, "Okay, guys, you know

why I called this. We're down four ACs as of today and no instructor pilot. If anyone wants to volunteer for the instructor position, let me know. If no one volunteers, then I will select. The choice is yours: volunteer; I select; or you guys collectively browbeat someone into taking the job, with my approval. Now for ACs. Of the right-seaters, we have seven that have the time and hours. First is Mr. Dumas with eight months in-country and over six hundred hours. By a show of hands, who's in favor?" As usual, not one hand went up.

"Oh, come on now. He's not that bad," the CO argued.

"I don't see you raising your hand, sir," Mr. Sinkey pointed out. Sinkey was a young fellow, as most pilots were. He had attended Southwest Oregon College for one year before joining the Army. With his lean and muscular build, he could easily be taken for a competitive swimmer. The spiral passes he made with a football were hallmarks of a pro. His sense of humor never ceased, or was it immaturity? He was quick-witted and probably a ladies' man back home.[4]

The CO said nothing but just gave him the stink-eye. Tossing Dumas's file to the side, he picked up the next candidate's file.

"Moving right along, how about Captain Wehr?" He had more than enough hours and had been in the unit for four months. Everyone raised their hand. "Thank you," Major Sundstrum said.

After going through the stack of eligible candidates, the CO had three new aircraft commanders. To be eligible for consideration, pilots had to have four hundred hours of combat flying, generally four months in-country and a vote of confidence from the majority of current aircraft commanders.

"Thank you, gentlemen. I'll fly with each of them and sign them off for AC until we get an instructor pilot, which I expect will happen in the next twenty-four hours," the major announced, meaning that the pilots would have to choose someone pretty damn quick.

After the CO left, the discussion turned to who the new instructor pilot would be. As far as the warrant officers were concerned, there was a likely choice, CWO2 Barstow. He was on his second tour and had been a flight instructor at Hunter Army Airfield. He had been an AC for a month and had been in the unit for two months, just long enough to learn the area of operations. He had even been an instructor for some of the newest pilots when they had gone through Huey transition in the second half of Advanced Flight Training. As all eyes turned to him, he began objecting.

"Hey, not me. I've done my time with instructor duty. One of you guys needs to take on that responsibility," he protested.

"But, sir," Mr. Bailey chimed in, "you have all the prerequisites and the experience. You're the best choice for the job." Bailey didn't really need to address him as sir, as rank amongst warrant officers was like virtue amongst whores, but the effect was notable.

"No, I don't want the job and that's final," Barstow continued to protest.

"All those in favor of Mr. Barstow, raise your hand," directed Lou. In truth, most guys thought Lou should be the instructor pilot, but he was halfway through his second tour. He also kept the fact that he had been an instructor at Fort Rucker pretty quiet, so it was known only to a few people. Of the fourteen ACs, fourteen hands were raised.

"Looks like you've been elected, Rick," Captain Beauchamp said. "I'll tell the CO." Captain Beauchamp was the senior platoon leader in the company as well as an AC. A field artillery officer, he also served as the Operations officer for the unit.

"Son of a bitch!" Barstow fumed. "You guys railroaded me

on this one. God help you if the old man puts any of you up for a check ride with me." Standing and picking up his beer, he headed for the door. "I'll tell the CO right now. Might as well get it over with," he mumbled over his shoulder as he departed.

Looking over at Lou, Captain Beauchamp smiled. "You know, Lou, if he ever finds out you were an IP at Rucker, he's going to be unmerciful on you."

Smiling back, Lou said, "Hey, sir, what's he going to do? Bend my dog tags and send me to Vietnam?"

"There are fates worse than that," Captain Beauchamp said as he pushed back from the table. "It's late and I got a letter to write, so I'll see you ladies in the morning. Night, all."

"Night, sir" was heard as everyone started finishing their beers and leaving as well. Even though the NVA had taken a beating in Cambodia two months before, that didn't mean that combat operations in III Corps were over with. Not by a long shot.

Keep reading, get your copy of Medal of Honor today.

# APPENDIX 1

## Some Gave All

The following are members of the 227th AHB who were lost during the period from 1969 through 1970. Each may be found on the National Vietnam Memorial Wall as indicated.

### Company A:
DateNamePanel/Row

- 1/16/69CPT David A Carlin34W 013
- 1/16/69CWO George F Lapan34W 015
- 1/16/69SP5 John C Deaton34W 014
- 1/16/69SP5 Paul R Dew34W 014
- 1/16/69SP5 Frederick L Holder34W 015
- 1/16/69SP5 John Mirich34W 016
- 09/03/69WO1 David R Hanna18W 028
- 09/03/69WO1 William E Tittle18W 029
- 09/03/69SGT Mark C Alford18W 026
- 09/03/69SP5 Michael L Collins18W 026
- 11/05/69WO1 Ken A McCartney16W 033
- 11/05/69WO1 Gerould M Rumble16W 035
- 11/05/69SP4 Charles A Posey16W 035
- 11/05/69SP4 William T Quillin16W 035
- 02/18/70WO1 Paul E Ash13W 025
- 02/18/70WO1 Eric W Taylor13W 030
- 02/18/70PFC James N Diedrich13W 027
- 02/18/70SP4 Maxie D Linam13W 029
- 03/15/70 WO1 Robert F Young12W 002
- 05/13/70PFC Randy G Kittleson10W 034
- 07/29/70WO1 Karl T Anteau08W 064

- 07/29/70SP5 Jack H Dillon08W 065
- 07/29/70SP4 Ricky J Hills08W 066

**Company B:**
DateNamePanel/Row

- 5/4/69LT James P Flagella26W110
- 5/4/69LT William D Britton26W112
- 5/4/69WO1 Milton W Remmler25E001
- 5/4/69WO1 Michael E LeMaster26W110
- 5/4/69SGT Norman L Plemmons25W001
- 5/4/69SGT Don L Ross25W002
- 5/4/69Billy R Stubbs25W002
- 5/4/69Robert L Thomas25W001
- 7/15/69WO1 Fred A Fedder20W118
- 01/02/70LTC Roger W Kvernes15W119
- 01/02/70LT Robert E Carmichael15W117
- 01/02/70SFC Eddie L Spivey15W120
- 01/02/70WO1 Dennis E Debner15W121
- 06/30/70LT Leslie F Douglas Jr9W104
- 06/30/70LT Richard Dyer9W104
- 06/30/70S/P5 John L Burges9W104

**Company C:**
DateNamePanel/Row

- 10/10/69WO1 Thomas F Brown17W060
- 10/10/69WO1 CPL Robert Lazarus17W063
- 10/10/69S/P4 Shelby M Long17W105
- 10/28/691LT James F Spencer16W020
- 10/28/69WO1 Ralph D Tadevic17W129
- 10/28/69S/P4 George H Ayala17W125
- 10/28/69CPL Charles C Terrace17W126
- 05/22/70CPT Richard A Larson10W081
- 05/22/70WO1 John C Reilly10W081
- 05/22/70S/P4 James L Abler10W077
- 05/22/70PVT Richard W Mehlhaff10W082
- 05/23/70CPT Charles D Foley10W084
- 05/23/70CPT Ellis D Greene10W08406/30/70S/P5 Garry M Shannon09W107

**Company D:**
DateNamePanel/Row

- 04/07/70PVT Joe B Gibson12W 104
- 12/13/70S/P4 Earl E Shannon06W119
- 12/13/70S/P4 John T Kile06W119

It should be noted that three members are listed both under Company D and Company B. They are 1LT Carmichael, SGT Spivey and WO Debner. As they were listed under Company B, they have not been posted here.

# APPENDIX 2

## Unit Citations and Individual Awards

### UNIT CITATIONS DURING THE PERIOD 1965 TO 1971

1. 227th AHB Presidential Unit Citation, Pleiku Province, 23 October to 26 November 1965

2. Co A & Co D, 227th AHB Presidential Unit Citation, Binh Thuan Province, 27 Jan to 04 April 1967

3. 2nd & 3rd Platoons, Co D, 227th AHB Valorous Unit Award, Quang Tin Province, 01 to 31 October 1967

4. 227th AHB Valorous Unit Award, Bien Hoa Province, 6 March 1969

5. 227th AHB Valorous Unit Award, Fishhook, 01 May to 29 June 1970

6. Co A, 227th Valorous Unit Award, Fire Support Base 6, 31 March to 16 April 1971

7. 227th AHB Meritorious Unit Commendation, Vietnam 1965–1966

8. 227th AHB Republic of Vietnam Cross of Gallantry w/Palm, 1965–1969

9. 227th AHB Republic of Vietnam Cross of Gallantry w/Palm, 1969–1970

10. 227th AHB Republic of Vietnam Cross of Gallantry w/Palm, 1970–1971

11. 227th AHB Republic of Vietnam Civilian Action Honor Medal, 1st Class, 1969–1971

*Appendix 2*

## Individual Awards

1. Individual awards received by crew members could not be
   determined as individual awards were not categorized by unit.
   It is sufficient to note that every crew member received the Air
   Medal and in most cases multiple awards of the Air Medal.
   Many received higher awards for actions to include the
   Distinguished Flying Cross and Silver Stars. Most notable are
   the following awards, received over the course of the unit's time
   in Vietnam.

## Congressional Medal of Honor

1. Major William E. Adams, Company A, 227th AHB
2. Chief Warrant Officer Frederick E. Ferguson, Company C,
   227th AHB
3. Distinguished Service Cross
4. Captain John D. Curran, Company A, 227th AHB
5. Specialist 5, Thomas E West, Company A, 227th AHB

**AC**. Aircraft commander; also alternating electrical current.

**ADA**. Air defense artillery.

**ARA.** Aerial Rocket Artillery, commonly referred to as Blue Max.

**BC.** Battalion commander.

**C-Rations.** Canned food that could be eaten cold or hot, used by the military from World War II until the late 1970s or early 1980s.

**CWO.** Chief warrant officer.

**C&C.** Command-and-control aircraft.

**DC.** Direct electrical current.

**det cord.** White cord approximately 1/4-inch around that is highly explosive and used to quickly cut trees or blow up other objects.

**GCA.** Ground control approach, a technique used for landing aircraft, with a ground controller watching an approaching aircraft on radar and giving the pilots information as to runway alignment and altitude.

**klick.** Measurement of distance used by the military, consisting of 1,000 meters (one kilometer).

**LZ.** Landing zone, the designated location for the insertion of troops. Once an established firebase is present, it is named with the prefix LZ.

**MP.** Military police.

**medevac.** Medical evacuation.

**NCO.** Non-commissioned officer, those enlisted personnel in the military with a rank between E5 and E9; commonly referred to as sergeants in the Army, Marine Corps and Air Force and chief in the Navy and Coast Guard.

**NDP.** Night defensive position, usually established by company-sized or smaller units for their stationary position after dark.

**NVA.** North Vietnamese Army.

**PX.** Post exchange, the military version of Walmart.

**PZ.** Pickup zone, a location to pick up passengers or supplies.

**RLO.** Real live officer, a term applied to commissioned officers, versus warrant officers, who are appointed officers.

**SF.** Special Forces.

**S-2.** The title for the officer responsible for the overall planning, coordination, collecting and analysis of intelligence information.

**S-3.** The title for the officer responsible for the overall planning, coordination and execution of actions by an organization.

**S-3 Air.** The title for the officer responsible for coordination with aviation elements to support the actions of an organization.

**thermite grenade.** A grenade that is designed to destroy objects through heat rather than explode; burns at approximately 4,000 degrees.

**TOC.** Tactical operations center.

**WO.** Warrant officer, junior to CWO.

**Warrant Officer Protection Association.** A fictitious organization consisting of warrant officers, which allowed us to complain about RLOs and Army policy.

**XO.** Second-in-command of a unit.

# ACKNOWLEDGMENTS

This work would not have been possible without the help of so many people. My thanks and appreciation to all of you. First to all the members of the company that kept me in the air and out of trouble during those nineteen months. I hope I have done justice to you and to those that gave all. May they soar with the Angels on the wings of Eagles; may they watch over those they loved and those that loved them; may they rest in peace until we all gather at the final formation together. To Howard Burbank for encouraging me to undertake this mission and coordinating with so many to contact me. To Mike and Dusti Scovel for the original cover picture and design. The cover is the most important feature as it catches readers' attention. If they don't pick the book up, they will never know our story. Unfortunately we could not digitize that picture for publication. Thank you to Joe Leonard, Ted Grossman, Ron Fender, Martin Beckman and Bill Hess as well as Bruce Sinkey and Joe Lyle for filling in some blanks and providing some details. To Eliza Dee, my editor, for putting up with my changes and coaching me through this process. I never knew before what an editor did except correct my grammar and spelling, but now I know they do so much more. To James Rosone, who has published so many of his own works and who provided me with encouragement and guidance. To Infidum, LLC (www.infidiun.net[1]), who took my hand-drawn maps and turned them into incredible pieces. To my wife, who has read this so many times she is able to recite it from memory and finally told me to find an editor. To LTG (Ret) Robert Clark, who I first met on a PZ in Vietnam, and LTG (Ret) Hugh Smith, a fellow Vietnam aviator, for their guidance and suggestions.

# NOTES

## Chapter 1

1. It was years later that I found out that Crawford was actually a Criminal Investigation Detective planted in the company to find drugs and drug dealers. He was already a warrant officer.

## Chapter 4

1. A klick is a common term for one kilometer or 1000 meters, about 0.6 miles. Military topographic maps are measured in klicks.

## Chapter 8

1. Maximum torque on the UH-1D is 43 pounds. On the UH-1H it is 50 pounds. We flew both at the time.
2. Map created by Infidium LLC for Matt Jackson Books.

## Chapter 9

1. A unit call sign with a response of India indicated that instead of taking to the commander, you were actually talking to the commander's radio operator.
2. Each piece of equipment in the Army has an operator's manual, which is referred to as the -10. For the UH-1D and UH-1H helicopters, it is TM55-1520-210-10. TM stands for Technical Manual.

## Chapter 16

1. A named landing zone was commonly referred to as Firebase or LZ. LZ and Firebase (sometimes called FSB, for fire support base) were interchangeable.
2. Camp Gorvad, previously Phuoc Vinh Base Camp, was named after LTC Gorvad, who commanded an infantry battalion at LZ Grant in February of 1969. The LZ was attacked and LTC Gorvad was severely

wounded, losing both legs to a mortar, but refused to leave the battle, putting others on the medivac aircraft. He died of those wounds.

## Chapter 22

1. He wrote to my mother that this was the worst ass chewing he had ever received in his military career.

## Chapter 35

1. Det cord is basically composition C-4 explosive in rope form, used for wrapping around trees and blowing them over.

## Chapter 38

1. Official reports indicate that this landing zone was created by a daisy cutter bomb. That is not correct, and no landing zones that were employed in air assault operations were created by daisy cutter bombs.
2. Map created by Infidium LLC for Matt Jackson Books

## Chapter 39

1. Other sources indicate the operational name was Operation Dong Tien II, which may have been the name employed for Republic of Vietnam operations operating in concert with the 1st Cav operations.
2. Map created by Infidium LLC for Matt Jackson Books.

## Chapter 40

1. For his actions that day, Sergeant West was recommended for the Congressional Medal of Honor, which was downgraded to a Distinguished Service Cross. He went on to retire from the military.
2. The ground commander did not know that Blue Max had departed, leaving only two Cobra gunships to cover the insertion.

## Chapter 44

1. A policy was enacted that aircraft taking fire in approaching or departing a PZ/LZ would drop a smoke grenade to mark the shooters' position for

the Cobra gunships.

## Chapter 45

1. He would spend six weeks in a coma, only coming out of it after he was at the Army Burn Center at Fort Sam Houston, Texas, and would spend another year in recovery. Today, he is doing very well.

## Introduction

1. Because the medal is presented "in the name of Congress", it is often referred erroneously as the **"Congressional Medal of Honor"**. However, the official name of the current award is "Medal of Honor". Within the United States Code the medal is referred to as the "Medal of Honor", and less frequently as "Congressional Medal of Honor".
2. Map Created by Infidium LLC for Matt Jackson Books.
3. Map Created by Infidium LLC for Matt Jackson Books.

## Chapter 1

1. Aircraft commanders, ACs, flew left seat in our unit.
2. Lou served a total of three years in Vietnam flying helicopters. I am told he entered the corporate world and became a financial advisor for a major corporation.
3. Captain John Wehr would go on to retire from the US Army as a Lieutenant Colonel.
4. Mr. Sinkey would return to college and today has his own architectural firm.

## Acknowledgments

1. URL Inactive

# ABOUT THE AUTHOR

## MATT JACKSON

The author enlisted in the US Army in 1968 and served on active duty until 1993, when he retired as a colonel. In the course of his career, he commanded two infantry companies, one being an airborne company in Alaska, and commanded an air assault infantry battalion during Operation Desert Shield/Storm. When not with troop assignments, he was generally found teaching tactics at the United States Army Infantry Center or the United States Army Command and General Staff College, with a follow-on assignment as an exchange instructor at the German Army Tactics Center. His last assignment was Director, Readiness and Mobilization, J-5, Forces Command, and Special Advisor, Vice President of the United States. Upon retiring from the US Army, he went into private business. He and his wife have been married for the past fifty-two years and have two sons, both Army officers.

Matt Jackson Books

Sign Up For Book Updates
https://frontlinepublishinginc.eo.page/mattjacksonbooks

**<u>Undaunted Valor Series</u>:** Follow a young man from the time he joins the military in 1968 after two worthless years in college and watch his progression from a private to an accomplished combat instructor pilot over the course of two years. All events are true, and most of the characters are people he flew with.

### *Undaunted Valor, An Assault Helicopter Unit in Vietnam 1969-1970*

### *Undaunted Valor, Medal of Honor*

### *Undaunted Valor, Lam Son 1971*

### *Battle of Quang Tri, 1972*

### *Battle For An Loc, 1972*

**<u>Crisis in the Desert Series (coauthored with James Rosone</u>):** How much different would Desert Shield and Storm have been if Saddam had carried his attack through Saudi Arabia and into the UAE? This series examines the difficulties and challenges that would have faced the allied forces if Saddam had carried the attack as well as received assistance from the crumbling Soviet Union at the time.

### *Project 19*

### *Desert Shield*

### *Desert Storm*

### * * *

Visit Matt Jackson's website:

www.MattJacksonBooks.com

Contact:

info@mattjacksonbooks.com

Sign Up For Book Updates Via Email

https://frontlinepublishinginc.eo.page/mattjacksonbooks

# COPYRIGHT

This book is a work of historical fiction. The characters, incidents and dialogue are drawn from public sources and personnel interviews as well as some fictional characters. Conversations between characters are fiction.

**eBook-Kindle ISBN: 978-1-960249-03-6**
**Paperback Print ISBN-13: 978-1-960249-04-3**
**Hardback ISBN-13: 978-1-960249-05-0**
**Printed in Ruskin, Florida, United States of America**
**Library of Congress Control Number:** 2023906260

Made in the USA
Monee, IL
19 April 2024